# Waking
# PATRICK

## AN ORDINARY MAN FINDS HELP
## FROM EXTRAORDINARY FRIENDS

# BOB DOLAN

# Waking Patrick

An Ordinary Man Finds Help From Extraordinary Friends
Bob Dolan

Cover image: iStockphoto.com and Shutterstock.com
Cover and book design: Tau Publishing Design Department
Author photo: Julie Wolf

For information regarding permission, write to:
Tau Publishing, LLC
Attention: Permissions Dept.
4727 North 12th Street
Phoenix, AZ 85014

ISBN 978-1-61956-042-0

First Edition September 2012
10 9 8 7 6 5 4 3 2 1

Published and printed in the United States of America by Tau Publishing, LLC
For additional inspirational books visit us at TauPublishing.com

TauPublishing.com

*Words of Inspiration*

# Ackowledgements

The characters in this book are based on historical figures. While portions of the conversations between the author and the historical figures contain actual quotes from the figures, the conversations as a whole are fiction, as are the descriptions of their appearances and attire.

I am grateful to the following men for their wisdom and perspective:
 Donald Hying, Auxiliary Bishop of Milwaukee
 Fr. John Yockey, a priest of the archdiocese of Milwaukee
 Fr. Michael Berry, OCD, Vocation Director for the Province of the Immaculate Heart of Mary

Research material included:
The Catechism of the Catholic Church
Butler's Lives of the Saints
Inspirational Quotations by Frank S. Mead
John Paul II, An Invitation to Joy: publisher, Simon & Schuster

Thank you to the Reverend Monsignor Robert T. Ritchie, Rector of the Cathedral of Saint Patrick's, for allowing the author private access to the magnificent Cathedral.

# Dedication

To my family for giving me the example and inspiration to keep me close to the proper path. Your presence in my life is an absolute joy.

And for all those who, like me, ask questions, admit to having doubts and wonder about one's role in life: keep asking, keep searching, for it shows you want and need faith in your life.

# Contents

# I

# *First Time*

I was a young man once and it doesn't seem so long ago, either.

I'm only 55 years old but I've never defined 'old' as a number. For example, if the 27 year old man who lives down the street dies tomorrow in a tragic accident, is he not already much older than me?

I'm 55 but if God gives me until 80 then I'm not old at all. However, if God only gives me until next week, then at this precise moment, as I sit on a bench in Central Park in New York City, I am very, very old.

I am certain of only this: every breath I take makes me older than I've ever been before. Every breath brings me closer to death. Thus, I define 'old' as not how many years one has been on this earth but rather how many years one has left.

I do not at all believe this is a morbid or depressing point of view. The way I see it, I am simply facing facts, which I've been told is always a wise and mature thing to do. Thus, even though my driver's license and birth certificate say that I am age 55, the truth is that I really don't know how old I am.

And that's the part that scares me.

Truly, I don't often think of death. I am not afraid of it, for why fear something that is inevitable? For me, death only comes to mind when I hear of the passing of a friend or relative; it is quite common and natural to think of our own mortality when we attend a funeral. Naturally, at age 55, that occurs with greater frequency than ever before: friends, relatives and acquaintances my age, even younger, are dying, it seems, far too often. These

 Waking Patrick

days when I read the obituary section in the daily newspaper it's
not just because I have nothing left to read; rather, it's because
there's probably a name in there that I recognize.

A few years ago I saw my own name in the newspaper
obituary. In bold type were the words **Dolan, Robert Matthew**.
No relation; I didn't even know the guy. In the accompanying
photograph he looked to be about 112 years old but it still scared
me for a few seconds. I felt like Ebenezer Scrooge near the end of
*A Christmas Carol* when the Ghost of Christmas Future shows to
him Scrooge's own tombstone. And then I thought of what would
be written one day when it really was me who had died. After
'Husband of Elizabeth, father of Erin and Caitlin, beloved brother
of Timothy, Deborah, Lisa and Patrick' what would it say? And
days later at my funeral, what would someone say during the
eulogy? How would I be remembered? All these things, oddly,
I thought of when I saw that one obituary of an unknown Robert
Dolan. One day, it really will be me.

I remember my parents, so many years ago, telling me that
'life is short' and that 'you won't believe how quickly the time
passes as you get older.' They were right. My first 55 years have
gone by rapidly so it stands to reason that this last phase of my
life will pass even quicker. Sometimes, for no apparent reason
but usually when I am in the presence of my daughters, now in
their mid-twenties, I am reminded of the haunting song from the
musical *Fiddler on the Roof*:

> *Is this the little girl I carried?*
> *Is this the little boy at play?*
> *I don't remember growing older,*
> *When did they?*
> *Sunrise, Sunset,*
> *Sunrise, Sunset,*
> *Swiftly fly the years.*
> *One season following another,*
> *Laden with happiness and tears.*

It's hard to come to terms with the rapid pace of the passing

10

of time. Sadly, one doesn't realize that until too much of your time has passed, until it is too late to do anything about it.

Sometimes I feel as if I have already cheated death, that I'm already living on borrowed time. My dad died at age 51; his dad and brother were in their fifties, also, when they passed away. Family history is not my friend.

I remember thinking at 7am on July 24, 2008, that at that specific date and time I was *exactly* the same age as my dad when he dropped dead at his desk at work, precisely age 51 years and 6 months. At 7:01am that morning, I had officially out-lived my father, and as I reflected on that, I didn't feel old at all. I felt I still had many things to do and plenty of time to do them. I could not imagine dying on that day, at that age, as my dad did. I felt I was too young to die at that time, age 51 years and six months exactly. I felt that by dying when he did that dad got cheated. He missed too much. He never knew my wife or kids. We all got cheated.

I have all these thoughts, unusual I admit, as I sit on a bench in Central Park on my first visit ever to New York City. It is a beautiful spring day. The trees and flowers were showing off their colors, boasting that they had survived yet another hard winter. There is a soft breeze and a bright sun in the cloudless sky as I sit and watch the thousands of people walk by.

I see a man and woman, probably husband and wife, slowly strolling arm in arm, bundled up as if it was still the dead of winter, each wearing a coat, scarf and gloves. They look to be about 70 years old. They look happy, content, in complete comfort in the other's company. I wonder to myself if that will be my wife and me in about 15 years. I hope so.

Yes, long ago I used to be a young man. I felt it. I looked it. Now, every day, it seems, in different ways my body tells me that I am getting old. My knees hurt. So do my hips and back. I've gained weight. I've lost some of my hair. I look in a mirror and wonder who it is that is staring back.

On long drives in the car, I have problems with my sciatic nerve. It used to be that I could drive non-stop for as long as six hours, only stopping because the gas tank was nearly empty. Now, I have to pull over every 90 minutes to stretch and walk

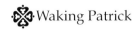 

because of that painful sciatic; not to mention having to go to the bathroom once again. That's something new, too.

I take a daily dose of Lipitor for high cholesterol and a generic green pill that promises to keep the prostate healthy. I'm not sure I believe that, but that's what my doctor tells me.

I can no longer play daily games of racquetball or tennis or handball; the best I can hope for is a vigorous hour on the elliptical machine or a brisk walk on the beautiful state park trails near our home in Wisconsin. In golf, my tee shot doesn't travel nearly as far as it once did; in addition, I use a belly putter, a sure sign of surrender to age and nerves. When I jog, my distance limit is now just a few miles; and my pace is so slow that I no longer use a stop watch to time myself, I use a calendar.

"Bob, you used to be pretty good," I tell myself as I sit alone on this wooden bench, holding a cold can of a yet another tasteless diet soda. "You had your moments. Well done."

I smile as I recall the baseball season when I went a full year without once striking out and finished with a .472 batting average. I remember consistently shooting 85 or lower in golf and once even driving the green on a short par-four. Of course, I also remember taking three putts on that same hole and being mad for a week because I failed to get my birdie. I recall the soccer game played in freezing rain when at one end of the field I stripped the ball from an attacker, passed ahead to a teammate and then ran the length of the field to receive a return pass and blast the ball in to the top right corner of the net for the game-winning goal. The goalie never had a chance. I briefly laugh out loud, a strange sight and sound indeed to all those walking past this bench, when I remember the street hockey game as a teenager against the bullies from the other side of town when I scored seven goals to lead my team to a huge victory. When I was 40, I recollect beating a much younger man in tennis, a man who was a college *tennis coach* at the time, even though I hadn't picked up a racquet in over three years. Heck, even just a few years ago, just as I was beginning to feel old, I won the city YMCA racquetball tournament.

'Those were good days,' I tell myself, 'and now, it's going

to hurt just getting up off this bench! What happened to me?' Whatever it was, I didn't like it.

I look down the path leading to the Central Park zoo and I see a man, clearly younger than me, in a wheelchair. Across the lawn I see another man, a war veteran I presume, with one leg. These two men make me realize how good I have it. It's a lesson I learn every day as far too often I see people less fortunate.

Reality sinks in. I am healthy. I am happy. How many people can say they are both? I am blessed, indeed. So I happen to be getting old; so what? Join the crowd.

I am very proud of my wife and two daughters. I love them and for some reason they love me. I am close to my siblings and I enjoy their company. I have a few very good and loyal friends. I've had some success professionally. Financially, we're certainly not rich but we are comfortable: we are able to afford a few nice vacations every year; we eat out at nice restaurants when we choose, and we are able to keep up with our monthly payments and bills. I am lucky. I know that.

I like New York so far. This is my third and final day of a business trip and I plan on using these last few hours walking around the city. My business here is complete so, naturally, I want to see some of the famous sights, beginning with Central Park because it is close to my hotel.

I've traveled to many places in my life, not only in this country but Europe as well. I love to travel, despite the fact that the 'getting there' and the 'getting home' parts are far more frustrating than ever: baggage fees, long security lines, delayed or cancelled flights, rude airline employees, hidden fees on rental cars, and more. I love to travel to other countries because I enjoy meeting the people, experiencing their culture, eating their delicious food, drinking their tasty wine, and seeing their beautiful cities and countryside. Sometimes my wife and I walk, sometimes we train, and sometimes we even rent bikes. In Ireland, one of my favorite countries, we rent a small car and enjoy the challenge of driving from the right side of the front seat, shifting gears with my left hand, and concentrating very hard on staying in that left hand lane as my wife holds both a map and the rosary beads.

In all European countries, I prefer the small towns and villages over the big cities. The people are more genuine and the pace is less hurried than what I find in big cities like Rome or Dublin or London. Those cities are wonderful, no question, but give me Orvieto or Siena, Italy or Kilkenny, Ireland or Toledo, Spain any time, any day.

I feel the same way about cities in the United States, too: the smaller, the better. In fact, that's one reason why this, at age 55, is my first visit to New York. I have intentionally avoided this city. For years, others have told me that I would not enjoy New York for it included too many of the things I detest, including heavy traffic, large crowds, unreasonably high prices and rude people. So far, I've found none of that to be true. Yes, there's heavy traffic but it hasn't rattled me because I either take a taxi cab or I walk. Yes, there are many people on every street corner, but everyone seems to get where they are going without any hassle or incident. Yes, if you feel like eating a $15 omelet or hamburger, you can easily find it, but I've also discovered good meals at fair prices several times in my first two days here. And the most pleasant revelation for me so far has been the people of New York; almost without exception, they are kind and helpful, especially the police officers.

Central Park is massive, over 60 city blocks long. I didn't realize that until I studied my *Streetwise Manhattan* map last night in my hotel room. I won't have time to walk the entire park because there are too many other things I want to see on this final day of my trip, but at least I've already covered a few of the highlights: the Jackie Kennedy Reservoir, the Great Lawn, Strawberry Fields, the Wollman Rink and a quick tour through the Metropolitan Museum of Art. I also had my first New York soft pretzel, with mustard on the side for dipping, purchased from a street corner food cart. It could have been served a bit warmer, I thought, but it was good, especially for just two bucks. Honestly, a few of the other items offered from that cart seemed lethal, e-coli on a stick, botulism in a bun, but you can't go wrong with a soft pretzel. Those street food carts are everywhere in this city, as are sidewalk scarf and jewelry sales, some of them perhaps even legal, Duane Reade convenience stores, Starbucks, Dunkin' Donuts, and cops.

I finish my pretzel and get up from my bench, slowly because of my aching knees, to begin a long walk to my next destination, Ground Zero. It is early afternoon. My map shows me to exit the park at Columbus Circle and then proceed down Eighth Avenue. I estimate the walk to be about four miles, leaving me plenty of time to daydream about other 'first times' in my life, in chronological order of course, because if nothing else I am at least orderly and organized, probably to the point of being a fanatic; some would define me as 'anal' but I prefer the much softer 'fanatic'. The currency in my billfold is in numerical order; my credit cards are stacked alphabetically; all cupboards and drawers in our home must always be closed tight; my sock drawer is arranged by color; canned goods must be stored with the labels facing to the front; and on and on. I even put my T-shirts on hangers.

As I approach the Hearst Tower at Eighth and West 57th, I remember my first school; Holy Infant Grade School in small town Ballwin, Missouri. We all went there, my four siblings and me. We were educated by nuns who came to Ballwin directly from Ireland: including Sister Ida, Sister Catherine, Sister Monica, Sister Bosco, Sister Rosario and the scariest of them all, for me at least, Mother Gertrude, who looked like a linebacker. I think she even had sideburns. Those were eight great years at Holy Infant. The nuns were terrific teachers. And the things they could do with a ruler were amazing. And quite painful too.

Those were good days, when I was a kid. There wasn't anything to worry about. Mom would cook great meals, especially fried chicken or spaghetti and meatballs; Dad would play ball with me in the yard and allow me to cut the grass with a real lawnmower and help him burn the leaves; my older brother and sister would let me hang out with them every now and then; and there was always an event at church or school to attend. We'd listen to St. Louis Cardinal's baseball games on KMOX ("The Voice of St. Louis") with announcers Harry Caray and Jack Buck while dad and some of the neighborhood men cooked pork steaks on the outdoor charcoal grill and drank cold Budweiser

or Falstaff purchased from the 9-0-5 liquor store down the street.

It was during this time, I recall, that I had my first crush. Her name was Carol. She was a girl in the neighborhood and I asked her to sit next to me on the bus for a school field trip. That may have been the longest bus ride in human history because neither one of us could think of even one thing to say. When we broke up, two minutes after the end of the bus ride, we didn't even talk *then*; it was just the obvious next step in our short relationship. No words were needed.

Carol was soon followed by Mary, another girl from the neighborhood. I don't think I ever talked to her, either, but she was sure nice to look at as she walked by our house.

My first crush in high school, when a crush can finally mean something, was Cindy. She was small with coal-black hair, quiet, sweet, and nice. I thought Cindy was the cutest girl on earth.

She never said anything to me, either. A few times I attempted to begin a conversation with her, but I never knew where to go after 'Hello'. Usually, a jock would come by at that very second and I'd watch as Cindy walked to her next class with a burly athlete at her side carrying her algebra and biology books. And I'd stand there and ask myself just when it was when I became invisible.

Those were good days, when I was in high school, John F. Kennedy High School in Manchester, Missouri, class of '75. I had a great group of friends. We'd play sports after school and we'd go to dances and concerts and parties on weekends. We took turns driving and we chipped in for the gas. Many times we enjoyed blueberry pancakes or pigs in the blanket at 2am at the local International House of Pancakes, where once a buddy mistakenly, drunkenly, poured a bottle of hot peppers on his waffle. And still, he ate it, pausing more than once to remark that the syrup was "unusually hot tonight." The rest of us never said a word.

My buddies and I could have worked much harder scholastically but somehow most of us managed to frequently make the Honor Roll. We took interesting electives, including an English class called 'I Wish I'd Said That' in which we studied some of history's greatest speeches.  My term paper assignment in Advanced United States History class was 30 pages on 'Boss Tweed and Tammany Hall'; a subject I'd never heard of before and never once thought of since.

We played soccer and baseball and football.  We worked on the student newspaper and even joined the Chess Club for a few months. And, constantly, we talked about cheerleaders and all the other cute girls in school.  The fact that we were pretty much unknown to these members of the opposite sex only strengthened our bond, only gave us one more thing that we had in common, one more thing to joke about.

When I arrive at the corner of West 42$^{nd}$, I can see a portion of Times Square off to my left and many of the huge billboards and marques with the flashing lights promoting the musicals and plays.  Strangely, this reminds me of my first concert: freshman in high school, Kiel Auditorium in St. Louis, Elton John.  This was in his *Crocodile Rock* days.  He wore feathers and oversized eyeglasses that lit up like a Christmas tree.  I couldn't believe my parents allowed me to go.  I really didn't enjoy the concert but still I told everybody at school the next day that it was the best night of my life.  They were so jealous.  The girls even almost talked to me: I could tell they at least thought about it, which for me was a moral victory.

As I cross the busy intersection, weaving in between the taxi cabs and limousines, I remember my first car: Ford Pinto, 1972, ugly green with scratches and rust spots.  I bought it with money earned at my first real job: clerk at the local A&P grocery store.  I had to join the union, Local 655, and I still remember learning my first union lesson: I was helping the Produce Manager, Jim, wipe and stack the cucumbers and I got yelled at because, according to the union rules so thoughtfully written to protect me, only Jim was allowed to touch the vegetables and fruit.  Local 655 taught me to never, ever offer to help anyone.

A&P paid great.  That same union gets credit for that.  I was making $3.35 an hour at a time when all my high school friends were earning half that.  I felt rich.

I was not a very good employee at A&P, however.  Often,

the other clerks and I would be in the back room, playing soccer behind the milk section, leaving the floor unattended. I'd organize the game. It usually began during a break period. We didn't use a regulation soccer ball for that would have been too obvious and too hard to hide from the boss when we arrived for our shift; so we used a worn yellow tennis ball instead. One could kick that thing to reach speeds of about 70 miles per hour. If you missed the net, the ball would ricochet off the glass that protected the frozen food case and then usually off someone's nose. We'd scream "Goal!" each time someone would score until the manager would finally hear us and order us back to the aisles. I was the store's best backroom soccer player. To this day, I am proud of that.

Also, a customer once asked me where she could find the peanut butter. I didn't know, probably because I was usually playing soccer behind the milk, but I lied and confidently replied, "Peanut Butter, both creamy and chunky, aisle 5, left side." I thought she'd believe me if I gave her more information than she requested, that's why I threw in the 'creamy and chunky' and 'left side' comments. Then I ran into the back room to hide so she couldn't scream at me moments later when she discovered that aisle 5 was actually toothpaste and toilet paper.

My walk through Manhattan has now taken me to West 34th Street and Eighth Avenue. The famous Macy's Department Store is off to my left. This street corner is overwhelmingly crowded. Suddenly, I am uncomfortable, even claustrophobic. There are approximately seven billion people in the world and at this very moment I'd swear six billion of them are at this intersection bumping and pushing me from every direction. I pushed back. I had no other choice. It was either push back or die.

I have no desire to go in to Macys, I have no desire to ever go in to *any* store, but I do at least want to see the front of it, the section that was featured in the great Christmas movie, *Miracle on 34th Street,* starring Maureen O'Hara and the young Natalie Wood. We still watch that movie every Christmas season and even now at age 55 I usually have to wipe away a tear when the judge declares Kris Kringle 'to be the one and only Santa Claus'.

I stop halfway through the intersection and turn around to see the facade of Macys. 'Pretty cool,' I think to myself.

Stopping is a mistake; I'm nearly trampled to death so I literally run through the rest of the intersection against a red light, leaving behind the multitudes of Macy's shoppers and fellow tourists, vowing to never again come to this specific intersection for as long as I live.

As I reach the other side, I stop to catch my breath and I see the famous Madison Square Garden just ahead. Strange, but this is my first 'wow' moment of my visit. I'm a big sports fan and for many years I even made a living as a television and radio sportscaster, and now here I stand in front of perhaps the most famous arena in America, the sight of so many memorable sporting events, including the greatest heavyweight championship fight in my lifetime, Ali versus Frazier. It is here that I take my first photo in New York, meekly asking a young woman if she would mind taking my picture.

This walk has been longer than I first thought. I'm already a bit fatigued. At the end of Eighth Avenue, I turn left on Greenwich, which according to my map will take me through the heart of historic Greenwich Village, then through the Tribeca neighborhood, famous for its' film festival, and at long last directly to Ground Zero.

❖❖❖❖❖❖❖

It is Tuesday, September 11, 2001. My wife and I are traveling in Ireland. We are with a tour group consisting of close to one hundred people.

We arrived on Saturday. It'd been a great experience already. We've visited the Cliffs of Moher, The Ring of Kerry and the bustling, beautiful city of Killarney. We've kissed the Blarney Stone. We've enjoyed pints of Guinness. We've met many friendly and fascinating Irish men and women. We love this country after only three days.

On this day, Tuesday, we are on our way to Waterford where we will spend the night and tour the famous crystal factory the

next day. First, however, will be a stop in Cobh, pronounced 'cove', formerly called Queenstown, located near Cork. This was the final port of call for the Titanic. We are visiting the Cobh Heritage Center, from where millions of Irish left their homes to start anew in the United States.

When we board the bus to soon begin the drive to Waterford, our two Irish tour guides are both standing in the parking lot, well away from our group. We could see they were both talking on a cell phone in animated conversations, but they were too far away for us to hear any of it.

Here in Ireland, it was early afternoon.

After the rest of us were in our seats, the tour guide in charge of our bus finally entered. He whispers something to the driver. The driver excitedly whispers back.

Both men look shaken and upset.

Many of the tourists on our bus do not notice. Some are talking to the people around them. Others are writing in their journals. A few are already resting, eyes closed, hoping to sleep as we travel to Waterford.

My wife and I, however, do notice. We are leading this tour so at every stop we try to make sure everything is running smoothly and on schedule. Thus, we are attentive and constantly on alert. We'd become quite friendly already with the two tour guides, both funny and charming men. We notice their unusual behavior at this time because it is very much out of character.

Soon, the driver pulls out of the parking lot. Our tour guide sits silently in the jump seat next to him. He still hasn't talked to any of us, not even "How did you like the Heritage Center?" or "You're going to love the Waterford crystal." No small talk, no niceties. A silent Irishman? "Something isn't right," I say to my wife in our seat near the back of the bus.

We are about five minutes into the ride when our tour guide stands and turns down the volume on the Irish music playing on the speaker system. He holds a microphone and turns to face us.

"Ladies and gentlemen, I have news," he begins. "I have been in contact with our home office several times in the past hour. The news is very bad."

With that, he has our full attention.

"Your country has been attacked. Your President has called it an act of war. Airplanes were hijacked. Two airplanes were flown into the Twin Towers in New York. The towers have collapsed. Another plane crashed at your Pentagon. The loss of life is expected to be enormous. I don't have any other information for you. I am very sorry for all of you. I pray for your country."

He then turns on CNN International Radio and we listen to the coverage for the next two hours as we make our way to Waterford. Nobody speaks. We listen in stunned silence. It is difficult to grasp the magnitude of the attack because we haven't yet seen any of the video or photographs.

When we arrive at our hotel, hours after leaving the museum in Cobh, many of us skip registration and go directly to the bar off the lobby so we could watch the television coverage. It was now that the horror of the event finally hits home, for there we see the constant video replays of the airplanes slamming into the buildings, people leaping out of windows, rescue efforts by brave firemen, reports from both the Pentagon and a field in Pennsylvania, and the towers crumbling to the ground. The group at my table are nursing a pint and we join in prayer.

My wife and I try in vain for several hours to call our two daughters back home. We want, even need, to assure them that in spite of the terror they are witnessing, that everything will be alright. We ache to tell them that we are safe, that *they* are safe, and to pray for all the victims and their families. Gratefully, we are able to contact them nearly seven hours after we arrive in Waterford. Just talking to them helped us a great deal.

The people of Ireland are very kind and sympathetic to us over the next several days. Everywhere we go, every small town, every pub, every shop, every hotel, every carriage ride, we are told how much the Irish love and respect America, that many of them have relatives there, that their hearts are broken as are ours.

Three days after the attacks, Ireland comes to a stop for a National Day of Mourning and Prayer. Everything closes down, except churches, where standing room only crowds gather from Dublin to Derry, from Tuam to Tralee. We attend Mass at the

cathedral of Galway, and in the ten minutes of silence and prayer after communion, well over a thousand people quietly cry to the haunting sound of a bagpipe.

Everyone remembers their first trip to wonderful Ireland. My lasting memory, however, was the overwhelming desire to get back home.

❖❖❖❖❖❖❖

I think of all of these things and more as I stand at the corner of Greenwich and Vesey in lower Manhattan. The site is now a huge construction zone. The Freedom Tower will stand here one day. It is very noisy from the trucks and tools and machines. Hundreds of people stand with me, watching. And, I'm sure, remembering.

"Where were you on 9-11?" I ask the man standing next to me.

"I was at work," he replies, softly. "We watched from the cafeteria. At noon, they sent us home."

I turn to the woman to my right and ask, "What about you?"

"Believe it or not, I was in a hospital room in St. Paul, Minnesota," she replies. "I had just given birth to our second baby. Even now, all these years later, we celebrate her birthday on September 10th. Celebrating anything on the 11th just doesn't seem right."

We all remember where we were on that day. Two generations back had December 7, 1941. One generation back had November 22, 1963. And we have September 11, 2001.

The world is crazy. I suppose it always has been. There has been hatred and evil and terror in every generation, every century. And as I stand on this historic street corner and look up at this new building, I recollect what used to be here, and I sadly realize with confidence that all generations still to come will most assuredly have a day that they, too, will always remember, their own day that will live in infamy.

❖❖❖❖❖❖❖

It's 6pm as I leave the Freedom Tower site. I follow West Broadway to Washington Square Park, where I pick up Fifth Avenue. As soon as I see the street sign, I think of the Judy Garland song in the movie *Easter Parade*, one of my family's favorites. Our daughters used to sing that song constantly when they were small:

*"On the avenue,*
*Fifth Avenue,*
*the photographers will snap us,*
*and you'll find that you're on the rotogravure."*

I hum the song; and then I wonder what exactly is a rotogravure? After all these years, I still don't know. I've never bothered to find out.

I'm hungry. It just hit me that I haven't eaten since that soft pretzel in Central Park so many hours ago. I duck into an Irish pub and order a bowl of lamb stew and a Guinness.

That combination cost $23.75.

Maybe I should have gone back to the pretzel.

After dinner, I continue up Fifth Avenue and soon I find myself in the shadow of the Empire State Building. I saw it several days ago from my airplane window seat but it looks much bigger when you stand across the street from it and look up to the top.

There is no way, I tell myself, that I would ever go up there. I have a better chance of being elected as Pope than I do of ever finding myself on the observation deck of the Empire State Building. I'm afraid of heights. That fear, for a reason I don't pretend to know, has grown worse as I've aged. I'm fine with flying but not at all fine with tall buildings; that contradiction doesn't make sense to me. In fact, I am so bad with heights that as I stand on the ground, looking up, my legs shake and my knees go weak. As I am *standing on the ground*, mind you, I can feel my fear of heights!

A friend once gave us free tickets to see a popular play in Milwaukee. The seats were in the balcony. I walked through the balcony entrance and felt like I was going to tip over and fall

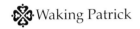 

down to the stage far below. I couldn't stay. I *listened* to the play from the lobby.

"How was the play?" my friend asked later.

"I loved it," I replied. "Best play I've ever heard."

I am also very claustrophobic. I can't do small elevators, crowded rooms and MRI machines. I once crawled out of an MRI machine about two minutes after the test had started; I couldn't breathe. The nurse tried to be nice but I could tell she thought I was nuts.

This is one reason I may chose to be cremated; I fear I will feel claustrophobic in a casket. I'm afraid that even after death I will know I am in a tight space. How crazy am I?

I also don't like being out on the open water. A good friend owns a sailboat and for years has kindly asked me to join him for a ride. "We'll stay close to shore, I promise," he tells me. I can't do it. I've turned him down every time.

Roller coasters, scary movies, snakes, mean dogs, sitting in the passenger seat as someone else drives a car; I am afraid of all of them. Especially, though, heights and tight spaces.

'I am *so weird* as I get older,' I conclude as I continue my walk.

It's nearly 7:30pm as I arrive at West 49th and Fifth Avenue and see, to my left, Rockefeller Plaza. This is where the large Christmas tree stands for over a month in the winter. The famous ice skating rink is located here, although now in springtime it has been replaced by an outdoor café. NBC's world headquarters are here. This is where tourists stand to see the daily live broadcast of *The Today Show*. This is where Johnny Carson hosted the first years of *The Tonight Show*.

My family loved that program when I was a kid. My older brother would watch Carson most every night in our small town Missouri home on our tiny black and white television set. Most nights, my dad would also watch, even though his alarm clock was set for 4:45am the next morning. We'd usually watch Johnny's opening monologue and the first comedy skit (Aunt Blabby, Carnac the Magnificent, Stump the Band, Art Fern and the Tea Time Movie, etc.) and then we'd go to bed. We rarely stayed up to watch the guests. We just wanted to watch Johnny.

We thought he was the best. My dad and older brother would laugh so hard.

"Did you know that Ross Perot," Johnny once asked in his monologue during the 1992 campaign, "is the shortest presidential candidate in history?"

On cue, Ed McMahon replied, "Is he?"

"Yes. Unless you consider Michael Dukakis." Pause. "But nobody ever does."

That one still gets my brother and me.

As I turn to leave this plaza area, I notice I am standing in front of an American Girl store. God, help me. Most parents who have ever had young daughters know what these stores are all about: this is where girls enter looking very normal but when they exit, several hours and hundreds of dollars later, they look like girls from 150 years ago. It's like a real-life episode of *The Twilight Zone.* 'Do they have a time machine in there?' I ask myself. 'Is Rod Sterling the cashier?' This is one scary place. Add this to my list of phobias.

To be fair, I suppose, we did the same thing with our daughters when they were children; not with American Girl dolls but with Barbie dolls. They must have had over a dozen. Plus, they also had the Barbie mansion, clothes, convertible car and yacht. I often wondered just what Barbie did for a living to allow her to afford such a nice lifestyle. Maybe Ken just paid for all of it. Maybe that's why Ken always looked like he was in such great pain.

Our daughters would play with Barbie constantly. They'd often bathe with the dolls and then leave them in the tub when bath time was complete, which meant that the naked Barbies were still there when I'd later come in to take a shower. I was frequently showering with nude dolls surrounding me. I never once told Ken. That's probably the one thing that would have wiped that silly smile off his face.

Those were great days, when our girls were small. Christmas mornings were always joyful as they opened their gifts and saw what Santa had left for them. We took many family vacations to places like Disney World and Washington D.C. and beaches in Florida, and during every one we thoroughly enjoyed each

other's company. Decades later, we still share stories from our vacations and we still laugh at the memories.

Our girls both played soccer in the fourth-grade. I volunteered to coach. I'm not sure how much they learned about the sport but we all had a good time, I made sure of that much at least. At this age, at this level, the girls from both teams are usually all within about ten feet of the ball and every five minutes the ball will miraculously squirt out of the pack of players and roll harmlessly down the field. Then the entire group of eighteen girls from both teams would chase it.

One game, I told my daughter to go in and take over for Stacy. "And Erin," I instructed her, "stay away from the pile! I want you to stay downfield. Sooner or later, that ball is going to pop out from the pile and you will have a clear shot on goal. OK?"

She nodded her head and ran into the game. Stacy's mom and dad, of course, glared at me for daring to take their precious daughter out of the game. The worst part about coaching is the parents, overbearing and opinionated. And those are the nice ones.

Sure enough, about three minutes after entering the game, with Erin standing alone downfield, the ball squirted out of yet another pile and rolled directly to her, giving Erin a clean breakaway on the opposing goalie. She dribbled in to the penalty box and easily scored the winning goal. Her teammates mobbed her. Erin looked at me and thought that her dad was a coaching genius.

And I let her believe it.

Those were good days. My wife loved being Mom, I loved being Dad, we laughed as they took their first steps, we taught them how to ride a bike, we watched their school plays and concerts, we dressed them in costumes on Halloween, we carved pumpkins, we made cookies and ordered pizzas for their first sleepover with friends, we lit sparklers on the 4th of July, we packed picnic baskets and ate off blankets in the neighborhood park, we cried as we put them on the bus on their first day of kindergarten, we hosted birthday parties at Chuck E. Cheese, we colored eggs the night before Easter, we counted down to midnight on New

Year's Eve and then five minutes later we all went to bed.  Then, after 18 years, we cried again as we dropped them off at college. We taught them well, I think.  I hope we did.   It was so fulfilling and gratifying to watch our kids grow and become responsible and compassionate adults.  In no time at all, it seems.

I had a strange dream just as our youngest daughter Caitlin was preparing to leave for college.  I dreamed I was bowling and there were two pins left standing side-by-side at the end of the lane.  When I rolled my bowling ball down the lane, perfectly on line to knock over the remaining pins, they moved on their own, as if they could walk, and my ball went right by them, falling harmlessly into the back channel.  I told a friend of mine about the dream and he suggested that the two pins represented my two daughters walking away from their previous 18 years in our home, under our care, and there wasn't anything their dad could do about it.  I hated to admit it, but he was probably right.

At least he didn't charge me for the interpretation.

I leave the American Girl display window and continued my walk up Fifth Avenue.  My hotel is nearby.  This has been a good day.  I've seen many things.  I've walked many miles.  I am very tired.  It's late.

Just one more stop, I tell myself.  It's just a block ahead.  I can see the top of it from where I stand.  I check my map to confirm it.  I'll just go in for a quick visit; at least then I can tell everybody back home that I saw it.  Then I will go back to my hotel.  I still need to pack and organize for my return trip tomorrow.  I look forward to going home.  I always do.

'I'll just drop in for ten minutes', I tell myself as I walk up the front steps of St. Patrick's Cathedral.

# II

# *The Cathedral*

Saint Patrick's Cathedral is huge.  It occupies an entire New York City block, bordered by Fifth Avenue, 50th Street, Madison Avenue and 51st Street.   Inside, it looks even larger; from the entrance where I now stand, the far back wall looks as distant as Brooklyn.

The first thing I do is grab a brochure to provide me with a few facts.  This is, after all, my first visit ever to the cathedral. Immediately I notice I've made a common mistake: I, like so many others, refer to this church as 'St. Patrick's Cathedral' or even the shorter version of 'St. Pat's' but according to this brochure the official name is *The Cathedral of Saint Patrick*.

'Well, too bad,' I inform the brochure, as if I was carrying on an actual conversation with it.  I knew that if I jumped in to any taxi cab in this city and told the driver to 'take me to St. Pat's', he'd know exactly where to go; but if I told him, 'Take me to the Cathedral of Saint Patrick' he'd probably have to check the GPS.

I don't like things that sound too 'official'; I like Bob, not Robert; I prefer Bill, not William; while in Washington D.C. I visit the zoo, not the National Zoological Park, its 'official' name.  Just keep it simple.

Thus, for *my* visit at least, this is St. Pat's Cathedral.  Everybody else can call it whatever they want.

I don't have a lot of time.  They lock the doors in about a half an hour.  Besides, I'm tired.  I just want to see some of the highlights. I just want to tell family and friends after I return home, "I went to St. Pat's."  That's the only reason I am here.

As I stand at the back pew, I glance at my brochure and read

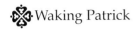

several quick facts.

For example, this is the largest gothic-style Catholic cathedral in the United States. It seats approximately 2200 people. The exterior spires rise 330 feet from street level. Construction began in 1858, stopped during the Civil War years, and was completed in 1879.

This brochure is putting me to sleep.

'Here's something interesting!' I tell myself as I continue further down the page. This is the second St. Patrick's Cathedral: the original one, located at Prince and Mott Streets near the SOHO and Little Italy neighborhoods, was built in 1815. Today, that place is a Basilica, the highest honor for a church in Catholicism.

Here's something else; over five million people visit here every year! They come from all over the world and they are people of many faiths, certainly not just Catholics. That's more visitors per year than Cape Cod, The Boardwalk in Atlantic City, even the Grand Canyon. Now, to a man like me who'd never go to Cape Cod because of his illogical fear of the open water, a man who would never go to Atlantic City because he'd lose his shirt gambling, and a man who'd never go to the Grand Canyon because of his enormous fear of heights, that fact makes perfect sense: five million people visit this cathedral because there's nothing to fear in here, not to mention its historical relevance and impressive architecture.

I see in my brochure the mission statement of the cathedral: 'In a city and nation of immigrants, it has greeted countless waves of people seeking freedom and anchors us all to such basic human virtues as charity, love, decency, strength and justice. It was built to affirm the ascendance of religious freedom and tolerance.'

That's an interesting mission statement, I thought, especially that last part. I may want to forward it to some of the folks in Washington, D.C.

From the back of the cathedral, about twenty feet inside the two large bronze doors at the entrance, flanked by giant statues hanging on the wall of Saints Peter and Paul, and standing at the row of votive candles which are placed at the back pew (suggested donation, two dollars per lighted candle, please) I decide to quickly circle the cathedral, beginning with the right side aisle and using the brochure as my tour guide. I know that I have to hurry. They lock the doors soon.

First, there are plaques commemorating the papal visits of Pius XII in 1936 and Benedict XVI in 2008. The brochure tells me that Popes Paul VI and John Paul II were also visitors to this cathedral. Popes travel a lot. I wonder if they ever cash in their frequent flier miles.

In just a few steps I reach the cathedral's gift shop, located in the far back right corner. I see inside countless books and medals and small wooden statues; plus a sign which guides the visitor to a much larger cathedral gift shop located across the street.

Next, I pass the window dedicated to St. Vincent de Paul, a man known for his great charity and kindness. He's got me beat on both. But then again, he should. He's a saint; I'm not. That's why Vince has a window and I have a brochure.

There's a story, it seems, every few steps at St. Pat's. The next window, for example, includes Saint Elizabeth, Queen of Hungary, who lived in the early 13th Century. In her image on the window she bears a basket of roses. It is said that when her husband asked what she held in her mantle, the bread she was carrying for the poor turned into roses.

I like that story. In addition to the miracle, it proves that even husbands back then asked silly questions of their wives.

Nearby is a statue of St. John the Evangelist holding a chalice from which springs a serpent. The legend is that John was given a cup containing poison and, after he made the sign of the cross over it, the poison came forth as a serpent. I'm thinking, if I was John, that would have really freaked me out.

Further down the aisle is the Shrine of Elizabeth Ann Seton, the first American born saint; wife, mother and educator. Upon the wall hangs a likeness of Seton by famed sculptor Frederick Shrady.

Beyond that is a window honoring Saint Patrick himself. My brochure tells me that Pat has two windows at the Cathedral, the second of which depicts eighteen scenes from his life. He also gets a statue in front of a huge column on the left side of the

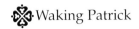 

white marble liturgical altar.  His statue shows Patrick vested in a chasuble, the chief vestment of the Mass, and holding a sprig of shamrock.

If I had made that statue, I would have skipped the shamrock and instead have him holding a small glass of Jameson.

It is here, as I stand at the communion rail in the very center of the cathedral, immediately in front of the six steps leading to the altar and sanctuary, that I feel for the first time something vaguely familiar, a sense that I've seen this somewhere before.

Then it hits me.  Of course this area looks familiar.  This is the most famous cathedral in America.  It's been included in many Hollywood movies and television programs.  Some years, St. Pat's Christmas Eve Mass at midnight is nationally broadcast.  I've watched it.  Plus, through the years I've seen countless newspaper and magazine photographs of this specific area.  This is why it feels as if I have been here before.

Babe Ruth's Requiem Mass was held here.  I've looked at black and white photos of that event; the Babe's casket resting right here where I now stand.  They buried Roger Maris from this spot; Vince Lombardi, too.

I'm a sports fan so it suddenly strikes me as a big deal that I'm standing in the same place where these sports giants were ushered to their eternal rest.  Maris once hit 61 home runs in a single season while playing with the Yankees, breaking the Babe's record of 60 set way back in 1927.  Maris and Ruth did it without steroids, so I still consider their home run marks to be baseball's true record.  Maris played his final few years with the team I followed in my childhood, my beloved St. Louis Cardinals, and he was always one of my favorites; he was a quiet, classy player, not at all like many of the athletes we see today.

And Vince Lombardi?  I've lived in Wisconsin for most of my adult life so I know all about the Lombardi legend.  He was buried from this spot at St. Pat's in 1970 and many of his former Green Bay Packer players attended the funeral, including quarterback Bart Starr, another one of my favorites as a kid.  It's no wonder why I feel a special bond to this precise spot in the cathedral.  I linger for a few minutes to take it all in.

Bobby Kennedy was buried from here, as well. I remember that event vividly. I was 11 years old when he was assassinated in June 1968 in California. I remember my parents being very upset when they heard the news of the shooting and his eventual passing. Especially, I recall Teddy Kennedy's eulogy delivered right here in St. Pat's, literally just a few feet from where I now stand.

"My brother need not be idealized, or enlarged in death beyond what he was in life; to be remembered simply as a good and decent man, who saw wrong and tried to right it, saw suffering and tried to heal it, saw war and tried to stop it.

"Those of us who loved him and who take him to his rest, pray that what he was to us and what he wished for others will some day come to pass for all the world.

"As he said many times, in many parts of this nation, to those he touched and who sought to touch him: 'Some men see things as they are and say why. I dream things that never were and say why not.'"

That is so good. I studied that speech in my high school English class. It was wonderfully written and beautifully delivered. That may have been Teddy's shining moment.

Too bad about all the other moments Teddy gave us, the ones you can't talk about in front of children.

Finally, I leave the front of the altar. It is very quiet inside the cathedral. There are very few other tourists at the moment and those who are here are lingering near the exit. I see a few security guards looking at their wrist-watch. A custodian is sweeping the floor in between the pews. I can see through the windows that it is dark outside; night has fallen.

To the side of the altar and sanctuary, I come across the Altar of St. Andrew, elevated three steps from the main floor. Above it is a window which includes the figure of St. Thomas the Apostle in the scene where Christ is confronting him because he would not believe the Lord had risen until Thomas had touched His wounds.

Sometimes I feel sorry for old Tom. Sometimes I feel he only did was most of us would have done; refuse to believe that a

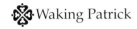 

man could literally rise from the dead. Who in their right mind would believe that? After all, it had never happened before in all of history. So, for this all too human reaction, two thousand years later all he has to show for his saintly life is the common phrase 'doubting Thomas.'

I think perhaps he deserves better. After all, he was an apostle, one of only twelve, so he must have done *something* right. I mean, haven't all of us at some point in our lives doubted or questioned something about our faith? This fellow does it *once* and that's all he's known for until the end of time. Poor guy.

That would have been me. I would have done what Thomas did. If I would have witnessed Christ being crucified, dying such a painful death, his dead body removed from the cross by the guards and soldiers and placed in a tomb; and then a few days later I am told by the others, 'Hey, guess who we saw today, looking as good as new!' I wouldn't have believed it either. I would have responded, 'Nice try, fellas' and then asked someone to please pass the bread. Really, I feel bad for doubting Thomas; I can relate to him.

In the far back corner of the cathedral I come across the replica of Michelangelo's masterpiece, the Pieta. This copy is three times larger than the real one which sits inside St. Peter's Basilica in Rome. I've seen the one and only several times. I am hardly an art expert or historian, but in my mind the Pieta is the single most beautiful and remarkable individual work of art ever created.

I still remember the first time I saw it. I was 18 years old. My brother was attending school in Rome at the time and I went to visit and tour for six weeks. We traveled throughout Italy and beyond, including Germany, Switzerland and Austria. The trip was great, all of it, but the best part was exploring Rome by foot; the churches, the museums, the ruins, the back alleys, the cappuccino bars, and one trattoria after another. For me, though, the gem was St. Peter's Basilica and more specifically, located inside, the Pieta. Used to be, it was placed within just a few feet of the tourist with only a velvet rope and a Swiss Guard keeping one from touching it. Now the Pieta is protected by bullet-proof acrylic glass after a maniac named Laszlo Toth attacked the sculpture with a geologist's hammer while shouting, 'I am Jesus Christ!'

Turns out, he was not. He was just an idiot.

To the left of the Pieta is the Lady Chapel. I am now in the far back of the cathedral, directly behind the sanctuary and altar. My brochure informs me that this area is the most sacred part of the building for it is here where the Blessed Sacrament, the consecrated bread that Catholics believe is the real presence of Christ, is on display.

This is a favorite place for prayer for many visitors. Countless numbers of couples have taken their marriage vows in this small chapel.

My brochure instructs me to turn around to notice two green doors. These lead to the steps of the crypt, where lie the remains of the archbishops of New York and a few others closely associated with the parish and the history. There are two kneelers placed at the entrance to the crypt, where one can pray to or for any of the men buried nearby. Here, too, one can even pray for the canonization of, reading from the provided prayer card, 'the Servant of God, Archbishop Fulton J. Sheen.'

High above the crypt, hanging from the ceiling of the cathedral, are the large broad-brimmed tasseled honorary red hats once worn by Cardinals of this archdiocese. They are positioned directly over the tomb of the man who once wore it.

I am now walking up the left side of St. Pat's towards the place where I first entered almost thirty minutes ago. My first stop is the altar dedicated to St. Joseph, the earthly father of Jesus and the husband of the Virgin Mary. This altar is strikingly plain and basic. The brochure tells me the design is fitting for a man whose life was the very model of simplicity. In fact, in the entire Bible, there are no recorded words from Joseph. We literally have no quotes from this man! Proof, I think to myself, that even two thousand years ago we had a husband who knew the less he said the better.

Of course, when your wife is the mother of Christ and your son is Christ Himself, what can you ever say that would trump the other two?

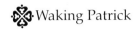

Nearby Joseph's altar is a window featuring St. Joachim and St. Anne, the parents of Mary. The in-laws, hanging around Joseph, every minute, every day, for over 150 years in this cathedral. No wonder he never talked.

I am very tired. I am halfway up this aisle so my round trip of the cathedral is nearly complete. I'm very glad I came in here. I've learned a lot. It's a beautiful building.

Now I come across the Altar of the Holy Face, which features the only mosaic portrait in St. Pat's; the image of Christ on the veil of Veronica. The eyes of Christ appear open or closed, depending on where the viewer is standing.

I test it. I stand still and sure enough they eyes are open. I move away just a few feet and now the eyes are closed. 'How do they do that?' I wonder silently.

Veronica is the woman who encountered Jesus on the Via Dolorosa on His way to crucifixion on Calvary. When she used her veil to wipe the sweat from His face, His image was imprinted on the veil. Today it is called 'Veronica's Veil' or 'the Holy Face' or even simply 'The Veronica'. Many people believe the story to be true; they believe this really is the face of Christ.

I love things like this! I love the mystery of the Shroud of Turin of whether or not it is the burial cloth of Christ. I'm fascinated with the story of the Blessed Virgin Mary leaving her image on the apron-like tilma of the peasant Juan Diego in Guadalupe, Mexico. There are so many stories like this. I have no idea if they are true or not, but just the possibility that they *may* be true leaves me shaking at even the thought of this unfathomable power.

I often wonder about the legitimacy of some of the places which claim sightings of Mary. I believe that she appeared to three peasant children in Fatima, Portugal. I believe she was seen by Bernadette in Lourdes, France. Guadalupe? Sure. But, c'mon, some of these other supposed apparitions could not have occurred. There must be hundreds of people and places which claim to have been visited by the Virgin Mary. It's as if Mary works for Publisher's Clearinghouse.

And what about these people who claim to see Mary on top of their grilled cheese sandwich or in the remains of a melted ice cream cone?  My God, what's missing in their lives?  What's next for these people; will they see Mary sitting in an Adirondack chair on their patio, cooling off with a glass of iced tea?  Would she request a packet of Splenda?

I also wonder why Mary only allows herself to be seen by very small groups of people, usually children.  Obviously, who am I to be second-guessing the mother of Christ, I get that, but wouldn't it be far more effective if, for example, she just hung over a Super Bowl for about ten minutes?  Maybe she makes herself the halftime show.  She'd be seen in-person by 100,000 people and on television by many millions more.  Nobody could doubt it.  Seeing is believing.  We'd all listen to whatever she had to say.  Most of us would be so frightened that we'd certainly follow her instructions.  Why doesn't Mary do that?  Wouldn't that have far greater impact than every 50 years or so appearing to a teenage peasant girl who immediately and understandably will be called, at best, an imaginative dreamer, or, at worst, mentally ill?

All these strange thoughts as I stand before this altar of the Holy Face.  I'm ashamed to even be thinking these things but I can't help it.  I usually question things or look at things from a different perspective.  I'm not the type to believe things only because I am told to believe them.  I'm weird.  I know it.

I'm near the end of my self-guided tour.  I walk past a few more side altars, including the final one which is dedicated to Saint Jude, and I slide into one of the back mahogany pews to sit and rest.  I don't see any other tourists.  The overhead lights were dimmed about five minutes ago.  Several candles are still flickering up front.

I'm very glad I saw this cathedral.  How can a Catholic on his first-ever visit to New York City not come to St. Patrick's, right?

I am so very tired.  I can't wait to order a sandwich and soda back in my hotel room as I pack my belongings.  I'll go there in just a moment.  First, I tell myself, I'll just rest my head against this massive pillar next to my pew and close my eyes to quickly pray and reflect on everything I've done and seen today.  'It's been a fascinating visit', I whisper, as the weariness of a very long day settles in.

# Chapter
# III
## *My First New Friend*

My few minutes of silent prayer were interrupted by the sound of footsteps inside the cathedral. I opened my eyes to see a man approaching from the middle aisle.

'He must be security,' I thought to myself. 'I hope I'm not in trouble.'

A quick look around the cathedral showed me that I was the only person inside, at least as far as I could tell. I'd stayed too late. The place is probably closed by now. He's going to tell me to get out. I'll just apologize and move on, no big deal. Heck, I want to leave anyway. I have a lot to do back at the hotel.

As the man got closer, I noticed his unusual clothing. He was wearing long black stockings. His pants, brown, covered only to below his knees. His shoes were red and pointed, looking more like high slippers than shoes. He was wearing a huge gold belt around his waist, a camel-hair coat and a surcoat of linsey-woolsey. He looked like he just stepped out of a Broadway play just a few blocks away, something set hundreds of years ago, like a Shakespearean drama or a scene from medieval times. His hat, though, was the strangest of all for it didn't match the rest of the outfit; he was wearing a St. Louis Cardinals baseball cap. I have one just like it in my closet back home.

He looked strange, indeed. He certainly looked out of place. And as he stopped in front of my pew, he even looked scary. For a few seconds, I was frightened.

'Perhaps he is a homeless man', I thought to myself. Often the homeless will wear any odd collection of clothes that they've found in garbage cans and dumpsters. Perhaps, I wondered, this

poor guy was only looking for a warm place to sleep for the night and I happened to be in his desired pew.  If so, he can have it, and I'll get out of here.

"Bonjour!" he said, pleasantly, in a French accent.

Hesitantly, I replied.  "Bonjour."

"Parlez-vous francais?"

Why was this guy speaking French?  But I continued to play along.

"Je parle un peu," I replied.  ("I speak a little.")  "But *very* little," I continued, this time in English.  "I took four years of French in high school but that was about forty years ago."

"Good for you!" he responded happily.  "I love the language myself.  I wish more people would speak it.  It seems like everybody is learning Spanish these days but French is a far more beautiful language, at least in my opinion."

He was a decent looking fellow, I thought to myself. I wouldn't call him handsome, but he was far from ugly. I could see his dark hair sticking out from under the cap.  He had bushy eyebrows. He face was long and thin.  His ears and nose, however, were large and seemed to be out of proportion to his skinny face.  He looked to be about my height, 5' 11", and he had a muscular frame. I guessed his age to be around 35.  'Maybe he is an athlete,' I thought.  'Soccer, perhaps.  Soccer is big in France; they even won the World Cup a few years ago.'

"How much do you remember?" he continued.

"How much do I remember about *what?*" I asked.

"French!  You said you learned it in high school.  So, other than 'Je parle un peu,' what else do you know?"

What's up with this guy?  I hate conversations with total strangers.  I'd rather he just got to the point and leave the small talk to some other person on some other night.

I answered.  I didn't want to be rude.  At least not yet.

"Well, I can recall how to ask the time of day.  'Quelle heure est-il?'"

"Tres bien!" he replied.

"That means 'very good'.  I remember that, too.  And thank you, by the way.  Merci!"

I continued. Suddenly I was having some fun with this little game of his.

"I also remember, 'Ou est le restaurant?'"

"Tres bien a second time! 'Where is the restaurant?' Not bad."

"And, 'Ou est la toilette?' I figure I better remember that phrase if I was first going to find the restaurant."

"Yes," my friend replied with a friendly chuckle. "It is a good thing to know where to find a bathroom. Especially in France. Escargot may move slowly on the ground but they are known to move quickly through one's body!"

I still couldn't get a good read on this unusual yet friendly man. He couldn't be a member of the St. Pat's security team. He wasn't dressed the part and he hadn't yet asked me to leave.

"Well, Mister, it's been nice talking with you but I better get going. I think the place has closed. Besides, I have things to do at my hotel. I go home tomorrow."

"Don't leave on my account," he responded. "In fact, stay as long as you wish."

I stood to get a better look at him.

"Are you with the cathedral security staff?" I asked.

"Not at all."

"Do you work here?"

"Sometimes."

"Are you a tourist?"

"It would be more accurate to say I am a visitor."

He smiled. He was enjoying my interrogation.

"Look, Mister, you seem like a nice guy but…"

He interrupted me. "Louis."

"Excuse me?"

"My name. It's Louis. You just referred to me as 'Mister' and I want you to know my name."

"OK, Louis," I said as I accepted his offer for a handshake. "I'm Bob. I'm an American. I am from Wisconsin. Obviously, you are French, correct?"

"I am."

"Then what are you doing here, late at night, inside St. Patrick's Cathedral in New York City?"

"I could ask you the same question, could I not?"

This guy wasn't going to give me anything. This was becoming a game of verbal tennis and he was winning. He was starting to get on my nerves a little bit. Why wouldn't he; he *is* French, after all.

"Fair enough," I replied. "I am visiting the cathedral for the first time in my life. I've been in New York for a few days for business and I spent today seeing some of the famous sites, including St. Pat's. This was my final stop."

I squared my shoulders to directly face him. "Now, Louis, it is your turn," I stated, sounding just a touch irritated. "You know who I am, where I am from and what I am doing here."

"And I also know that you speak a little French."

I ignored him. "Yet, even though you seem like a good guy, you haven't told me anything about yourself other than your first name. So, either you cooperate in this most unusual conversation or it is time for old Bob here to return to the hotel to pack."

He was still smiling. He wasn't upset at all with my tone. "What would you like to know?"

"Well, with all due respect, what's with your clothes? Are you an actor? Did you just come from a performance?"

"No, I am not an actor. And no, I did not come from a performance. These clothes are what someone in my position would regularly wear in my day. For you, they may seem unusual; for me, they are quite normal."

"But not the baseball cap!" I argued. "That hardly goes with the rest of it!"

"You are correct, Bob. I just added the cap a few weeks ago. Every now and then I like to wear something very new. I have a great fondness for the Cardinals baseball team."

"I do, too. I grew up in St. Louis."

"I know that."

His smile got even bigger. He knew he had me. He knew I couldn't leave now for I had far too many unanswered questions.

I was no longer irritated. He had disarmed me within seconds. I was curious, puzzled, and a bit intrigued. I had a live one on my hands. He seemed completely harmless; so why not stay until I get a little more out of him?

"What do you mean?  How could you *know* that I grew up in St. Louis?  We just met."

Silence.

"I told you I was from Wisconsin.  That's where I live.  I never mentioned to you my place of birth.  I never said anything about my childhood."

Still silent. Still smiling.

"Wait a minute.  Your name is Louis.  Is that true?  No joking around, OK?"

He finally responded.  "Yes, Bob, my name is Louis.  In English, an acceptable rendering would be Lewis, L-E-W-I-S, but I am most commonly spelled in the French version, L-O-U-I-S."

"Why are you playing 'Wheel of Fortune' all of a sudden?"

"What's that?"

"Forget it.  Sorry I even went there."  I regrouped.  "OK then, Louis, what's your *last* name?"

"We really don't use last names where I come from.  For example, my mother, God rest her soul, was Blanche of Castile.  That's all she was ever called.  No last name was necessary."

He noticed I was studying him very closely, looking for a mannerism or a nervous twitch that would give him away as either a fraud or some sort of improvisational comic.

"Ask me instead what my *first* name is," he volunteered.

"I thought your first name is Louis."

"Let me rephrase that then," he said as he adjusted his cap.  "My name was preceded by a title.  Actually, two titles.  Ask me.  Then you may know me."

"C'mon, Louis, I am so sure I really have to ask.  Just tell me!"

He nodded.

"Of course.  My first title, in life, was King.  As in King Louis IX of France."

I laughed out loud.  I couldn't help it.  This nice guy is nuts after all.  He's harmless, he seems intelligent, he obviously has a wild imagination, but he is clearly nuts.

I'm hardly an expert on French history or even church history but I do know what became of the real King Louis IX of France

about thirty years after his death. I wondered if this guy also knew.

"Well, then, Mr. King of France, suppose you tell me by what other title you are called?"

"I said 'My first title, *in life*, was King.' So that means that my second title came after death; and that title would be 'Saint'. I am Saint Louis. And, Bob, it is very nice to meet you."

❖❖❖❖❖❖❖

For a few seconds, I didn't know how to respond. Why would I? I decided to try sarcasm.

"Well, hello, Saint Louis. It is nice to meet you, too. I'm the Easter Bunny."

"You don't believe me?"

"Do you believe I am the Easter Bunny?"

"I do not." Pause. "You don't have his ears."

I just stared at him.

"So," he resumed, "not in a joking mood, are we?"

"You tell me, Saint. Can I call you 'Saint' or do you prefer 'King'? Or maybe I'll just call you Lou. I like that."

"You're angry."

"Lou, trust me, you haven't seen me angry. This is not anger. This may be impatience. This may be frustration at wasting these most recent minutes of my life talking to someone I initially liked who then turns out to be a crazy man, but no, Lou, I am not angry. I don't get angry often. I'm proud of that. But when I do, it's not good. You'll know it if you ever see me angry."

"Like the night your dad died?"

I took a step back.

"Excuse me? What did you say?"

"I said, 'Like the night your dad died?' That was April 1, 1977. If I recall correctly, you were angry *that* night. A person who had come to your home to offer condolences had too much to drink. This person heard you laughing with your friends in another room as you finished telling a funny story about your father. This person thought it was quite inappropriate for you to be laughing at such a sad time. This person tracked you down, told you to knock off the laughter, and then added, 'Besides, you have nothing to feel good about; he's dead because of all the stress you gave him.' You got in that person's face and screamed back. Your friends had to take you in to another room."

I was stunned at what I was hearing. I leaned my hands on the top of a pew to keep my balance. And I looked at this man called Louis as if I had just seen a ghost.

❖❖❖❖❖❖

I sat in the pew. I looked up at this most unusual man. "Who are you?" I asked in a whisper. "There are only about five people in the world who know what occurred that night; the people who happened to be in that room at that particular time. I've never told anyone. Who… are… you?"

"I told you. I am Saint Louis. I was canonized in 1297. When I was alive I was King Louis IX of France. I reigned for decades."

"Well, forgive me for still not believing you, Lou," I shouted, the sarcasm having returned to my voice. "If what you say is true, then I'm sitting here talking to someone who has been dead for about eight hundred years."

"Seven hundred and forty two."

"What?"

"Seven hundred and forty two. I've been dead for that many years. I died in 1270."

"Did you now? Well excuse me, Lou, I stand corrected. Let me continue if that's OK with you. If what you say is true, then I've been talking to a man who has been dead for seven hundred and forty two years. Sorry, but I don't buy it."

"Why not?"

"I'm not supposed to believe in ghosts. I'm Catholic."

Lou smiled again. "So am I."

"Oh, that's right Lou, I forgot, you're a saint. I thought I was just talking to the King right now, my mistake."

I pulled out my handkerchief from the back pocket of my blue jeans and wiped the small beads of perspiration from my brow. I

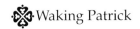 

was losing this argument. All I wanted to do was get up from the pew, shake his hand, wish him well and walk out of this cathedral and forget whatever it was that had taken place over the last ten minutes. I just wanted to pack my suitcase and go back home.

But I couldn't move.

"Let's start over, Lou," I said, calmly. "You are telling me that you are the former King of France. You died over seven centuries ago. Now you are a saint. You are Saint Louis. You are the man after whom my hometown is named. Am I right so far?"

"You are correct. Let me add, however, that I have many places named after me, not just your hometown; your Saint Louis, Missouri, just happens to be the largest and the most famous. There is a Saint Louis in Oklahoma, for example. There is also one in Michigan. The capital city of Mauritius, Port-Louis, is named after me. Sao Luis do Maranhao in Brazil is mine. Plus, there are many churches or cathedrals or basilicas named after me, including one in New Orleans."

He paused for a few seconds and looked down at the floor. "I am very humbled."

"Yeah, I'm sure you are, Lou. Otherwise, why would you bring up all those other facts?"

He had no reply. I just trumped a King. Too bad we weren't playing chess.

"So, Mr. Humble, Mr. Great King, Mr. Big-Shot Saint, may I continue?"

He nodded.

"You've been dead for almost eight hundred years, you have many buildings and cities named after you, you were a big deal in France, now you're a big deal in the Catholic Church, and yet you're standing here talking to me, a very common man with a very ordinary life, inside Saint Patrick's Cathedral in New York City. Am I right so far?"

"Yes."

"Let's move on then. Why are you *here*, in *this* cathedral? I mean, if you were going to haunt somewhere, shouldn't it be in one of those cities or churches that are named after you? Why St. Pat's?"

"I have an altar here. You walked by it a few minutes ago."

"Did I?"

"You did. It's a side altar. I share it with Michael."

"You *share* it? That's a blow to your ego, isn't it?"

"Not in the least, Bob. Michael is an archangel. That's pretty good company. That's like sharing a dugout with Babe Ruth. Plus, there are thousands of saints who would trade places with me in a heartbeat. They don't have a side altar inside the great St. Patrick's cathedral. I do! I am honored. I am blessed."

"So you are here a lot then?"

"Not really. I get around. I split my time. But I do love it here."

"Why are you visiting with *me*?"

"You said it earlier. You are from Saint Louis. I pay special attention to people like you. That's my territory. It's part of my job. I watched you grow up."

"Prove it."

"I think I already did."

I caught his meaning.

"Oh, you mean that story about the night my Dad died. I need more than that, Lou. You could have heard that story from a friend of a friend of a friend. Or maybe it was a lucky guess. I mean, many people get angry at the death of a loved one. That doesn't prove anything to me. You'll have to do much better than that."

The man took a seat next to me in the pew. I held my spot. I was determined not to give in to this guy. I was not going to back down. We now sat shoulder-to-shoulder with our faces only about two feet apart.

"I understand," he said, with compassion. "Let's see if this helps."

He removed his Cardinals cap before he continued.

"You were born in 1957. You grew up in Ballwin, Missouri, a western suburb of St. Louis. Your parents were Robert and Shirley. You had two brothers and two sisters. You are the middle child."

"Well, congratulations Lou, you have my basic biography.

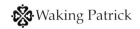

You could have found that on Google."

"Your home was very small, especially for seven people. The three brothers shared one tiny bedroom until your dad constructed a guest room in the damp basement to be used by the oldest son. Your home was located at the end of the cul-de-sac. The property featured a huge yard. You loved that yard because you were always playing sports in it. However, as you got older, you hated the yard because it was a lot of work to cut the grass and rake the leaves. You had a gravel driveway. Sometimes you'd take rocks from that driveway and throw them at birds perched in the trees; every now and then you'd hit one and watch it frantically fly away. The family car was always in need of repair.

"You had one air conditioner unit which hung very unstably from a window. St. Louis summers were extremely hot and humid so that one unit didn't do a very good job of cooling off the house. Often, you'd sleep with the windows and doors open to let the air circulate. A box fan was strategically placed at the top of the hallway which led to the bedrooms.

"You broke your arm when you were eight years old when you fell off the monkey bars at the school playground. You attended Holy Infant grade school. You played soccer there. You had your first fist-fight on that soccer field with a boy named Tony. He was waiting for you after school and all the kids gathered around to watch the fight; Tony had tipped them off. Your teachers were nuns from Ireland. They were excellent teachers but every now and then you'd get slapped on the open palm or the back of the wrist with a ruler as a result of some trouble you had caused. You sang in the school choir. At midnight Mass on Christmas Eve, the boy's choir sang while holding lit candles and the dripping hot wax would burn your fingers. You served as an altar boy. At one funeral mass you spilled the wine all over you and the priest and both of you tried very hard not to laugh because it was, after all, a funeral.

"When you were six years old you went trick-or-treating on Halloween with your older brother and sister. They were mad because your parents made them take you along. You were dressed as a cowboy. You had a hole in the bottom of your bag so the candy would fall out as soon as you left someone's front door. When you got home, you cried because you didn't have any candy. Your brother and sister got yelled at because they failed to notice the trail of candy in your wake.

"Ballwin back then was a very safe place. Everybody knew everybody. Doors were never locked. That all changed one day in the 1960's when a neighbor was murdered in her home…"

At that, I interrupted. "My God!"

"Her name was Betty. She was killed by an intruder; turned out to be a kid from the neighborhood who was burglarizing the home. It was traumatic for everyone. That next Sunday at Mass, your priest's entire homily was one sentence: 'Usually at this time every week we thank God for all the things that have happened to us; this week, let's thank God for all the things that have not.' And then everybody cried for about two minutes."

"How do you know this? This is impossible," I screamed.

"You won an academic scholarship to high school. I was very happy for your family because without that scholarship, you couldn't have attended the high school of your choice because your parents couldn't afford it. For the first time in your life, you felt jealousy from others who believed they were more deserving.

"The best Christmas gift you ever received came from your dad. He gave you two tickets to a St. Louis Blues hockey game. You were a huge fan but you couldn't afford to buy tickets on your own. The team was very popular so tickets were very hard to acquire. Your dad called in many favors and pulled a few strings to land the two tickets. He placed the tickets in a wristwatch box in order to fool you when you opened it. You were eleven years old and you felt like crying.

"The *worst* Christmas gift you ever got was one you very much deserved. The five siblings each randomly selected a name from a hat, and that name would be the person for whom they'd buy a gift. Your youngest brother was only four years old and he picked your name. Immediately, you balked: 'I got ripped-off! What's a four-year old going to buy me, a candy bar?' On Christmas morning, you opened that gift and inside, appropriately, was a Milky Way. And over on the couch, your dad looked you dead

in the eyes and you saw a trace of a smile. That candy bar taught you a lesson you still remember today."

"OK, Louis, that's enough. I can't do this anymore," I pleaded quietly. "This is like watching a movie of my life that I don't really want to watch."

Louis knew he held the upper hand. He knew he was in complete control. He even seemed to enjoy it. So, he went on.

"You liked high school but didn't love it. Frequently, you thought it was a waste of time. You had good friends. You played sports. You didn't date but it wasn't for a lack of effort; the girls kept turning you down."

"Feel free to skip that part if you wish."

"You couldn't wait to leave high school so you accelerated your class load and graduated in the middle of your senior year. Your baseball coach was pissed off because you were his starting second-baseman and you weren't going to be around for your final season."

"Hey, Louis, watch your mouth! I don't even let my daughters talk like that, much less my saint."

"Sorry. Anyway, it was during these high school years when you learned how to drive a stick shift; you passed your first driver's test with a score of 86; you held down a few after-school jobs to earn money for all your social events like school dances and concerts and Cardinal baseball games; your older brother moved away from home; your older sister went off to college; your Grandma died on Christmas Eve; you started playing golf and racquetball and tennis; you had your first beer; and you even thought about the priesthood for about five minutes."

He stopped and looked around the empty cathedral. "Have you heard enough?" he asked.

"Yes." I was stunned. I had no idea on how to get my arms around this. I believed, but I did not comprehend.

"How do you know all of this? You just said some things that even I didn't remember," I stated.

"Like I told you, I watched over you from the day you were born, January 24, until the day you left St. Louis for a job in Illinois at the age of twenty one. I enjoyed watching your family. You were good people. Sometimes I have to hang around some real losers but your family was a joy. I take my job very seriously; I think that's the least I can do when they name a huge city in my honor. That's what saints do. If one ever asks for my help or guidance, I try to step in. The hard part is when I am told to just stand-by and watch, to not interfere with what is happening, to allow people to experience pain and hardships and learn hard lessons."

"Who would tell you that? Do you have a boss?"

He leaned in a bit.

"We all have a boss, Bob."

❖❖❖❖❖❖❖

"So, what's with the cap?" I inquired, pointing to his red Cardinals baseball hat. We had left the pew and were standing in the center aisle, each leaning against a pillar. We were talking in normal volume because we were the only two people inside the cathedral. Well, at least I was sure there was *one* person in here; I still wasn't sure about this other guy.

"For obvious reasons, I'm a big fan of the Cardinals. They are *my* team! Do you know they've won more World Series than any other team in baseball history except for the New York Yankees?"

"I knew that. I'm a fan, too. When you grow up in St. Louis, you become part of the Cardinal culture. It never leaves you. I've lived in Wisconsin for most of my adult life but I still cheer for the Redbirds."

"Did you have a favorite player?"

"Through the years, I've had lots of them. As a kid, my favorites were Bob Gibson, Lou Brock, Ken Boyer, Orlando Cepeda and Roger Maris. Later, I liked Willie McGee and Ozzie Smith. But my all-time favorite Cardinal is Stan Musial. He was a man of great character, humble, married to his childhood sweetheart for over 65 years, and he was one of the greatest hitters ever. What's not to like and admire about him?"

"You met him once, didn't you?"

"Ah, yes, I did! Thanks for reminding me. We were picking

up my dad from the St. Louis airport after a business trip and as we walked to the parking garage, he spotted a man standing near the curb, hailing a taxi. The man was wearing a fedora hat pulled well down over his forehead, but my dad immediately recognized Musial's large nose. We walked over and he was very gracious. He signed an autograph. I still have it today."

I looked again at Lou's cap. "Do you ever wear your crown?"

"My King of France crown, you mean? No, not often. It's kind of heavy and burdensome. I have it packed away somewhere and every now and then I'll wear it for a few minutes just to remind myself of the good old days, but crowns don't mean very much in the places I hang around. I mean, who am I kidding? You think the Boss is impressed by the fact I was a king? He wore a crown, too. It wasn't made of gold, it was made of sticks and thorns. He wore it on the day He died. His crown is far more powerful and influential than mine or any others, don't you think?"

He had me there. This guy just can't take a compliment.

I changed the subject. "Tell me about this cathedral. Who do you hang around with?"

"Oh my, I'm never hurting for companions, if that's what you mean. There are many people here just like me with either a side altar or a window or a painting; we talk all the time, we just shoot the breeze, nothing real heavy."

"Even Mary?"

"No, we don't feel real comfortable approaching her. She's way out of our league. She is so kind and gracious and beautiful, but unless she starts the conversation we just wave or bow and stay out of her way. Her story is far better than any of our stories. Her contribution to human history puts the rest of us to shame. We're just lucky to be able to see her every now and then. Sometimes one of us will wisecrack to her: 'Say hello to your Son for me' and she'll good-naturedly smile. We think she is perfect. We are certainly *not* perfect, so we stay away for the most part."

"Saints aren't perfect?" I asked in mild surprise.

"Heavens, no. Pardon the pun, by the way." I could see he was quite pleased with himself for coming up with that turn of phrase.

"Most every saint I know, Bob, was first a sinner," he continued. "A saint is a sinner who keeps trying. Finally one day we get it right. Then our goal is to make goodness attractive. But we are all called to sainthood, Bob; we all have that capability. Even you."

I couldn't tell if he was mocking me or encouraging me, so I returned him to where we began.

"Well, if not Mary, then who are your pals in here?"

"Well, just off the top of my head, there's Bernard, Brigid, Columbanus, Martin of Tours, Thomas More, Cecilia, Catherine of Siena, Casimir, Jude, Charles Borromeo, Alphonsus, Agnes, James, Rose; shall I go on? There are dozens more."

"How do you keep them all straight?"

"At first we had to wear name tags. Columbanus had the worst penmanship; we couldn't even read his name tag so we used to kid him that he must have been a doctor. But now we just kind of know each other. We've been hanging around each other for centuries."

"Are you a patron of anything," I asked, as I ducked into a pew to sit. My legs were tired.

"As in 'the patron saint of' a specific profession or life issue? Yes. Most saints are selected as protectors or guardians of one or more topics or items."

"Give me a few examples."

"Well, Matthew is the patron saint of accountants and tax collectors. Joseph is the patron saint for anyone selling or buying a home. Teachers go to Gregory. Journalists and writers go to Francis de Sales; he, too, was a writer. If you work in television, your patron is Clare of Assisi."

"How did television get a patron saint," I asked. "Clare never knew TV."

"True, but one Christmas when she was too ill to get out of bed to attend Mass, she still saw and heard the local Mass even though it was being held many miles away. Thus, she gets television."

"You're kidding, right?"

"I am not."

"Did she try to turn the channel? Maybe catch an episode of *The Ed Sullivan Show*?"

Silence. I have to work on Lou's sense of humor.

I continued. "And what about you, Louis?"

"I am the patron saint of all of France."

"That makes sense."

"I am also the patron saint of French monarchy."

"That makes sense, too."

"And, finally, I am the patron saint of hairdressers."

"That does *not* make sense. Why did you get hairdressers?"

"I have absolutely no idea! I suppose there weren't any volunteers so they just gave it to me, knowing I probably wouldn't be terribly busy handling my other two responsibilities from France. I don't hear from too many monarchs these days, they're not exactly taking up a lot of my time."

"And what do hairdressers and barbers ask of you when they pray to you? Good tips? Sharp scissors?"

Silence.

"Hey, Lou, is there a patron saint of humor? If there is, you may want to email him."

Still nothing.

"Lou, I will make you this one promise: before I leave here tonight, I am going to make you laugh."

I'm already *talking* to a ghost, I thought to myself; so how hard can it be to make one laugh?

❖❖❖❖❖❖❖

My friend and I were now walking, slowly, around St. Pat's. We weren't really looking at anything specific; we just needed to stretch our legs.

"Lou, you seem to know a lot about me," I began, "but I know very little about you. So let's level the playing field. I know you were a king and I know you are a saint, but what else? Fill me in."

"Wow, Bob, that's very kind of you to even ask. People are always asking something *from* me, not about me. It's been a long time since I've talked about me. I hope I don't bore you."

"That'd be just my luck: of all the gin joints in all the towns in all the world, a boring ghost walks into mine."

Silence.

"That's a very famous line from a very good movie called *Casablanca*, Lou.  In the film it was an old girlfriend, not a ghost, who walked in."

He still just stared at me.

"Sorry, Lou.  I guess you never saw it.  Go ahead."

He immediately perked up.  It was obvious he was anxious to finally talk about himself, his life.

"I was born in 1214.  I was the oldest of twelve children."

I interrupted.  "My gosh; you really were Catholic!"

Again, I got the Louis stare down.

He continued.  "My mom used to tell me, "I love you, my dear son, as much as a mother can love her child; but I would rather see you dead at my feet than that you should ever commit a mortal sin.""

I didn't know how to respond to that.  "That's very… severe, Lou." was the best I could do.  His mom sounded like a real head case.

"I became King of France when I was twelve years old."

"Twelve?" I shouted in disbelief.  "You sure got me beat.  When I was twelve, I was eating boxes of Kraft macaroni and cheese and waiting for the next neighborhood game of kickball to begin."

I think Lou was beginning to get mad at me.  I thought I saw a trace of anger in his eyes.  What's that say about me that I can try the patience of even a saint?

Still, he went on.  "My wife, Margaret, and I were blessed with 11 children.  Her brother, Henry, was King of England."

"I have a brother-in-law who is a meat cutter," I jumped in.  "Isn't that sort of the same thing as your brother-in-law as King of England?  Both are butchers."

He ignored that, too.

"I was engaged in both the Sixth and Seventh Crusades.  I was captured and imprisoned in the Sixth.  Every day in captivity I recited the Devine Office, even at the threat of death.

"I had a great love for the Church and enormous respect for many of its priests and leaders; however, I was not blind to the injustices of a few of the leaders and I, as King, let them know about it. I did not tolerate false or hypocritical Priests or Bishops!

"I did not use or condone profanity or vulgarity. Ask my friends and they'll tell you they never heard me swear or speak ill of anyone in the company of others."

"Boy, Lou, I sure wish I could say the same thing of people today, including our leaders. We gossip, we speculate, we spread rumors, we look for the worst in others; it's all very disheartening."

"I believed in justice. I tried not to play favorites; rich and poor were treated equally in my reign. I tried to protect the poor from oppressive lords. Often I used the fines collected by my courts for religious and charitable works."

"Good luck trying that today. These days we push religion aside. It's not even supposed to be part of the public discussion. A public school cannot hold a *Christmas* party; it must instead be called a *Holiday* party. This, too, is very distressing."

He went on. "I kept my word. I was known as a man of high integrity. I founded a hospital to serve the blind. I often fed the poor and homeless.

"And in 1239 I got an unbelievable gift."

"Was it a gift that was even better than the Milky Way candy bar that I once received?"

Once again, he just skipped over my comment. Cleary; he didn't get my type of humor.

"Baldwin II, the Latin emperor at Constantinople, gave to me the Crown of Thorns."

Of all the unbelievable things he'd told me so far, this was the one I found most incredulous.

"He gave you *what?* How could that be? I am sorry to doubt a saint but c'mon! The crown would have been over twelve hundred years old by then; how could it have still been intact? And how did he get it in the first place? Don't you think you were a bit gullible to buy into that, Lou?"

"Baldwin was thanking me for my largesse to the Christians in Palestine and other parts of the East," he went on, deflecting what I thought was a sensible objection. "I tore down the chapel of St. Nicholas and replaced it with the Sainte Chapelle to house the crown.

"To be honest, I gave away some of the thorns in golden reliquaries, one of which I understand is in the British Museum today, but very little of the original crown remains. That makes me sad."

Louis stopped for a few seconds to gather his thoughts. Then he placed his right hand on my shoulder.

"I died, Bob, in 1270. And here's the really great part about it: I died at 3pm, the same time our Lord died on the cross! And my last words were: 'Into thy hands I commend my soul.'"

His voice cracked a bit. He looked at Christ on the cross above the main altar and then turned his gaze back to me.

"And that, my friend from St. Louis, was my life."

With that, he walked away and knelt in front of the first altar he saw that wasn't his own.

❖❖❖❖❖❖

I left him alone for a few minutes. This, I thought, would be a good time to leave. I still wasn't convinced I was really talking to King Louis IX anyway. Maybe I was hallucinating from that bowl of Irish stew a few hours ago or from complete exhaustion from a very long day and a very long trip. I picked up my backpack from the pew and put the strap over my left shoulder and turned to leave. I wasn't even going to say goodbye.

Lou was standing there as I turned around.

"Leaving so soon?"

"I thought you were up front? How'd you…well, never mind. Yes, Louis, I am leaving. It's been a great experience to meet you but I must go. Take care. Text or email sometime. Let's keep in touch."

"Why not hang around for a few minutes? We still have a few things to discuss."

"Do we now?"

"Yes."

"Like what?"

"Why don't you tell about growing up in St. Louis?"

"You seem to know all about it anyway, don't you? You've already told me that you watched me from the day I was born until the day I left St. Louis some twenty years later. What is there that you possibly don't know?"

"You've got it turned around, Bob. It's not that I need to hear it; it's that you might need to remember it."

"Look, Louis, leave me alone, will you please? I'm not the type of man who likes to talk very much. I'm not really into things like sharing my feelings or long, emotional discussions. Besides, aren't there some St. Louis alumni out there somewhere who needs your help? Do me a favor and go save somebody."

He gave me an icy stare. "I am."

❖❖❖❖❖❖❖

I removed my backpack and placed it in the pew.

"I don't really have a choice," I asked, "do I?"

"You are free to leave anytime, Bob. I'm not holding you hostage. We all have a free will. But, why not stay? Have I not been an interesting friend thus far? How often do you get to talk to a guy who used to be a king? How often do you speak to saints these days? Besides, what's waiting for you back at the hotel other than an empty room?"

He had me there. It was either watching a midnight rerun of ESPN Sports Center or stay here for a few more minutes and talk. Plus, I admitted to myself, I was curious to see what this guy was up to.

"So what do you want to know, Louis?"

"What do you want to tell me?"

"Nothing. I just explained that to you; I don't like to share things."

He ignored me. "What is your earliest memory?"

I paused to think about it.

"Now that's a good question, Lou! How early in life can anyone go back? Let me think about that for a few seconds."

"Take your time. Hey, I'm glad I finally stumped you; so far, you've been a cool customer."

"I'm not sure that there is a specific moment or event that would be my earliest memory," I finally replied. "I suppose my recollections would go back to when I was five years old, perhaps, just like most other people."

"That's fine; let's start there. What do you remember from those first few years?"

"Well, there were only three siblings in the family at that time; my older brother, my older sister and me. Dad worked a lot; not just at his main job but also picking up weekend work or evening work from time to time in order to earn additional income. Mom stayed home to take care of the kids.

"I remember waiting for my brother and sister to come home from school for lunch. Our home was only about a quarter-mile from school, Holy Infant. They got a full hour every day for lunch and recess break, so often they'd walk home to eat a bologna sandwich and drink a glass of chocolate milk. Usually, because I was just a kid with nothing to do, I'd set up in advance a board game for them to play with me as they ate. I was only capable at the time of playing games like *Chutes and Ladders* or *Checkers* so they patiently played those with me all the time. I think they always let me win. Sometimes I'd make them play *Bowling* in our hallway with my plastic pins and large black ball. They'd finish their lunch and walk back to school and I'd take my afternoon nap so I could be good and ready and rested when they came back.

"My family loved games. As the kids got older, we had dozens: *Clue, Monopoly, Life, Scrabble, Risk, Operation, Password, The Match Game, Jeopardy, The Newlywed Game, Concentration* and many more. I was usually the game-show 'host' for the ones which required an emcee. I loved that role. The family got a kick out of it.

"I would often play sports-themed games. I had table-top hockey and I even had names for all the players; my team usually had Glenn Hall as the goalie and Jean Beliveau from the Montreal Canadians as my center and Bobby Orr of the Boston Bruins as one

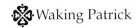 

of my defensemen. I kept statistics, too. One game, Orr scored twelve goals. His table top slap shot was the best in history. I say that with pride because, after all, I was the one at his controls.

"I had electric football. That game, however, was very frustrating to play, even for a sports nut kid like me. It took 'the coach' about ten minutes just to set up in proper formation the eleven teammates to run a play. Then you had to stuff that small football-shaped piece of white cotton in between the quarterback's body and right arm. The quarterback was also your running back because never in the history of electric football was there ever a completed pass: the few times one would even attempt a forward pass, the piece of cotton would either fall at the feet of the quarterback or would fly off the field and land in the kitchen; one game, it landed in mom's pot of tomato soup. Finally, after all this set-up, you'd turn the switch to 'on', the field would vibrate, the players on both teams would scatter aimlessly around the field, and about ten seconds later the quarterback had turned around and gone the wrong way and all the other players on the field had run head-first into the sideline. This was a horrible game but every kid had one. If you got one for Christmas or a birthday, you thought it was a great gift; but then about two weeks later you hated it and it was forever placed on the top shelf of your bedroom closet, never to be seen again."

"I remember watching you spend hours playing a baseball board game," Louis said.

"Oh, I loved that game, you're right! It was called *All-Star Baseball*. It was made by a game company called Codaco. On the box cover it said, 'Play Real Baseball With Real Major League Stars.' One year my team had these players: outfielders Babe Ruth, Mickey Mantle and Hank Aaron; Lou Gehrig, Bobby Doerr, Honus Wagner and Mike Schmidt in the infield; Bill Dickey as my catcher; and a pitching staff of Dizzy Dean, Sandy Koufax, Whitey Ford and Bob Feller. I can't believe that team ever lost a game. Like table top hockey, I kept stats in this game, too. One season, Koufax threw nine consecutive no-hitters and Mantle hit ninety home runs."

I paused. "And remember, Lou, this was *before steroids.*"

Silence. I still couldn't get this guy to laugh.

"I did love that game, Lou" I went on. "I'll let you in on a little secret: I *still* have it. The game is displayed on a top shelf in my home office.

"And do you know what I have on the next shelf down?"

He played along. "What would that be?"

"I have my collection of *The Hardy Boys* books! Yes, I still have them, even at age 55. I loved to read about the adventures of Frank and Joe Hardy. They were amateur detectives, the son of the 'world famous detective Fenton Hardy,' a phrase that was used literally in every book. Their pals often assisted as they investigated a case; Chet Morton, Tony Prito, Biff Hooper, Jerry Gilroy; but it always seemed to me that the pals usually made things worse for Frank and Joe. A couple of platonic girlfriends, Callie Shaw and Iola Morton, were sometimes involved in the case, too. The gals were always making brownies for the guys or planning picnics, pretty much just getting in the way of their investigative work. In one book, Frank, the older of the two brothers, held hands with Callie; that was as scandalous as the books ever got. They were a great read for a kid. My two favorites were *The Tower Treasure* and *The Great Airport Mystery* but there had to be close to a hundred of them total. I remember wondering once how one author could have come up with so many books but later in life I learned that the books were written by many ghostwriters but published under the pseudonym Franklin W Dixon.

"Strange, but I recall being disappointed when I discovered that fact. I wonder why that would have upset me," I revealed as I slowly shook my head.

"Anyway, my brothers loved *The Hardy Boys*, too. And my sisters read *The Nancy Drew Mystery* series and *The Bobbsey Twins*. Sometimes we three boys would pretend we were Fenton, Frank and Joe Hardy and our two sisters would pretend to be Nancy Drew and her best friend Bess Marvin and we'd walk around the house trying to solve a mystery, like where did mom and dad hide the Christmas gifts or how many beers did the men drink last night at dad's cookout."

"Tell me more about this book shelf in your home office

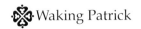

today," said Louis. "Do you have anything else on it from your childhood?"

I thought about it. It's a brown bookshelf, probably purchased from Target decades ago, and it stands about five feet high in the back corner of my den.

"Off the top of my head, I can think of two other items. One is a very small, no more than six inches in height, soccer trophy presented to me by my players when I was a coach."

"Ah, yes, I remember."

"I was only fifteen years old. I was a sophomore in high school. I was asked to coach one of the fourth grade boy's soccer teams back at my old grade school, Holy Infant. Soccer was hugely popular and they had so many boys who wanted to play that they had to split the fourth grade into two teams. When I accepted the offer to coach, I didn't know that the other team's coach, a longtime parishioner, had already stacked his team with the boys who had played soccer in the past; he gave me all the kids who had *never* played! Many of them didn't even know the rules of the game, much less how to dribble, pass, shoot, score, defend and tend goal.

"After the first week of practice, when my boys were still learning the basics of the sport, the other coach challenged us to a scrimmage. I accepted, even though both of us knew that his guys would destroy my guys. And, sure enough, that other squad won, 8-0, which for a soccer score is an absolute annihilation. But, in my madness of agreeing to the scrimmage in the first place, there was a method, a reason.

"My team had to listen to their classmate's ridicule for the next two months; they never lived it down that they were on the 'bad' fourth grade team. The two teams went their own way during the season; my guys were placed in the lower division and that other team was assigned to the more experienced division. We only encountered one another at the beginning or end of a practice session on the Holy Infant soccer field. For two months, that other coach looked down his nose at me and his players looked down on my boys. What he didn't realize was that as he ignored us for those two months, my team improved significantly.

"At the end of the season, I returned the favor. I asked the other coach if he'd like to scrimmage us once again. I told him it'd be a good way to wrap up the year; get the classmates back on the field for a friendly little game. He eyed me suspiciously but he agreed to play; how could he not?

"Well, do you know, Lou, what happened next?"

"Yes, I do."

"My boys won, 2-1! You should have seen them run off the field after the final whistle. They felt like they had just won the World Cup! They had been mercilessly mocked by their classmates for months and now they had earned a very sweet revenge. Their parents were overjoyed. And we let that other team hear about it for a long time, believe me. The next week, the boys and their parents presented me with that small trophy that I still have today on my bookshelf."

"Why did you keep it?" asked Louis.

"What do you mean?"

"Well, Bob, you did many things in sports. You didn't keep other awards or trophies. You didn't keep your high school letter jacket. You didn't keep the letter offering you a soccer scholarship to tiny Quincy College."

I jumped in. "I'd forgotten about that!"

"I didn't," he said bluntly. Then he continued. "So, why, I wonder, do you have that small soccer trophy from a group of fourth graders some forty years after they gave it to you?"

"I suppose because it reminds me of the unbridled joy those kids felt. If you could have seen their faces…"

"I did."

"Well, then you should understand. That joy is what I think of when I look at that old trophy. That was a great moment for them. It taught them about the benefits of hard work and the importance of working together towards a common goal. That trophy also reminds me of the gratitude of their parents for they were very tired of the ridicule their sons had endured."

"Was that all it was?"

"Meaning what, Lou?"

"Could that have also been your first experience with the

feeling of revenge? And perhaps you liked how it felt?"

"Well, Louis," I replied rather testily, "so what if I did? I was only fifteen years old. That other coach, an adult mind you, had treated my boys and me poorly for two months. The kids on his team were arrogant and made my boys feel inferior. So, yes, Mr. Saint, maybe revenge did feel good."

"Confucius said of revenge: 'Before you embark on a journey of revenge, dig two graves.'"

I shot back. "Well, I bet Confucius never coached fourth grade soccer."

Louis continued. "And Gandhi said: 'An eye for an eye only ends up making the whole world blind.' Francis Bacon, a buddy of mine, as a matter of fact I just had dinner with him last week, said: 'A man who contemplates revenge keeps his wounds green.'"

"Give me a break, Lou, I was a teenager. We're not all saints, Lou, especially at fifteen years old. Besides, now that I'm wiser and more experienced in this ugly world, I can respond to your Confucius and Bacon and Gandhi with a Shakespeare: 'If you prick us do we not bleed? If you tickle us do we not laugh? If you poison us do we not die? And if you wrong us shall we not revenge?' It's a normal, natural, understandable human reaction and emotion, Lou. Yes, I admit it, I liked the temporary feeling of revenge, but that's not why I kept the trophy. I was very happy that I was able to teach those kids the game of soccer. They probably never forgot that one game against their classmates. I'm glad I was able to do that for them."

"And how do you feel about it now, Bob?"

"I just told you."

"I'm not talking about that long ago soccer game. I'm talking about revenge. Do you still seek it today? Do you still enjoy it?"

My reply came out higher in volume than my usual tone. "Let me get this right; I'm getting a lecture about revenge from a man who once led two crusades?"

"Who better then to teach you?"

He paused for a few seconds. "Let it go, Bob. You have to believe me on this one. If you've been wronged, let it go. Even if you just *think* you've been wronged, let it go. Remember this: there is no revenge so complete as forgiveness.

"Seeking revenge is a waste of time. And the fact is…" He stopped talking.

"Yes?"

"And the fact is that time is growing short."

❖❖❖❖❖❖❖

"What is the other item on that bookshelf?" Louis asked after several moments of silence.

I didn't know what he meant. I was still taking in what he had just said about 'time is short.' For the first time, I was shaken by something my new friend had said.

"What are you talking about?"

"You told me you had *The Hardy Boys* books on that shelf and the All-Star Baseball Game and the coaching trophy: but you left something out."

I thought about it. "Oh, yes, you are right. I also have an eight ounce beer glass inscribed with the autographs of every member of the 1964 St. Louis Cardinals."

"That's the team that beat the powerful New York Yankees in the World Series!"

"Yes. The Cardinals won the series in seven games. I listened to every game on the radio."

Lou grinned: "I *watched* every game." The same guy who just spoke to me about revenge apparently had no problem at all with one-upmanship.

"Who are some of the names on that beer glass?" he went on.

"To begin with, the starting line-up: Tim McCarver, Bill White, Julian Javier, Dick Groat, Ken Boyer, Mike Shannon, Curt Flood, Lou Brock. The starting pitchers included Bob Gibson and Ray Sadecki. That one small glass has every signature on it. And every now and then I pick it up and look at those names. Sometimes I even drink a cold beer out of it. It's just another reminder of my upbringing."

"Baseball was a big part of your childhood, wasn't it?"

"You should know that, Lou, hanging around St. Louis as much as you did. When one grows up in St. Louis, you are a huge fan of the Cardinals. I think it's even a part of one's baptismal ceremony; first, the holy water on the forehead, then a small Cardinal's cap, then a ticket to your first game."

Lou just stared at me. He was very good at that. I still couldn't make him laugh. Heck, right now, I'd take a giggle.

"In fact, sweet Lou" I continued, "it was a baseball game that made me cry for the very first time, at least as far as I can remember."

"Let me think. Ah yes; 1968, correct?"

I nodded my head. I still didn't get how this guy knew so much.

"It was game seven of the 1968 World Series between my Cardinals and the Detroit Tigers. I watched the game on television. I was only eleven years old. I walked home from school for lunch and my dad allowed me to stay home with him for the rest of the afternoon. He was working an overnight shift at the time. He had just made me one of his classic lunches; a bologna sandwich with mustard and peanut butter, and…"

"He made you *what*?"

"A bologna sandwich with yellow mustard and peanut butter," I repeated.

"I am surprised I didn't remember that," Louis responded.

"Don't look so disgusted, Lou. Try one sometime. It is outstanding! Even now at age 55, I enjoy one on occasion. Dad also used to put peanut butter in our grilled cheese sandwich. That was great, too. When I had kids, I made the same things for them. They loved them, also.

"Lou," I teased, "you shouldn't be so quick to judge."

I laughed. He didn't.

"Anyway, I was so happy to be able to watch that game with my dad. The next day I found out I was one of only two kids in my class who did not return to school from lunch that previous day. Everyone in my class thought that the other boy and I had the coolest dads ever."

"Those Irish nuns probably did not share that opinion on that particular day," Lou stated.

"Whatever. As Mark Twain once said, 'Never let school get in the way of an education.' That's where I stand. Sometimes it's beneficial to keep the kids home from school if you are providing a worthwhile experience. My wife and I did it on occasion with our daughters. They remember those days far more than a spelling lesson.

"Anyway, back to the World Series. It was the final game. The contest was played in Busch Stadium in downtown St. Louis. We had our best pitcher, Bob Gibson, and they had their best, Mickey Lolich. It was scoreless in the top of the seventh inning. It was very tense. Dad and I were biting our nails as we watched on our small television set. He was drinking a beer and I had a Vess cola. We never bought Coke or Pepsi; it was always a generic or secondary brand. Vess was my favorite. I was wearing my Cardinal hat, similar to the one you have, Lou.

"The Tigers had two runners on base in that seventh inning. Then, Jim Northrup hit a ball very well but right at our center fielder Curt Flood. He was an excellent defensive player and had won several Gold Glove awards in his career. However, on this play, Flood mis-judged it. He initially broke in on the ball, and by the time he realized his mistake, the ball flew over his head and rolled to the wall. Northrup had a two-run triple and my Cardinals were in serious trouble. They didn't recover from that Flood mistake.

"Detroit won, 4-1. When the Cards made the final out of the game, I started to cry. Honestly, I cried! I couldn't imagine my Cardinals ever losing a World Series for they had won the other two in my lifetime, 1964 over New York and 1967 over Boston. This time, they lost, and in such a heartbreaking manner, too, with our best pitcher on the mound and the mistake in center field. Dad turned off the television set and went outside to rake the leaves. I stayed inside and cried. So, Lou, yes, baseball was a big deal to all of us.

"Heck, I remember being allowed to take a county bus, called The Redbird Express, to Cardinal games all by myself when I was as young as eight! Dad would drive me from our home in

Ballwin to the West County Shopping Mall about twenty miles away to pick up the bus. Many people rode that Redbird Express, young and old, male and female. It only cost a dollar for a round-trip from the mall to Busch Stadium and back. Sometimes I went with a few friends, sometimes I went alone. Even the game ticket only cost one buck. Dad was always there, sometimes as late as midnight, to meet the bus after the game and bring me home. We always met under the light pole with the giant dove on top. He'd ask me, 'Who won?' even though I knew he had listened to the game on the radio back home. When I proceeded to tell him the details of the game, he acted like he didn't know. Sometimes he had a McDonald's cheeseburger waiting for me when I jumped in the car. And a real Coke with lots of chipped ice in the cup.

"Can you imagine, Lou, any parent allowing their kid to do that *these days*? Times were so different then; a parent knew it was safe to let their eight-year old ride a bus, alone, at night, to a downtown area to watch a major league baseball game, surrounded by tens of thousands of strangers, then walk back to the bus terminal after the game to get the ride back home. That would never happen today. I never allowed *my* kids to do anything close to that!"

"You *played* baseball, too, didn't you?"

"I sure did," I responded quickly. "I was pretty good, but as I get older I probably exaggerate my ability. Don't we all? I mean, when we're adults we all believe we were superstars at *something* in our past. A friend of mine talks so often about his soccer talent on our high school team that you'd swear his name was Pele or David Beckham. Same thing with me; to hear me talk now you'd think I was in the baseball Hall of Fame, but like anyone else I did have my moments."

"I remember one in particular," Lou said. "Big game, big moment, you were the man at bat in the key situation, your dad and some of his buddies were watching from the bleachers."

"I recall that one very well! We were playing our rivals. They were in first-place at the time. It was the bottom of the eighth inning, the game was tied 3-3, we had runners at first and second, there were two out and I was up next. The other team's manager walked to the mound to bring in his ace relief pitcher. I stood near home plate to watch the guy warm-up. He was huge. He had a scowl on his face. The kid was even working on a real mustache! He threw very hard. However, the more I watched him throw, the more confident I grew. I had been hitting the ball very well for the last two weeks. I was in a zone. I was hitting line-drives from foul pole to foul pole. 'This guy has a nasty fastball', I thought while watching him, 'but I can hit it.' I wanted to wipe that ridiculous scowl right off his face.

"I worked him to a full count: three balls and two strikes. I was late swinging on his first heater. I fouled off his next one. Then he nibbled at the corners on the next three but I didn't bite.

"I stepped out of the box for a few seconds. I knew he didn't want to walk me because then the bases would be full, placing the winning run at third base. I knew, too, that his best pitch was his fastball. So, as I stepped back into the box, I expected him to throw his very best seed right over the plate."

Lou jumped in. "And that's exactly what he did."

"Yes! And I pounced all over it. I hit from the left-hand side and I jumped on that fastball and hit it so hard that it was over the right-fielder's head before he could get his glove above his shoulder. It rolled to the fence. The two runners scored, I had a triple, and we had a 5-3 lead.

"As I stood on third base and bent over to catch my breath, placing my hands on my knees, my third base coach came over and slapped me on the back. Then, for just a few seconds, I glanced to the bleachers and saw my dad's three friends standing to applaud and dad, still sitting, with a look of pride on his face that I had never seen before."

I turned to look at Lou directly and took a slight bow. "And that, my friend, was the highlight of my baseball career."

"*Which part* of that story was the highlight?" he asked.

"Well, my game winning triple, of course. What other part was there?"

He said nothing. He just shrugged his shoulders.

❖❖❖❖❖❖❖

"Do you remember another time you cried?" resumed Louis.

"In my childhood, you mean?"

"That's what I mean. That was my jurisdiction, remember; from your birth to the time you left St. Louis. You already told me the time you cried after that World Series, but I also recollect a time you cried just about a year later."

"You make it sound like I was a crybaby. I sure hope not."

"No, you didn't cry any more or less than any other kid. It's just the things that made you cry were unique."

"Remind me. What's the other one?"

"You really don't remember? Here's a hint: card game."

I remembered immediately. "Oh, yes, the card game. You are right; once again I cried like a baby. What a stupid and annoying kid I must have been."

Lou didn't reply.

"Feel free to disagree if you wish."

He didn't budge. "Go on with the story."

"You know, Lou, as I remember all these things from my past, I can't help but wonder if all you ever did was watch. Why didn't you ever step in and stop me? It would have been nice, for example, for you to somehow intervene and stop me from that card game. You could have saved me a lot of money."

"Bob, was not the money lost worth the lesson learned? Like I told you earlier, sometimes the Boss won't allow us to step in. It's all in His plan. Now, get on with the story."

"One night, my older brother and his college classmates were at the house for dinner. After the meal, they began a card game at the dining room table. Dad joined in. I was just twelve years old so I was standing off to the back but watching with interest.

"I had been cutting grass, raking leaves and picking up various other minor jobs at school and around the neighborhood all summer, trying to earn enough money to buy a ticket to the new Six Flags over Mid-America amusement park. All my friends were going to the park at the end of summer and I knew the only way I could join them is if I paid for the admission myself. At the time of this card game I had earned about $12, which was very close to the amount I needed.

"The game that most grabbed my attention was called In Between. I was interested because the rules were much easier for me to understand than were the other games they had played, including five-card stud or seven-card draw where every other card, it seemed, was wild. During those games, time after time I watched as one of the players somehow came up with five aces to win a hand. I couldn't grasp that because even I knew there are only four aces in a deck of cards. That whole 'wild card' thing was way beyond my skill level.

"In Between, however, was an easy game to understand. Each player would receive two cards face-up and the player had to bet on the chances of his third card being *in between* his first two. For example, if a player was dealt a five and a nine, the player would only win if the third card was a six, seven or eight. In this scenario, the wager would be a small one because the odds of winning were very low. If a player's first two cards, however, were a three and a king, then the bet would be a much larger one because the player would win on a third card of anything from a four to a queen. A tie was a loss. If a player lost his bet, his money would go in to the pot and the game would continue until someone was willing to bet everything in the pot and then drew a winning third card. Does all of that make sense, Lou?"

"It does. I especially like the 'king' part."

"So, long story short, I decided that In Between was a game even a twelve year old could play.

"I asked Dad if I could join in. He thought before answering, took two puffs off his Pall Mall cigarette and told me to pull up a chair.

"I was nervous; after all, this was my first card game involving real money. Before this I had only wagered with Monopoly money, toothpicks or potato chips.

"I gathered my money from my cigar box in the bedroom. I gave two dollars to the banker, who happened to be my dad, and he gave me twenty nickels and ten dimes in return. I bet one nickel or one dime at a time for the first fifteen minutes, winning some bets and losing some others.

"Later I saw one of the players bet $10 after he drew a two and

a King on his first two cards. His third card was an eight. He just won $10 in about five seconds. I was very impressed.

"I was having a great time. I was playing real cards with real men and real money. Mom kept bringing in snacks and desserts and I was even allowed to have a second Vess cola. Life was good.

"About an hour into the game and with the pot now worth over $20 I drew a two and an ace. The others at the table shouted with joy. This was, they told me, the perfect draw! My odds were as good as they could ever be in this game. The only cards that could beat me were another two or another ace, and there were already a few of those lying in the discard pile.

"Here's what I was thinking: 'Do you know how many leaves I'd have to rake or how many lawns I'd have to cut to make as much money as what was lying in front of me at this moment?' I'd been working all summer to earn $12 and now I was staring at an opportunity to make all of that and more with just one more good card. Not only could I go to Six Flags, I thought, but I could also buy some food while I was there and still have most of my original money left over. 'Don't be a coward,' I thought. 'Do it!'

"I looked at Dad for advice or approval. He said nothing. I looked at my brother across the table. He just smiled.

"A few of the other players encouraged me to go for it. 'Bob,' one said, 'you just got the ideal hand. This is why we play the game!'

"I'd never been more nervous in my life, except perhaps for the time in kindergarten when I had to stand up in front of the class and recite the alphabet. When I got to 'L', I threw up.

"I can't bet everything I have," I finally announced, "but I will bet most of it. I'm in for ten dollars.

"I was hoping and expecting the others at the table to applaud my choice and my courage. Instead, nobody said a word. I got more nervous. I thought about taking back my bet but then I'd look like a scared little kid. Besides, I had a two and an ace! Others would kill for my hand. I was sure anyone else would bet the full pot if they had my hand. I had to go for it.

"I'm in," I repeated, this time with added emphasis. "Ten

bucks."

"The dealer slowly picked my third card from off the top of the deck. He looked at it before he placed it in front of me. I swear he lost all the color in his face.

"He dropped the card in between my two and my ace. 'Ace of Hearts,' he said quietly.

"I lost. I was stunned.

"I lost to one of the few cards that could beat me. I lost ten of the only twelve dollars I had to my name. I lost most of what it took me two months to earn.

"I looked at my brother. It was one of the few times in his life that he didn't know what to say.

"Next, I turned to Dad. He didn't say anything, either. For a few seconds I believed he would take my $10 out of the pot and hand it back to me. He did not.

"After a few painful seconds of silence one of the guys at the table said, 'Let's just call that a practice hand. We all get our last loss returned to us. We all start over. How does that sound to everyone?'

"That sure sounded great to me! Once again, I looked at my father.

"Dad was quiet. Then he looked me right in the eyes and declared: 'No, leave the money in there. He's been taking money out of the pot when he wins. He leaves the money in when he loses.'

"And that's when I cried, Lou. I mean it, I cried right there at the table, right in front of my dad and my brother and his buddies. Then I got out of my chair and went to my bedroom. I cried there, too."

"I remember. I actually felt sorry for you," admitted Lou. "Everybody there felt sorry for you." He briefly paused, then smiled. "By the way, you sure knew how to ruin a card party."

I grinned back at him. "You're right! I look back now and laugh about it but at the time I was very angry at myself. I was also mad at the dealer for not somehow switching cards once he realized I was going to lose. And I was especially mad at my dad for refusing to correct my mistake.

"I still had tears in my eyes and a strange, horrible feeling in my gut about twenty minutes later when my dad opened the bedroom door. Dads didn't knock back then, Lou, they just barged in. I was lying on my bed so he told me to stand up. He then pulled a ten dollar bill out of his pocket. 'This is your money,' he said. 'You worked very hard for it. Never once did you ask your mother or me for the money needed for Six Flags. You knew you'd have to earn it. You did it the right way. Take this money and I hope you always remember the lesson you just learned; never bet anything if you are unable or unwilling to lose it.'"

"I walked back in to the living room a short time later to find everyone had gone home; it was only Dad, Mom and my brother sitting at the table. They were drinking a final beer and finishing the chips and French onion dip. My brother picked up the deck of cards and held them out in my direction, asking with a smile on his face, 'Hey, Bob, do you feel like playing a little In Between?', and then he burst out laughing.

"I was the only one in the room who did not think he was funny. But I do now. That entire story is funny to me now, but it was sure painful at the time."

Then I looked at Lou eye-to-eye and said, playfully; "Hey, Lou, I bet when you played cards way back when, your favorite card was a King!"

He just looked at me with a blank expression on his face.

I tried again. "Were kings always wild?"

Nothing.

"Or, even better for you, maybe the *queens* were wild!"

Still, he had no reaction. Boy, on the day the good Lord was handing out senses of humors, this guy must have called-in-sick.

❖❖❖❖❖❖❖

"Do you remember the time, Bob, when your family thought you had drown?"

My new friend sure didn't mince words.

"No, Lou, I don't," I replied, dripping with sarcasm. "I mean, why would one recall a time when the rest of his family thought he was dead?"

Louis grinned. It was clear he had enjoyed that particular event. That made one of us.

"My family took a week's vacation to Kentucky Lake. This was unusual in itself because we didn't take many trips. Often, our vacations consisted of a weekend at a cabin in the Lake of the Ozarks or an adventure we called 'day trips' when Mom and Dad would pack the kids in the car, throw some beer and soda in a cooler, sandwiches and snacks in a picnic basket, and we'd literally drive as far as four hours to see something like Old Salem State Park in Springfield, Illinois or the Mark Twain sites in Hannibal, Missouri. Once at our destination, we'd tour whatever it was we had gone to see, we'd find a local park at which to eat our food and drink our refreshments, and we'd jump back in the car and return home. Many times, it was about a hundred degrees with oppressive humidity. Our car never had air conditioning. Invariably, one of the kids would vomit on the return drive. Once, we even hit the trifecta; within ten minutes, three of the kids all threw up. Dad was mumbling cuss words and he even got mad at Mom, as if it was her fault that we had all thrown-up on cue. That stopped day-trips for at least two years.

"One year, however, we splurged and spent a full week at Kentucky Lake. We did very little except swim and eat and rest. Each day, our most difficult decisions were: 1.) What to eat for dinner, and 2.) Should we go to the pool or the beach. It was a good time for all of us."

"Except for..." prodded Louis.

"Yes, Lou, except for that one day at the beach. We had been at the beach for several hours. Our parents were resting in the sun and my siblings and I were in and out of the water. No one was really paying much attention to what the others were doing. Even back then, at age thirteen, I couldn't sit still for long periods of time so I became bored and restless. I had a Coke bottle and the new issue of Sports Illustrated waiting for me back at the cabin so I decided to leave the beach and walk back on my own. The only problem was..."

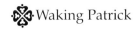 

Louis interrupted. "You didn't tell anyone."

"That's right. I neglected to tell Mom and Dad that I was leaving. I walked to the cabin, got my Coke and magazine, and planted myself in a lawn chair in the front yard. I was having a grand time, all alone, enjoying the peace and quiet, completely oblivious to what was occurring back at the beach.

"Eventually, Mom looked up from her book and didn't see me. She told Dad; and he, too, looked around the area. They got up from their chairs and asked my siblings if they knew of my whereabouts. They checked the restroom. They checked the concession stand. They couldn't find me.

"And that's when the panic set in. Dad told a lifeguard that his son was missing. The lifeguards spread out over the beach area. Mom began to cry. My siblings grew worried.

"Soon, the lifeguards ordered everyone out of the swimming section. Over a hundred people stood on the beach, watching in silence and shock as the lifeguards took turns diving to the water's floor, expecting to find a kid who had drowned."

"And while all of this is occurring at the beach, you are…"

"I am sitting in a lawn chair back at the cabin without a care in the world. I had no idea."

"Do you know there was a doctor at the beach and he gave your mother a pill to relax her nerves because she was hysterical?"

"Yes, I was told that later."

"What happened next?"

"Dad was told to drive Mom back to the cabin so the lifeguards could continue to search for what everyone was now assuming was a drowning victim. As our car turned into the cabin's driveway, they saw me in my chair, nonchalantly drinking my Coke and reading my magazine. They ran from the car and hugged me. 'I've only been gone an hour,' I thought to myself. 'This is a bit over-the-top.'

"Then they told me of the events of the past hour. They really did think that I was dead. They both laid into me. They couldn't believe I was so irresponsible and thoughtless."

"What did you say to them?"

"I'm not sure I said anything. What *could* I say? Somehow,

'Sorry you thought I was dead; can we go back to the beach after lunch?' didn't seem appropriate at the time. I felt like a complete moron.

"You know, Lou, looking back on all the stupid things I did as a kid, sometimes I wonder if Mom and Dad were ever tempted to trade me in for a case of beer and two filet mignons."

❖❖❖❖❖❖❖

"Let's talk about high school."

"Hey, Lou, what's going on here? What's this all about? Don't get me wrong, you're a nice guy. I respect your life; that King-Saint combination is pretty impressive, certainly better than anything I've ever done, but I'm not the type of guy who spends a lot of his time talking about the past or living in the past. These stories are fun and every now and then it's fine to reminisce but what's the point, Lou? I'm tired. I want to go back to my hotel room and sleep. Tomorrow I go home to see my wife and kids. I'm all talked out. Besides, you know it all, anyway."

My friend didn't respond. Instead he grabbed my elbow and guided me to a folding chair near the back of the cathedral. I knew by now that arguing with him wasn't going to work.

"Let's talk about high school," he repeated. "If I remember correctly, you went to John F. Kennedy High School, didn't you?"

"I did, but I have to be honest with you, Lou; I didn't have the greatest high school experience in the world. I'm not like so many people who look back on their high school years or college years as the best years of their lives. In fact, if it weren't for sports and my circle of friends, I would have hated high school."

"Did you not want to go to JFK?"

"Oh, no, that's not it at all. In fact, I *very much* wanted to attend Kennedy. It was the new high school in our county. There was great buzz and excitement about it. I wanted to be a part of it. Throughout the previous year, during my eighth grade at Holy Infant, I was preparing myself to attend our public high school, Lafayette High, because my parents couldn't afford to send me to JFK, a private school. My older sister went to Lafayette but

she was already graduated by the time I would have attended so I wanted to join many of my friends at Kennedy. One day in May I received a letter from the education department at the archdiocese of St. Louis informing me that I had earned a four year scholarship to Kennedy; a full-ride! Apparently I tested very well in all the high school entrance exams but I've always believed my family's economic situation played a big role, too."

"You were poor, you mean?"

"Well, Lou, I suppose if you want to be blunt, sure. We never thought we were poor, though. We thought everybody was just like us."

I stopped. "Lou, have you ever seen the Christmas movie, *It's a Wonderful Life*?"

"What does that have to do with your high school?"

"I'll get back to that in a minute. Answer the question. I've answered all of yours."

"I've never seen all of it. Sometimes I'm hanging around a stranger's home and they happen to be watching it, but then I usually get called away to go watch over someone else. What about it?"

"The end of the movie is terrific. Jimmy Stewart's character, George Bailey, is at the end of the rope because he's lost all his money. He literally has nothing. He thinks about suicide. His friends and neighbors came to his rescue. They raised money to save George. Then, his older brother Harry, a war hero, grabs a glass of champagne and offers a toast: 'To my big brother George, the richest man in town!' Everybody explodes in song and cheers and laughter. I get a lump in my throat every time I see it."

"It sounds like a fine movie," said Lou, "but why did you think of that now?"

"I told you, we didn't have much money when we were kids. But we had all the things that mattered, and so many times in my adult years I've looked back and realized, to paraphrase Harry Bailey, that we were the richest family in town."

Louis nodded his head. "Very good," he acknowledged. "Now, back to high school: you unexpectedly won a scholarship to allow you to attend the high school of your dreams and yet you tell me your high school experience was not at all a great one. What happened?"

I thought about it. "You know, Lou, it may have been because for the first time in my life I felt like I didn't belong. I felt out of place. I mean, as a kid in my neighborhood and in grade school, I was very comfortable, I felt very much at home, I was well-liked, other kids and classmates seemed to be drawn to me. Once I got to high school, however, I was just another guy. I wasn't special. I got lost in the crowd. It was my fault entirely; JFK was an excellent school, I just didn't know how to make the transition. I didn't play football so I never fit in with the 'jocks'. I got *good* grades but never consistently *great* grades so I never fit in with the Honor Roll kids. I was a bit on the shy side and very aware and embarrassed by my teenage acne so I didn't have any confidence with the girls. I was just your run-of-the-mill high school kid. I doubt if very few of the hundreds of other students even knew who I was. I didn't like that."

"You played sports, yes?"

"I did; baseball and soccer. That helped, but in my high school, football and basketball reigned supreme so the guys who played my sports were often overlooked."

"You had good friends?"

"I sure did. They were the best part of my high school years. My circle included Mike, Al, Marty, Steve, Bruce and Jeff. A few others would float in and out from time to time, but those guys were my core. We hung out together, played sports together, studied together, talked about girls together, went to parties together, and ate countless midnight meals together at IHOP or Pizza Hut or Steak 'n' Shake.

"We always took turns driving to events or parties. Those who weren't driving would chip in for gas: even fifty cents per person went a long way because gasoline was cheap back then. All of our cars were crap; a Pinto, an Impala, a Fairlane, a Volkswagen bug; but they all got us where we needed to go.

"Do you remember the movie *The Exorcist*?" I asked Lou.

"Remember it? Heck, I know the devil it was written about."

His face was expressionless when he said that. I didn't know

if he was kidding and I sure didn't want to ask.

"Well, my buddies and I saw it together. Everybody was talking about that movie. There were long lines at most every theater in the country. We decided to see the midnight showing because we thought that would further prove we weren't afraid of it. What sense did *that* make? Anyway, I was horrified during that movie but because I was with my pals I couldn't let on, so I literally looked at the red exit sign to the left of the screen for most every minute of it. I desperately wanted to turn my head away or close my eyes but I knew my buddies would never let me hear the end of it, so by looking at the exit sign they never knew I wasn't really watching the screen. Two days later, one of my friends confessed that he, too, had stared at the exit sign for most of the film. We laughed about that for weeks and never told any of the others."

"Do you believe in the devil?" asked Lou. "Do you believe that Satan can possess one's body?"

"I sure did then, after seeing *The Exorcist*. The movie, you know, was based on a true story."

"Of course I know that. The case occurred in St. Louis."

"You're right!"

"I'm always right; why does that still surprise you? In the movie, the possessed person was a girl but the real-life case in St. Louis involved a boy. The possession and the exorcism fascinated me, even scared me, as I watched over it. The power and influence of evil can be frightening."

"After the movie," I said, returning to his question about my belief in the devil, "I read a few books about other real-life exorcisms and demonic possessions. So, yes, I most certainly did believe it back then."

"And now?"

"Well, Lou, that's one of the many things I just don't know about these days. The older I get, the more I question things. Obviously, there is evil in the world. There always has been. However, the belief in one very specific supernatural source of evil may not be necessary to explain away all evil acts and thoughts. Man alone is quite capable of every evil and wickedness, would you not agree?  Have we not seen that throughout history?  Do you get what I am trying to say, Lou?  I'm not sure that there is one guy forever lurking out there somewhere with a pitchfork and tail and red pointed ears named The Devil.  Sometimes I think that all that is necessary for the triumph of evil is for good men to do nothing."

"My new friend Bob goes deep; where is *that* coming from?" he asked sarcastically.

"Hey, you asked the question.  I'm just being upfront with you. I am curious and confused about many things; the existence of one devil, one Satan, is just one example."

"Be careful, Robert, about what you question or doubt. Listen to me: The devil thrives where resistance to him is the least."

"Wow, you just called me 'Robert' for the first time in our friendship. Mom used to call me 'Robert' when I was in trouble."

"What did your dad call you as a tip-off you had misbehaved?"

"He'd call me 'Mister', as in 'You get over here right now, Mister!' or 'I am not happy with you, Mister.'  When he used 'Mister' instead of my name, I knew I was in for it."

I paused because I suddenly, inexplicably, remembered something.

"There was one incident, however, that went far beyond getting called 'Mister'.  God, that was bad.  He was so upset."

"Remind me."

I closed my eyes trying to erase that specific memory. "Maybe some other time, Louis.  Not now."

"Very well," he conceded.  "Let's return to your high school buddies."

"We just had good times; nothing more to it than that.  We were always laughing.  We were mischievous at times, yes, but nothing ever serious.  I remember two of us went golfing at the local course one day after school.  We weren't very good at the game but we enjoyed it and usually had a few beer cans hidden inside our bag.  The legal drinking age in Missouri at this time was 18 years so, admittedly, we often ignored that law.  Most everyone did, frankly."

"That's good to know.  Obviously that made it right."

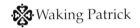 

I pretended I didn't hear him.

"I met my friend at the golf course. He came directly from football practice and when he arrived he realized he didn't have any other shoes with him other than his football cleats. 'Who's going to know?' he joked. 'Let's play.'

"On the seventh hole he hit the best approach shot in his life; he nailed a six-iron to within about two feet of the pin. As we walked to the green, he constantly talked about this upcoming short putt which would give him the first legitimate birdie ever; one accomplished without a mulligan or improving one's lie in the fairway, two things we often did during a round. He was ecstatic.

"I putted first, missed, and then tapped in for my par. As I walked off the green, I noticed a course official sitting in a cart on top of the small hill at the back of the green, watching us. I didn't think anything of it at the time and I turned around to watch my buddy attempt his birdie putt.

"He stood over that putt for a long time. I'd been in that situation before so I knew what was going on in his head; he was thinking of all the different ways he could *miss*.

Finally, he drew back the putter, struck the ball, and sure enough he missed it! He left it short! He had a two foot putt and he, inexcusably, left it short! He had choked. And he knew it.

"In his anger and frustration, he immediately began jumping up and down on the green, repeatedly, while screaming, 'I missed it!' Remember, he was wearing football shoes with long cleats, so with each jump he tore out a huge chunk of the green. Being the good friend that I was, I did what any good friend would do: I laughed at him.

"That's when I remembered the official sitting in the golf cart. I looked up to where he sat and watched him speed down the hill, taking a turn on two wheels, headed directly to my friend still jumping on the green."

"What happened?" asked Lou.

"That man got in our faces real good. He threw us off the course on the spot and warned us to never come back. Boy, was he ever mad!"

"What did your friend say?"

"He apologized, naturally, but then he boldly asked for a refund because we weren't being allowed to finish what we paid for."

"Did you get one?"

"No. Why would we? But we've laughed about that incident for almost forty years now and that fact alone makes it one of my best rounds of golf ever."

"Are you still in contact with your high school buddies? It's been almost four decades since you graduated."

"One remains a very good friend. Another I see twice a year when he is in my hometown for business and a third stays in touch via email or Facebook."

"What about all the others? What happened?"

"The same thing that happens to most of the people one meets in life; they just go away. You lose touch, you lose interest, and all of a sudden they've become just another part of your past. Sometimes I wish I could gather all of my close friends from all of the different periods of my life; childhood, high school, my first career job in Illinois, my decades in Milwaukee, and my current friends; and bring them all together. At those different times in my life, they were outstanding friends who shared with me many good times. I wonder if an event like that, where I could see all of them once again, would make me happy or sad. It'd be good to see them, yes, but also perhaps a bit melancholy because you cannot recapture what used to be. One always needs to look forward, would you not agree, Lou? Appreciate the past, fine; but never wish to re-live it."

"You've ventured pretty far off the path these last few minutes; you were talking about high school friends, remember?"

"Well, one good group of friends made me think of others, I suppose."

"Did you all like he same music?"

"Not at all! Some of us were into The Rolling Stones and The Who and JethroTull and Bachman-Turner Overdrive and Creedence Clearwater Revival; others, including me, liked The Kinks, Jackson Browne, Loggins & Messina, Seals and Crofts,

even Bread and The Bee Gees, believe it or not."

I chuckled. "It is kind of embarrassing to admit that now. What were we thinking?"

Louis waited for me to continue.

"Talking about music just reminded me of another story. One of the guys in my group would accept a bet on most anything; he was crazy enough to take on a humiliating challenge if it meant he could win a few dollars from the rest of us. One day at lunch in the school cafeteria, there were about ten of us around one large table, eating Twinkies and Fritos and drinking Cokes; our typical high school lunch. We were bored. We decided to liven up the lunch room which was packed with about two hundred other students by challenging our buddy to jump up on the table and sing, as loudly as possible, any song of his choosing."

'How much money?' he asked, eagerly.

"Right then, we knew we had him. The others at the table looked at each other and pulled a figure out of thin air. I spoke for the group. 'Ten bucks.'

I looked at Louis; this set-up to the story had his full attention.

"Sure enough, Lou, this guy jumps on top of the table and sings *Rocky Mountain Way* by Joe Walsh. He even plays the air guitar. He's pounding his right foot on the top of the table, keeping time with the song. He is doing all of this very loudly. Everyone in that cafeteria stopped eating and turned to watch our friend. Some began to clap; others even began to sing along. Our pal was really getting into it; it was like he really thought he was Joe Walsh giving a concert in a sold-out arena. The guys at our table were doubled-over in laughter.

"This went on for at least a minute before being noticed by a teacher standing inside the main office. He sprinted across the cafeteria and yanked our friend off the top of the table. He grabbed him by the back of his collar and walked him directly to the principal's office. The students cheered.

"They got close to the door when our buddy, still being tightly held by the teacher, stopped and turned. He yelled across the cafeteria to our table: 'Hey, don't forget my ten bucks!'

"We emptied our pockets and all we could come up with

was $3.75. After school, facing a two-day suspension, our friend accepted the money without remorse. He didn't even care that we shortened him by over six dollars."

Louis smiled. "I remember that guy. Watching over him was nearly a full-time assignment."

He went on. "Did you guys, your close circle of friends, ever fight?"

"Come on, you know how guys are; if there's ever a serious disagreement, you throw a couple of punches, you roll around in the dirt for a few seconds, then you get up and brush each other off and laugh about it. We got along great. We were pretty thick. However, in our four years of high school, there were two things that, honestly, were inexcusable. I was involved in both. Would you like to guess, Lou, what they were about?"

"Probably a girl."

"Right again, Lou. We had a phrase, 'cutting the grass', which meant one guy was hitting-on the date of a friend. Let me be clear: if the date was our buddy's steady girlfriend, then we'd stay clear, obviously. Very few of us in my circle ever had a steady girlfriend, however, so that rule rarely came into play. But if the friend met a girl at a party or dated a girl once every few months just for something to do, nothing at all serious in their relationship, then it was considered 'cutting the grass' if another friend tried to move in. Admittedly, there was a lot of grey area, the rules weren't exactly clear-cut black and white, so sometimes it was no big deal but other times it clearly crossed the line. One never really knew until one did it."

"And just where did you fit in, Bob?"

"Well, I was on the receiving end of a 'grass cut' once and I was on the giving end the other time."

"Do you mean…"

"Yes, Lou, I was a victim one time and, sad to say, the guilty party the next time. Frankly, neither time felt good. I'll start with the time I had the lawn mower. A good friend held a huge party at his home; there had to be over sixty people. Obviously, one did not know everyone at the party because there were many new faces. Near the end of the night, I noticed a cute redhead looking

in my direction. Believe me, Lou, this was a new sensation for me; usually girls looked beyond me, not at me; or if they really were looking at me, it was in disbelief that any high school boy could be so ugly. I got more stares than the Elephant Man.

"Anyway, a few minutes later the redhead walked over. Instinctively, I looked over my shoulder to see what guy was standing behind me for she certainly couldn't have been coming over to talk to me. To my surprise, I was the only boy in the area.

"She was very pleasant. Our conversation came very easily. I was not at all nervous like I usually was when attempting to say anything beyond 'hello' to a girl. And, Lou, she was a doll.

"She explained that she had to leave the party because she had come with a group of friends and the driver of that car was ready to leave. Then she said, 'If you'd ever like to go out, please call.' She wrote her phone number on a napkin, turned and left.

"After I picked myself up off the floor, I immediately tracked down my buddies. I couldn't wait to tell them that I met a very nice girl and she wanted to go out with me. I think I made it into the next room in one giant stride. Either that or I floated.

"I found my friends. I told them about the redhead and our conversation. Soon, one of my pals stopped me in mid-sentence to ask the girl's name. 'Pam', I responded.

"My friend got angry. He told me that Pam was his date for the party that night. He said they had gone out three times in recent weeks. He said he really liked her. He said that he thought she really liked him. Then he walked away.

"The rest of my friends glared at me; they immediately found me guilty of cutting the grass. 'I didn't know Pam was his date!' I protested. After a few minutes, they came around to my side of the story: they realized that I was only guilty of ignorance.

"It took me about 30 minutes to locate the other friend. He accepted my apology and graciously admitted that it really wasn't my fault. He told me he was more upset at Pam because he thought they had been getting along quite well. In fact, he was so nice to me that he encouraged me to call Pam.

"Did you?" asked Louis.

"No, I couldn't do that to a buddy," I responded.

I did not tell Lou, however, that every night for the next week I dialed Pam's phone number and then hung up each time she answered; I was very close to asking out a girl who had just hurt a good pal. That was pretty despicable of me. However, if you'd had seen Pam as she walked out of that room, you'd cut me some slack. I didn't want to go there with Louis; he'd never understand. He's a saint.

"Remind me of that other incident," Lou prodded. "Now you are the victim, not the perpetrator."

"I'm happy to. I am still seething about it. It involved a classmate named Molly. Everyone in my circle of friends knew that I had a massive crush on Molly. Heck, that crush was so big, Great Britain probably knew about it. However, I never dated Molly; I could never get up the courage to ask her. She was way out of my league.

"That's where it gets tricky. If I was never going to ask her on a date, is it allowable and acceptable if my friend asks her out? As I told you before, Lou, sometimes the rules of grass cutting are not clear.

"Well, you know where I am going with this. One of my friends began dating Molly. In fact, they became a couple. He never once asked me if I'd be alright with them dating. To make matters far worse, he once asked me for a ride home from a party. He had Molly with him. And as I drove home, alone in the front seat, my dream girl Molly and a guy who considered me a friend made-out in my back seat like they were Richard Burton and Liz Taylor.

"Lou, in my opinion, that was not only cutting the grass, that was using a riding mower. That was showing off. That was rubbing it in my face. That hurt. And I think he did it on purpose."

"What happened between you and the friend?"

"Our friendship was never the same. I didn't forgive him. He was still in our circle for the final year of high school but I shut him off pretty good. After graduation, I never spoke to him again. I have no idea whatever became of him."

"What about Molly?"

"They broke up after about three months. I certainly didn't want to date her anymore. I think she was just as guilty as my buddy. She had to know I had a crush on her. I hope she's old and fat right now."

Lou hesitated before making his next comment. Finally, he said, "You seem to have a hang-up with being wronged."

"Excuse me?"

"You have a hard time with letting go. You have a hard time with forgiveness. For example, you still remember how poorly you were treated by that adult soccer coach at your grade school. Now you're telling me of the rotten behavior by this friend and his girl. Both events occurred over forty years ago, Bob. Tell me, if you accidentally ran into this high school friend tomorrow, would you laugh with him about that incident or would you still be mad?"

"Honestly, probably both. I'd start by making a snide comment along the lines of, 'So, are you still cutting grass these days or did you finally grow up?' Then, after satisfactorily making him uncomfortable, I'd joke about it with him."

"Why, Lou, is there something wrong with that or do you expect all of us to live the perfect little lives of the saints?"

He responded. "Remind me again how your first friend reacted when you admitted liking his date, Pam."

I paused. I didn't like where this was going. "He understood. He accepted my apology."

"And today?"

"We are still friends."

"Now tell me again of *your* reaction to your friend and Molly."

I knew Lou was right but I wasn't going to give in too quickly.

"Look, Lou, you cannot condone what that guy did to me! I don't apologize for being upset and hurt."

"I repeat: Bob, it's been four decades! Do you really wish Molly was old and fat? Would you really give grief to your ex-friend if he showed up in your life tomorrow? Robert, you are better than that. The best way to get even is to forget. One shows no grace while holding a grudge. Besides, those who forgive most are often most forgiven; and may I remind you that there are many things you've done, many things we have all done, that need forgiveness."

With that, Lou quickly turned and walked down the aisle. I had the feeling that I was not his favorite person at the moment.

I caught up with him in a few strides. I knew he had made the appropriate point but I wasn't going to let it go just yet. I didn't like being judged.

"Hey, Lou, since you are the one who first asked me about high school, how about I also share with you my most vivid memory. Let's see how self-righteous you feel then."

Unexpectedly, my voice began to rise in anger. Louis had a look on his face as if he knew what was coming next.

"Let's talk about the month of May, Lou, of my junior year, shall we?"

Lou knew. He took a step back and removed his Cardinal cap and rubbed his scalp. "If you must," he said. He sounded sad.

"Let's see, how does the story go again?" I said, bitterly. "Oh, yes, now I remember. It's final exam week. I'm a junior. At our school, if you were finished with finals for the day, you had permission to go home early. It just so happens on this day in mid May, four freshman girls took their last exam. They began to walk home. It was early afternoon. It was raining very hard as they exited the school so they decided to take a short-cut through the thick trees on the hill overlooking the parking lot. The trees would provide cover for them from the rain."

I heard my voice grow in volume. I wasn't doing it on purpose. It just happened.

"By the time they got to the trees, the storm turned violent. Thunder, high winds, very heavy rain. The four girls, best friends, sought shelter under an elm tree. Would you like to take it from here, Lou, or shall I?"

He didn't respond.

"A bolt of lightning hits the tree and cuts it in half. The four girls were later found huddled together." By now, my voice was shaking. "They had been holding each other, Lou, when the lightning struck. They burned to death, Lou. Do you remember that? *They burned to death.*"

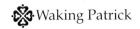

I briefly paused to catch my breath and calm down.

"This tragedy was front page news the next day in *The St. Louis Post-Dispatch* and *The St. Louis Globe Democrat*: 'High School Girls Killed by Lightning'. This was the lead story on television and radio. There was video of sobbing firemen as they carried the bodies out of the woods.

"Our high school had a student assembly the following day. Everybody cried, even teachers. The yearbook photos of the four victims were displayed near the stage. Our principal tried to give a speech to provide comfort; he couldn't get through it. He told us of visiting the families of the four girls the previous night. He broke down and cried uncontrollably. He was never the same, Lou. That moment changed his life.

"I'm not going to pretend that these freshman girls were my best friends; they were not. I didn't even know two of them and the other two I only knew well enough to say hello to as we passed in a hallway. So I'm not seeking sympathy here, Lou.

"I am seeking an answer. Explain *that*, will you, Lou? So far you are really good at explaining all this other trivial stuff in my life but what about this one? Explain why four girls aged fourteen and fifteen are killed while walking home from school. Explain to their parents, Lou, why their hearts just broke in half and their lives will forever feel empty. Explain to the victim's siblings and friends and cousins why these four innocent girls were taken away, in such a horrendous manner, with so much of their lives ahead of them, with men to marry, with children to raise, with contributions to make. Explain the reason for such indescribable pain felt by so many people. So far tonight, Lou, you're pretty good about soccer trophies and letting go of grudges but how are you on *this one*?

"Where were *you* that day, Lou? Were you watching another baseball game? Did you even think about stepping in to stop it? Did you even ask if you *could* stop it? Did you know it was going to occur?

"And while I'm at it: Where was *God* that day, Lou? Where was our compassionate and loving God the moment that lightning bolt cut that tree in half? Where was He when the four innocent teenagers burned to death?

"So, Lou, when you order me to talk about high school, I will tell you about good friends and playing sports and attending parties; and I will tell you about the times I behaved poorly; but I will also tell you about four girls who never got out of their freshman year. And how for forty years nobody has ever been able to explain that to me."

My anger had taken Lou by surprise. He clearly didn't know how to respond.

I sat in the pew and put my head in my hands. My anger had surprised me, as well.

I lifted my head and was about to apologize for my tone and disrespect when Lou took a small step in my direction and whispered, "Bob, sometimes even people like me don't have an answer."

❖❖❖❖❖❖❖

We sat in silence for several minutes. St. Pat's Cathedral was empty, other than us, and completely quiet. Finally, I spoke.

"Lou, I hope you don't think I'm some kind of atheist or agnostic. Of course, I believe in a loving and forgiving God. As I get older, though, sometimes I just cannot make sense of things so I ask myself a lot of questions about God, faith, church, and where I fit in on all three."

"That's quite common."

"It annoys me, though, that I can't quite seem to grasp it. I can't get my arms around all of it. Other people seem to be very content, even joyful, in their faith life. For me, though, it seems the more questions I ask, the more lost I feel, and more doubt creeps in."

"That's not necessarily a bad thing, Bob. If one is a real seeker of truth, doubt is often the first step. And when faith overcomes doubt, your faith is stronger."

He paused.

"Bob, our time together is nearly done. I don't want to leave anything on the table before I go."

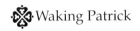

"I think we've covered it all."

"Have we?"

"Lou, if you have something to say, just say it! If you think there's something else, then tell me. You just said, 'I don't want to leave anything on the table.' I responded, 'I don't think we have.' And yet you still insist we are missing something. Some of these things we've discussed tonight, I haven't thought of in years. What else is there, Lou, from my growing up years in St. Louis? If you've got something on your mind, which you obviously do, just come out with it. Boy, for a saint, you've really got some annoying habits."

"Fair enough. Let's talk about your dad."

"Oh. So you want to go *there*, do you? Why? I just knew you'd eventually go there. Besides, if you truly are who you say you are, then you know him better than I do anyway; I only knew him for nineteen years, you knew him for the fifty-one years he was alive and the almost forty years since. What can I possibly add?"

"Let's go there and find out."

"And what if I don't? Will you tell all your ghost buddies that I'm a huge jerk? Will you haunt me tonight in my hotel room?"

"No. And no."

Louis wasn't going to budge. I could see it in his eyes. Apparently one needs to be very stubborn in order to become a saint. Who knew?

"OK, Lou, you win. Here goes. Dad was a very fine man. He worked hard. People loved him. Then he died. Are we done yet?"

Lou was in no mood for my playfulness. His expression didn't change. 'Let's get this over with,' I thought to myself. 'Give the ghost what he wants.'

I went on. "Dad was a Navy man, but I guess you probably already knew that, didn't you, Lou? He served on the USS Cleveland. He was in the thick of the action in World War II. He was proud of it.

"I have his navy dog tag on my keychain, engraved: 'Robert Matthew Dolan 8736961.'

"That's right; you are named after him."

"Hey, Lou, you catch on fast for a dead guy."

No comment, not even a flinch. I decided to end the sarcasm. "Yes, Louis, I am named after him. I am a 'Junior.'"

"Did he ever talk about his days in the war?"

"Not at all. I understand very few war veterans ever talk about their experiences; how would one put 'hell' into words, I suppose. Every year, he'd watch the Army vs. Navy football game. And every now and then he'd page through his battleship's commemorative yearbook, but I never heard him talking about the war. Perhaps my older brother and sister heard some stories but not me."

"What else?"

"I'm sure you've heard the expression, 'He's a man's man.' Well, that was my dad. Everybody liked him. Women liked him because he was funny and thoughtful and handsome and a solid family man. Men liked him because he was good at sports and games and a very hard worker and a great guy to talk with over a few beers.

"Our home was often the gathering spot for friends and neighbors. My parents were both very hospitable. They made sure all guests always had a good time. Dad would gather with the men on our patio, surrounding his charcoal grill, talking sports or politics or bad bosses and drinking coolers of ice cold beer. His favorite brands were Falstaff, Budweiser, Busch, Pabst and Schlitz; but truth be told, Lou, he enjoyed *any* beer, even if he'd never heard of it. Sometimes he joked, 'My favorite beer is the one which happens to be on sale.' During the cookout, as the pork steaks or chicken or hamburgers were settling in the aluminum sauce pan, the men would often step into our side yard for a lively game of horseshoes or lawn darts or bocce. Dad usually won; it didn't really matter what game they played. He'd keep everybody loose and relaxed, always cracking a joke, always handing over the next can of beer.

"The women, meanwhile, were usually gathered in our kitchen, preparing the side dishes for dinner; cole slaw, potato salad, chips, beans, deserts. Let it be said, Lou, that nobody

ever went hungry at our parties. The ladies would gossip about Hollywood or women at church or their hairdresser while sipping a vodka lemonade or brandy manhattan.

"After dinner, things picked up, as everyone would gather in the living room for games or music and singing. Dad had the great ability to make others feel special. One way he did this was to have many of the men sing a song; by the time they were finished, and always to rousing applause led by my father, the men believed they were singing superstars.

"He'd point at Al and ask him to sing 'Old Man River': next, Leo would belt out 'The Green, Green Grass of Home': then Ralph would do 'Won't You Come Home, Bill Bailey': finally, Dad himself would do his rendition of 'You Made Me Love You.' Later, the entire group would sing along to the songs of *Mitch Miller and the Gang*. The singing would last late into the night. Our parties were legendary.

"He loved music. It relaxed him. He had a nice voice, too. There was always music in our home. He loved Sinatra, Crosby, any Big Band, The Mills Brothers, The Ink Spots…"

Louis jumped in. "The Ink Spots? They're older than me!"

"Hey, good one, Lou!" I teased. "Saint Develops Sense of Humor; That Story Coming Tonight at Ten."

"He worked hard at jobs even though he often hated them," I resumed. "He never called in sick. He volunteered at the parish. He helped Mom with the household chores. He loved being with his wife and his five kids.

"He did not like pretentious people. He called them 'big shots'; that term applied to anyone with overwhelming arrogance or too much self-importance. As kind as he was to most people, he could be quite rude to these others, these big-shots.

"He didn't watch much television, other than the *CBS Evening News with Walter Cronkite* and *Combat*, the series about World War II starring Vic Morrow. He liked any movie about war or the Wild West.

"He was a solid and steady friend, father and husband. Many people looked up to him. Many people respected him and enjoyed his company.

"That's my dad in a nutshell, Lou. Is there anything else you want to know or are we done?"

He wasn't ready to stop just yet.

"Yes, there is. Earlier, you told me that your dad would call you 'Mister' if he was angry with you."

"That's right."

"And then you suddenly remembered an incident that apparently went far beyond being called 'Mister'."

I looked at Lou but did not respond.

"Let's go there."

I didn't want to.

"Trust me, Bob."

My anger returned as I replied. "What's with you, Lou? I came into St. Pat's Cathedral five minutes ago, five hours ago, I don't even know anymore, at the end of a very good day in New York. I took a quick tour of the cathedral and I sat down for just a few minutes to reflect. Then, seemingly out of nowhere, you popped up wearing weird clothes from eight hundred years ago and a baseball hat. You told me you were the king of France. You told me you've been dead for centuries. You told me that now you are Saint Louis, not the city but the *real* saint. You told me that your current responsibilities include watching over everyone who has ever lived in all the cities named after you. And yet you continue to urge me to tell you stories from my years in St. Louis, my hometown, that, if you've been truthful to me, you should already know! I don't get it. Why do you want to hear something you already know; what's in it for you?"

Lou was very stern when he replied. "I thought by now you would have figured this out. You disappoint me. You are not telling these stories for my sake, Bob. I'm doing this for your sake."

"Did I hear you right? Did you just say, 'I *disappoint* you'? Did you use that word on purpose?"

Lou didn't comment.

"You know how that word resonates with me, don't you?"

"Tell the story, my friend."

I began very slowly, with no emotion in the words. "I was

fourteen years old. It was summer. A neighbor up the street, not a close friend with my parents but an acquaintance and a fellow parishioner, bought into a business whose employees went door-to-door leaving items on door knobs: brochures, pamphlets, coupons, advertising, any number of things. The item was placed in a white plastic bag and then the bag would hang on the front door knob to easily be seen when the homeowner returned. The employees would canvas a different neighborhood every day."

My delivery began to quicken as I continued. My tone became animated.

"This neighbor hired a boy in the neighborhood and me to do his daily deliveries. This other boy was a year older than me. He was a friend. Our salary was based on how many drop-offs we could do in one day. It was hard work because we walked literally for nine hours with a large blue bag strapped over our shoulder. About once an hour, the boss would find us on our route to refill the shoulder bag with more stuffed plastic bags.

"It didn't take more than a few weeks for my friend and I to become bored and frustrated with this work. We started taking long lunch breaks. Our walking pace became more leisurely from house-to-house, neighborhood-to-neighborhood. More than once we were frightened by an attacking dog. Soon, we hated the job.

"One day as we ate a double cheeseburger at a Dairy Queen during a lunch break, my friend proposed a solution. 'Why not just throw the contents of our blue shoulder bag into a neighborhood dumpster?' he asked me. 'When the boss refills our bag every hour, we do about ten minutes of deliveries, just long enough to know that he's gone back to the office, then we dump the remainder and go sit in a park or a fast food restaurant. Who would know? We still get paid the same amount but our workload is much easier.'

"And you went along with that," stated Louis.

"I'm afraid I did. How bad was that? And for about two weeks, we pulled it off. We thought we had the perfect scheme. What we did not know, however, was that the business also hired part-time inspectors to check-up on their teenage employees manning the routes. We also didn't figure on the guys who unloaded the

My First New Friend

neighborhood dumpsters to call the main office to tell them that they'd found hundreds of stuffed white bags in with all the rest of the neighborhood garbage. We were caught red-handed.

"Our boss, the neighbor, picked us up one afternoon at the designated spot. The business owners at the main office had just informed him of our antics; they had intentionally kept him out of the loop during their investigation to determine if he was involved in our plot. They told him that his two employees had thrown away thousands of pieces over the last two weeks. They had to reimburse all the people who had paid to have their materials delivered. They fired my neighbor. He lost his investment. He was furious. He said he had already talked to our fathers. My heart fell into my stomach. I knew I had screwed-up big time. I knew I was in for it when my dad got home.

"When I walked in the house, my mom was standing at the kitchen sink preparing dinner. She had been crying. She looked at me and said only one thing: 'Your father will be home soon. He wants you to wait for him on the patio.'

"My God," I thought, "even Mom hates me. Dad might literally kill me."

"That was an agonizing twenty minutes, sitting in a lawn chair on our patio, waiting for Dad. I had no idea what punishment would be coming my way and I was very afraid to find out. I also knew, whatever it was, I deserved it.

"I heard Dad's car pull into the driveway. I heard the front door close behind him as he entered the house. I saw him walk into the kitchen and give Mom a quick kiss. He came to the patio immediately and sat down in a chair across from me.

"I couldn't even look at him. I stared at the concrete.

"I heard him strike a match to light a cigarette. Finally, after at least a minute of silence, he spoke.

'Son, look at me,' he began.

'He just called me son,' I thought to myself. 'That might be worse than Mister.'

"I looked up. I had never seen my dad looking so stern and so sad. He looked me in the eye and leaned in."

"I have never in my life been more disappointed," he said.

97

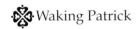

He sat quiet for a few seconds to let that sink in and then stood up and went back inside.

"That was it, Lou. That's all he said. I was expecting to be grounded for a month or being told to work part-time jobs to pay back my neighbor or being assigned many additional household chores. I had even imagined him taking me behind the storage shed and giving me my first whipping ever. Instead, all he did was look me in the eye and say, 'I have never in my life been more disappointed.' And by the way, Lou, that's a direct quote; I've never forgotten it.

"My dad could have done or said anything to me, Lou, and it would not have been as severe as what he did. This man was a kid in the Depression, he served in a world war, he was married, he had children, he had jobs he didn't like and bosses who treated him poorly, he struggled to pay the monthly bills, and yet he had just told me that his greatest disappointment was something I had done. I froze on that patio. I couldn't move. I didn't want to ever go inside that house again. I didn't know how to approach him. I couldn't think of one thing to say to make it right.

"Those nine words, Lou, were the most effective punishment I've ever received. Ever. To this day, I regret disappointing such a good and decent man."

Louis allowed me some quiet time before asking, "And now, Bob, in your adult years, how has that carried over?"

I forced a smile. "You'd make a good attorney, Lou: always ask a question to which you already know the answer. You know how I feel. I live in fear of disappointing people and I hate myself when I do. Do you understand what I am telling you, Lou? I live *in fear* of disappointing the people who are closest to me. I am sure that there have been times in my life when I made a specific decision or selected a particular path only because I thought I'd disappoint someone if I had chosen the opposite. And all because of some stupid and reckless thing I did when I was fourteen years old. Go figure."

"How were things between you and your dad after that?"

"Are you kidding me, Lou? Things were great. That incident was never mentioned again. I'm not saying he forgot about it but it never changed the way he treated me or loved me. He continued to support me and encourage me until the day he died."

"It sounds like he forgave you," said Louis.

"I suppose he did."

"Well, maybe it's time then, Bob."

"Time for what?"

"It's been over forty years. Maybe it's time to forgive yourself."

❖❖❖❖❖❖

Louis and I were walking towards the front of the cathedral, closer to his side altar. I had a feeling he was going to leave soon.

"Hey, Lou, you said something to me when we first met and now that we are talking about my father, it just came back to me."

"What's that?"

"When you were alive, when you were King of France, you hated vulgarity. You didn't curse. You didn't want others around you to curse, either."

"That's true."

"I would think in your position as king, it'd be difficult to avoid."

"Not at all. Truthfully it was *because* of my position that I didn't find it hard at all; a king needs to set an example. Now, why did that remind you of your dad?"

"He hated vulgarity, too. He rarely cursed, at least in my company. I'm like that, too. I'm not sure my daughters have ever heard me curse. I don't like it when others in my presence curse. I'm not talking about the occasional slip-in of a mild profanity, but I am very intolerant of those who consistently throw-in the big bombshells of curse words, you know the ones: f-bomb, s-bomb, and taking God's name in vain. I hate them all. It is unnecessary and ignorant and disrespectful of everyone in that conversation.

"The few times in my adult life, Lou, when I've used that worst word of all, it tells me that I've lost control. I don't accept that. I expect better of myself. It's inexcusable."

"I agree and I commend you for that point-of-view. I think, however, that you may hate that one specific word for one other

reason, as well."

"What's that?" I wondered.

"Think about it. You told me that your dad hated vulgarity. Good for him. How many times in your life did you hear your father say that one word?"

I knew right away where Lou was going.

"One time."

"And what happened the next day?"

"He died."

I hesitated for a few seconds. "You're not saying I equate that one word to death, are you? That's a bit of a stretch."

"I'm not implying that at all. You just told me, though, that you think that word means you've lost all control; for you, it is the ultimate sign of anger and stress. Naturally, I then wonder about your dad's emotions when you heard him that evening."

"His car had just broken down for about the tenth time in a month. OK, slight exaggeration, but you get my drift. He was so weary of repair bills and things never working properly and his inability to ever get ahead financially despite his hard work. He was angry, frustrated and stressed. For just a few seconds, he snapped. I was the only one with him at the time."

"And 12 hours later…."

"He dropped dead at his desk at work of a massive heart attack. He was only fifty-one years old."

Lou spoke slowly. "So maybe, just maybe, you think that losing complete control, even if just for a few seconds, is a sign of overwhelming stress. And certainly that level of stress isn't healthy. Not that you think you are going to die the next morning, but why risk it, why even go there?"

"It could be, Lou. It is possible, I will grant you that, but it seems like you've thought about it much more than me. It may be that I just hate that one word, nothing more to it than that. That, too, is possible. You're way too deep for me sometimes, Lou."

"Tell me about the day he died," he went on. "Did you cry?"

"What is your fascination with me and crying?" I exclaimed. "Already, I've admitted that I cried when I was twelve years old when I lost money in a card game; and that I cried when I was eleven years old when the Cardinals lost a World Series; and here's a shock, Lou, I bet I even cried when I was teething at nine months."

"And what about April 1, 1977: did you cry?"

"The day my dad died? I'm not sue, Lou. I'm not playing head games with you. I honestly cannot remember."

"What about at the funeral three days later?"

"I don't recall. I probably did, why wouldn't I?"

"Good question: why wouldn't you?"

"I remember intentionally *not* crying in front of my younger brother and sister when I told them Dad had died. My sister was only fourteen and my brother only twelve, so the last thing they needed to see was their older brother in tears. I also remember intentionally not crying when I told my older sister when she arrived at the house.

"I certainly remember many others crying. We had relatives and friends come to our home all day long to pay their respects. Everybody was stunned.

"I especially remember the reaction of my Uncle Bill, my dad's only brother and a very fine man. When he arrived at our house, I happened to be sitting alone on top of the picnic table near our back patio, just staring into the yard. I suppose I just wanted to get away from all the commotion inside. I heard the back screen door open and looked over my shoulder to see Uncle Bill approaching. He stepped on the bench and planted himself right next to me on top of the table. He put his left arm around me and said, 'I sure am going to miss the old guy,' and with that he sobbed uncontrollably for about thirty seconds. I never said a word. I didn't know what to say. When he stopped crying, he squeezed my shoulder and went back into the house. Poor guy.

"That's about it, Lou. It was so long ago, I really don't remember very much from that weekend, other than both the wake and funeral mass were standing room only.

"I'm not avoiding your original question. I do not know if I cried. I do know that a few times in my adult life that I've *felt* like crying; on my wedding day when I realized he'd never know my wife and on the days my children were born when it hit me that'd

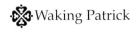 

he'd never know my daughters. But as far as that weekend in 1977 is concerned, I truly can't recall."

"I would think that'd be something easily remembered," offered Louis.

Again, I got aggravated with him. "Look, Lou, what do you want me to do, break down and bawl right now, right here; would that make you feel better?"

"Bob, it's not *me* I'm worried about."

❖❖❖❖❖❖❖

My friend and I had made our way to the front of his altar in the far back corner of the cathedral. I sensed our farewell was at hand.

"So, Lou, let me ask you a question for a change. You watched over me for about twenty years in Ballwin. You've heard me reminisce tonight. I've done a lot of talking, much more than usual. What do *you* think of my growing up years?"

He sighed while he gathered his thoughts.

"I think you were very fortunate, Bob. You had it so much better than most. You had hard working parents who sacrificed a great deal for their children. Yes, your father died young but it's always best to measure the *quality* of a loved one's life and impact, not the loved one's *longevity*. You had fun and loyal friends. Your family was well liked and respected. You belonged to a vibrant parish and school. Most people were charitable. It was a close-knit neighborhood where the families looked out for each other. Everyone took their faith very seriously. You had good examples all around you. I believe you've always realized that you were blessed indeed with your upbringing and childhood. I believe that's why your wife and you worked so hard when you became parents; you wanted to give your children that same foundation because you knew that would set them up for happiness and success for the rest of their lives."

I extended my right arm to shake his hand. "Lou, it's been good. I'm still not sure any of this really happened. I'm still not sure why you thought it necessary to visit me. But it's been a good experience.  I enjoyed our conversations.  I know I may never see you again, but please know I will never forget you."

Lou enthusiastically shook my hand.  "God bless you, Bob. And remember, He already has is so many ways."

He turned to walk up the step to his altar but stopped when I yelled out one final time.

"Hey, Lou, before you leave, let me ask you this: you give special attention and care to everyone who has ever lived in St. Louis, right?"

"That's right."

"Including my older brother?"

"Of course."

"So that would mean you remember the story he tells about spending the night with our grandparents so many years ago, right?"

"I see and hear many things, Bob.  Remind me."

"My brother spent a weekend at Grandpa and Grandma Dolan's home when he was a teenager.  On Sunday morning, after a huge breakfast of scrambled eggs, bacon and pancakes, the three of them left the table to get ready for mass.

"It turned out that Grandpa was in no hurry to attend church that day.  In fact, he was quite comfortable relaxing in his favorite chair, reading the Sunday newspaper and sipping on a mug of hot coffee.  Very soon, he told Grandma that he was going to skip mass that morning.

"And why are you doing that?" replied Grandma, testily.

"Because I can't stand that new priest!' he explained.

"To which Grandma immediately shot back, 'Yeah, well, you can't stand that new *bartender* up at the corner tap, either, but you sure as hell haven't stopped going there.'

"My brother says that Grandpa had no response.  He was literally speechless.  He got up from the chair without a comment, got dressed and went to mass."

Louis needed a few seconds to fully comprehend Grandma's effective response:  'You can't stand that new bartender up at the corner tap, either, but that hasn't stopped you from going there!' he repeated quietly to himself.

With that, he let loose with a loud, long laugh from deep within that echoed off the pillars and walls of the cathedral. He had tears in his eyes when he finally stopped.

"Oh, that's priceless! That's one of the great comebacks of all time. Your Grandma Dolan was a real firecracker! I remember that she sure loved a cold bottle of Falstaff beer and a game of cards."

I felt so pleased. At long last, I had heard genuine laughter from my new friend.

"Louis, you just made my day. Thank you. I finally got you to laugh."

"And Bob, you made my day, too: I finally got you to listen."

# IV
## *My Second New Friend*

"Testing! One, two, three. Testing; one, two, three."

I was still standing at the front of the altar of Saint Louis after having just watched my friend Lou disappear by seemingly walking right into the back wall, when I heard the voice of a male off in the distance over my left shoulder.

"Testing! One. Two. Three. Four," he counted, pausing dramatically in between each number.

I turned and looked across the high altar, trying to find the person who owned this booming voice. I saw the back of a man standing at the pulpit, speaking into the microphone. I circled around from behind the altar and approached the man from his left side as he looked out upon the empty cathedral.

"Testing. Testing," he repeated.

The pulpit was at the top of a winding marble staircase, six steps elevated from the floor. It is situated at the left front of the altar. I remember reading in the brochure that it is used for the reading of the gospel during Mass and often for a homily or an address. This figure loomed about fifteen feet above me as I entered his line of sight.

I stopped and leaned against the front of the first pew and looked up at him. I could now see his face for the first time. There was something about him that seemed vaguely familiar to me.

"Excuse me, sir; I don't think the sound system is turned on at the moment," I said loudly. "The microphone doesn't seem to be working. However, I can still hear you very well. Your voice carries a long way."

"It certainly does!" he replied, looking down to make eye

contact. "In fact, it carries all over the world."

Well, that might be a bit of an over-statement, I thought to myself. What is *this* guy's story, I wondered.

"Well, not to be rude, Mister, but I'm not sure it's *that* strong," I responded. "I meant to say that your voice is filling up this cathedral very nicely, even without the use of the microphone."

The man smiled but didn't immediately answer. Instead, he collected the loose leaf papers spread out in front of him, unnecessarily turned off the microphone, and turned to leave the pulpit.

He was out of sight as he slowly descended the steps. I decided this was as good a time as any for me to finally leave this place and get back to my hotel, so I turned to walk down the center aisle in the direction of the main exit.

I didn't get very far.

"Please don't go yet, Bob," came that same voice, this time from just a few feet behind me. "We have some things to talk about."

"Don't tell me that *you* know me, too," I responded, turning to face him. "Does every person and window and statue and altar in this freaky place know who I am?"

For the first time, I could plainly see this man with the golden voice. When he was on the high pulpit, I could only see him from the shoulders up, and because he was so much higher than me at the time, even that didn't present an accurate idea of his appearance. Now, however, we stood directly in front of each other, just a few feet apart.

He literally took my breath away for a moment. This was one good looking man.

He was solidly built. He had an athletic frame. He stood straight, shoulders back, with an obvious confidence and self-assuredness about him.

I estimated him to be just over six foot tall. His hair, combed straight back and perfectly manicured, was black with streaks of grey. He had a well-defined jaw and cheekbones. Truly, he looked like a Hollywood movie star, a mix of Cary Grant and Tyrone Power and Glenn Ford.

He knew it, too.  My first impression was that he might be a bit too cocky, but with an appearance like his it would be hard not to be.

In addition, he was dressed impeccably, although clearly his clothing was from a different era: a white dress shirt with a tight, thin collar; black Gab slacks, grey and black argyle socks, shiny black loafers, and a grey cardigan sweater buttoned to chest level. He looked as if he'd stepped right off a cover from a 1950's men's fashion magazine.

One other thing about his wardrobe; he was wearing a magenta cape, connected at the back of his collar, and hanging down to well below the back of his knees.

The man knew how to make an entrance, I'll give him that.

I felt inferior just standing close to him.  And I was sure it was about to get even worse once we started speaking; his intelligence level was probably off the charts.  He not only looked *good*, he looked *smart*.  Why I didn't immediately hate him, I don't know, but there was something about him, hard to put my finger on at the time, that seemed genuine and sincere.

"What was it you were saying, Bob?"

I was intimidated.  I sensed I was in way over my head, which I immediately proved with my reply.  "Huh?"

"You were saying something about the windows and statues all knowing about you; I didn't quite grasp your thought."  His voice was still very strong and confident, even though he was no longer pretending to be speaking into a microphone; this was probably his usual tone.

"Oh, yes.  It's just that you called me by my correct first name a minute ago even though we've never met.  The same thing happened to me earlier tonight.  A man named Louis knew who I was.  He knew my name was Bob.  He knew all about my upbringing. And now the same thing occurs with you.  It's strange, that's all.  I don't understand."

I paused, still hypnotized by this impressive man in front of me.

"I suppose this means you also know all about me," I asked him.

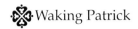

"I know enough," he answered gently. "I know nothing about your childhood but I do know a lot about your years as a husband and father."

"And why is that?"

"Well, Bob, you and I are connected. I know about you because you went to great lengths to know about me."

"Huh?"

I winced. For the second time, was that really the best reply I could come up with in this man's presence?

I tried to recover. "I'm sorry, sir, if I sound so unintelligent. It's just that I am very tired and very confused."

My new friend smiled. "You are fine, Bob. Let's sit down. Perhaps that will help you relax."

"I think the only thing that will help me is getting out of here," I smiled as I took a seat in the third pew on the right. "Either that or a good cold beer. You wouldn't happen to have one of those in that cape of yours, would you?"

He said nothing as he sat in the pew across the aisle. It was clear he was waiting for me to proceed.

Where do I go with this guy?

"It's been a most unusual night," I began. "I'm at the end of a sightseeing day in New York City. I came to this cathedral just before closing time. I just wanted to walk around it once. I must have lost track of time because I think I got locked in. Then I met some guy named Louis who told me he was the King of France and the one and only Saint Louis. He knew all about my life as a child and teenager. He got me to tell stories, a few of which I thought I'd forgotten. It was all just very weird, that's all. I still don't know what to make out of it. He turned out to be a very nice man but I am not at all convinced he was who he says he was. Heck, I'm not really sure I even met him and talked to him; I probably just *imagined* him. Then, he just disappears into a wall behind a side altar and the next thing I know I see and hear you standing at the pulpit. Like I said, Mister, it's been a strange night. I don't get it."

"I understand," he replied.

I stared at him. I couldn't get over his appearance. And I

couldn't shake the feeling that, somehow, I knew him.

"What's *your* story?" I asked.

"I think you know my story," he replied. "You know it well enough, at least."

"Funny you should say that. Do I know you? It feels like we've met."

"No, we've never met. But, sure, you know me. Many people know me."

"What's your name?"

"Peter John."

I thought for a few seconds. Did I know of someone, past or present, named Peter John? Perhaps a Pope I once read about? I came up empty.

I smiled as I asked: "Are you related to *Elton* John?"

"Not in the least," he said, returning my smile.

"Well, Peter, you're going to have to help me here. You say I know your story and I must admit you do seem familiar to me, but I just can't place a Peter John, either in my life or somewhere back in history."

"Bob, come on, you know this!" he urged. "Think! I didn't say my first name was Peter and my last name was John, did I? No! You asked my name and I replied with the name from my birth and baptism; Peter is my first name, John is my middle name, which means my last name is what?"

His tone wasn't at all condescending. Rather, it was encouraging me to come up with the answer he clearly knew I had.

I took the bait.

"OK, Pete, bear with me. I need to walk through this. Big voice, microphone, pulpit, magenta cape, handsome, you said that I 'know your story', you said that 'many people know me', you said your voice 'carries all over the world', and your birth name is Peter John. I think that covers it so far. So, all of this must mean that you are…"

I stopped, mid-sentence. It hit me. I leaned forward to look at him closely from across the aisle. I cannot be, I thought to myself, but *who else* could it be? Nothing else makes sense.

Oh. My. God.

"Yes?" he inquired.

"It must mean that you are Peter (pause) John (pause)…"

"Go on."

"Sheen."

"Yes!" he exclaimed. "I knew you knew! Better known worldwide as…"

"Fulton" I jumped in. "Fulton J. Sheen."

I was stunned. I had nothing more to add. I slumped into the back of my pew as my new friend stood and walked across the aisle to shake my hand for the first time to make his formal introduction.

❖❖❖❖❖❖❖

"I feel like such a fool," I managed, after several minutes of silence and gathering my thoughts. "I had the sense that I knew you. You looked familiar. I suppose I didn't connect the dots because, well, why would I believe such a thing, why would I think the great Fulton Sheen would ever be in my company? After all, you died, what, thirty years ago?"

"I passed in 1979. I remember it well. It felt like going to sleep, nothing more to it than that. I died in the small private chapel inside my Manhattan apartment, how cool is that?"

I didn't know him well enough to know if he was joking; he didn't seem to be, but I let it pass without comment.

"I just prayed for your canonization over there on that kneeler in front of the crypt," I resumed. "Sorry, but I can't remember exactly what the prayer card said."

"I know it by heart," Sheen said. 'Heavenly Father, you raise up within the church in every age men and women who serve with heroic love and dedication. You have blessed your church through the life and ministry of your faithful servant Archbishop Fulton J. Sheen. He has written and spoken well of Your Divine Son Jesus Christ and was a true instrument of the Holy Spirit in touching the hearts of countless people.'"

"That's pretty good, Archbishop. I suppose you've said it a

few times?"

"I'm not saying I believe I deserve sainthood, but since others believe it I figure it won't hurt to recite that prayer every now and then."

'Whatever,' I thought to myself, still perceiving that he was a bit on the cocky side.

I changed the subject. "Do you know Saint Louis?"

"I most certainly do! He's a good guy. He goes on too long sometimes about those precious crusades of his, but he's fine. We talk baseball from time to time because we are both fans of the Cardinals."

"I knew Louis was a fan," I said. "Why are you?"

"I was raised in Peoria, Illinois; that's Cardinal country."

"That's right, it is. Hey, did you know that I once assisted on the production of a one-hour video documentary about your life. Maybe that's why you seemed familiar a few moments ago when I first saw you; I researched your life for that video."

"I realize that. I appreciate that. I thought the documentary turned out quite well." He paused briefly and smiled before adding, "Personally, I would have included far more video clips from my television show, but that's just me."

"Great, just what I need," I laughed, "a dead critic."

"In fact, that's the reason for our visit tonight, Bob. You worked on my life so I began taking an interest in yours. But more about that later."

"*My* life? Boy, you must be bored in your dead days."

He ignored me. "Tell me what you remember from all you read about me in your project," he asked.

"Well, it's been a few years, but I'm happy to try." I stood in the pew as I gathered my thoughts. "First of all, I remember your very impressive academic achievements while being educated in Washington, D.C. and Louvain, Belgium and Rome, Italy. I probably recall that right off the top because I've been to all of those places, too."

"You, too, went to school in those cities?" he asked, clearly surprised.

"No, I went to *pubs* in those cities."

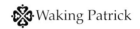

"Oh," he managed.

I went on.

"Also, Mr. Peter John Sheen, I recall why you are instead called Fulton. That was your mother's maiden name. By mistake, when you were very young, she once referred to you as her son, 'Peter John Fulton', and for some reason, 'Fulton' stuck."

"And the rest, as they say, is history," he commented. "Perhaps it was divine intervention for somehow, *'The Fulton Sheen Hour'* sounds better than *'The Peter John Sheen Hour'*. Would you agree?"

"I suppose so. I haven't thought about it as often as you apparently have. Your television program is another thing I most certainly remember from my work on that documentary. It was called *Life Is Worth Living*, but most people simply referred to it as The Fulton Sheen show. It was said your show inspired millions of people.

"You also hosted *The Catholic Hour* on the NBC Radio Network, so when one considered both your radio and television prowess, you were the most famous Catholic in the country for decades. You were a big star."

"I was a *very* big star."

"I'm glad to see it didn't go to your head."

"Hey, I'm proud of my broadcasting career, what's wrong with that? After all, I did win an Emmy Award."

"Yes, you did. In 1952, you won the Emmy as the Most Outstanding Television Personality. You beat Milton Berle. Congratulations!"

"That's even a big deal in this place, Bob; there are a lot of soul-savers and miracles and followers of Jesus in here, but there's only one Emmy winner. I good-naturedly bring it up all the time. It really ticks off Clare. She's the patron saint of television but she doesn't have an Emmy; only me. When I rib her about it, she always turns and walks away and pulls her rosary beads out of her pocket. Nice kid, that Clare, but she sure can't take a joke."

"I think I'm beginning to understand where she's coming from," I mumbled, looking down at the floor.

He went on. "Hey, do you remember what I said in my Emmy acceptance speech?"

"I do, but I bet you probably want to tell me anyway."

I'm not sure he even heard me.

"I stood up in front of the live audience and on national television, holding that Emmy statue in my hand, and with Milton Berle and other TV legends nearby I deadpanned, 'I feel it is time I pay proper tribute to my four writers; Matthew, Mark, Luke and John.' It brought the house down, Bob! Everybody laughed. That was sure a fine night. I even got an autograph from Bob Hope."

"That's great, Fulton," I said without enthusiasm. Clearly, I had momentarily lost my new friend as he took his ride on memory lane.

"I had a real knee-slapper once on a radio program, too," he went on. "I was going to talk about the sacrament of confession and to loosen up the crowd, I said, 'Hearing a nun's confession is like getting stoned to death by popcorn.'

With that, Fulton let loose with a big laugh, even clapping his hands three times for emphasis. "Oh my, those were some good days," he said, when his laughter finally died down.

I was a bit uncomfortable with his demeanor; this last minute or so he came off as superficial. He must have noticed my disposition.

"I'm sorry, Bob. I got caught up in the moment. I haven't thought about my television days in many years so I apologize for getting carried away. You must think I am something awful. You know the real me, right? You studied me. You know I always gave credit to God for my television and radio success. I'd always explain it this way: 'The only way to win audiences is to tell people about the life and death of Christ; every other approach is a waste.'

"Well, Fulton, you did kind of weird-out on me there for a few seconds, but that's alright. Heck, if you've looked at my life as you say you have, then you know all about my bouts with arrogance or being too self-centered."

"I sure do."

"Feel free to disagree if you like," I commented.

We smiled at each other as we began to walk side-by-side up

the center aisle.

"My dad used to watch you all the time," I resumed. "He was a big fan."

"I know. In fact, he used to watch me… religiously."

Once again, he laughed at his own joke.

"I've been using that line for sixty years," he continued. "It gets me every time."

"Hey, you just said 'I know' when I told you that my dad used to watch you. How do you know that?"

"He told me."

"He told you? He never met you."

"Not in this life, no. The first time we met was 1980. He told me then."

"1980? Dad was dead then."

"And I was, too."

"I don't believe you."

"Believe what you want, Hoot."

I abruptly turned my head to look at him.

"What did you just call me?"

"Hoot. That was your dad's nickname for you, correct?"

"It was. How'd you know *that*?"

"He told me."

"Whatever." Once again, I was losing a verbal bout with a dead man.

Sheen continued. "While we're at it, he told me one other thing just before I came to see you. He wanted me to tell you that he loves your wife and kids and he is sorry he never met them. And that he is proud of you."

First, Louis; and now this guy: it was really starting to hack me off that these two spirits seemed to know my dad better than I did. Certainly *longer* than I ever did. I had no response. Either I still didn't believe what he said or I was frightened beyond words to realize that I did.

I decided to return to the topic of my Sheen video documentary.

"Let's go back to something I can grasp. I was very impressed with how highly people thought of you at the height of your career and influence. One bishop said that you were a shining example of what it means to serve God.  Another bishop stated that being in your presence made him feel as if one of the original apostles was right there in front of him, speaking.  A priest from New York told me in my documentary; 'It was like Jesus Himself, who walked, who traveled, who went out and preached.  He went to the people.    That's what Archbishop Sheen did and that's what he inspires me to do, decades after his death.'"

My friend was touched.  "Really?  A priest who serves today, so long after my death, said that about me?"

"He sure did.  And didn't you yourself once say that the greatest tribute you ever received occurred during a meeting with Pope John Paul II, when he told you; 'You have been a loyal son of the Church.  You have written and spoken well of the Lord Jesus.'"

"Even now, when I hear that or when I am reminded of that, I am humbled."

"And what was it you said when asked once about how you wished to be remembered?" I asked.

"I said; 'Remember me as a missionary, a teacher and a humble servant of the Lord.'"

"Exactly," I stated.  "So I know all about the type of man you were, Fulton.  I know all about your character and your immense love for the Lord.  You have every reason to be proud of your TV and radio work because it enabled you to evangelize so effectively.  It helped you change people's lives.  I know you were humble about it.  In fact, I remember you once said that a proud man counts his newspaper clippings but a humble man counts his blessings, and that you counted your blessings every day.  You also once wisely stated that too much pride is an admission of weakness for it secretly fears all competition and dreads all rivals.  You were always on guard against pride and arrogance; they can be evil."

"Hey, Bob," he said as he tapped my right elbow with his left hand as we continued to walk, "you're pretty good at this!  I'm here to help you, yet somehow our roles have been reversed in these last few minutes.  I'll make it up to you, I promise, when we start talking about *you*!"

"Let's skip that part, shall we?"

He ignored me.

"Bob, sorry to backtrack but let me just say one more thing about my Emmy."

"OK."

He spoke the next three words very slowly. "God doesn't care."

"What do you mean?"

"Exactly what I said; God does not care. God is not impressed by trophies and honors and awards and blue ribbons and medals and titles. He doesn't care about your pride or prominence or popularity or prestige or power; he only cares about your willingness to be with Jesus on the cross.

"Do not think that on judgment day He will ask if you have ever won an Emmy. Don't think that He will ask about the awards and plaques hanging on your wall or a soccer trophy on your bookshelf. He won't ask to see your bank records and portfolio. Instead, He will ask if you fed the poor and visited the lonely and healed the sick and protected the children. He will ask if you treated others as if they were His Son. He will look at your hands to see if they have scars from giving; He will look at your feet to see if they were wounded in His service; He will look at your heart to see if inside you held a place for Devine Love.

"Remember, Bob, what does it profit you if you gain the world but in the process suffer the loss of your soul?"

❖❖❖❖❖❖

We found two folding chairs near the back of the cathedral and positioned them facing each other about five feet apart. I reached into my backpack for a small bag of salted cashews.

"Would you like a few?" I asked my companion.

"Thanks, but I'm allergic to peanuts," he said with a straight face.

"Oh. By the way, just what do you people eat, anyway?"

"What do you mean, 'you people'?"

"Well, I mean *you* for one; and *Saint Louis*, for another. You know, your average spirit or ghost or whatever you are, 'you people' who apparently hang around this cathedral waiting for someone like me to come in to give you something to do. Do you have a snack bar or kitchen to pass the time?"

"Where we are, we have all the nourishment we need."

"I see." That's the best I could do. I mean, how do you top that?

"So, Fulton, what's with the clothes?"

"Do you like them? I picked them out myself."

"Sure, they're nice, but what I meant was they are not exactly the clothes of a bishop."

"Well, that's why I kept my magenta cape; don't you just love it? The cape was a fairly common accessory for a bishop back in the day. Not only that, but every now and then it comes in handy when I pretend that I am Superman."

I had no reply.

"That was a joke, Bob."

"Oh."

"As for the rest of my outfit, well, this was the popular style back in my heyday. I'd often dress like this when I was alone in my apartment or rectory, certainly never when I was out in public. Priests don't always wear black pants, black shirt, black socks and black shoes. We do have normal clothes, too."

"I dropped by a priest's home one time," I said, "and he answered the door wearing grey sweat pants and a Notre Dame hooded sweatshirt. I thought I was at the wrong house!"

"I think some people believe priests even sleep in their blacks," said Sheen. "Heck, there were times, Bob, on a hot summer night when I slept in nothing but my boxers."

"Hey, Fulton…"

"Yes?"

"Too much information."

"Oh. Sorry."

I adjusted my position in the chair. "So, what am I supposed to call you? How would you like to be addressed?"

"What are you comfortable with?"

"Well, I usually like to show proper respect to people with a

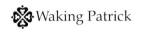

title, so I could call you 'Bishop', but after what you just told me about God not caring about titles, that seems unnecessary. I could stick with Fulton, I suppose, but even that seems a bit formal. I'm not a formal type of guy. How about Peter? Or Pete? Or Peter John? Or P.J.? Did anybody ever call you P.J.?"

"No, I can't say they did."

"That settles it, then! With your permission, from now on you are my friend P.J."

"Fine. I kind of like it. It makes me feel…normal. Sometimes I got very tired of always being so well-known. Sometimes I wished I could be like everybody else: common."

"Well, P.J., I know all about common. I'm as common and normal as you get. And sometimes I wish I could be more like people like you, people who are famous, people who have the power and influence to get things done, to change things for the better, like you did with your television and radio work. Take my word for it, common people often feel useless and lost. We feel as if there's nothing that sets us apart. I wouldn't necessarily wish for 'common' if I were you, P.J."

"Bob, you could not be more wrong."

"How so?"

He shot me a look which told me this portion of the conversation was over. "In due time, Bob; all in due time."

"I understand," I replied, even though I most certainly did not.

I quickly searched for a new topic. "Hey, P.J., I just realized why you are here in this cathedral. I don't know why it didn't hit me before now. You are buried here!"

"Yes. I am in the crypt below the main altar. I am there with men such as Spellman, O'Connor, McCloskey and Hughes. All former archbishops of New York are buried here."

"But you weren't an archbishop of New York; you were an auxiliary bishop. They made an exception for you as a lasting tribute to the impact of your life. That's quite an honor."

"You are too kind. The honor was also given to two other men who were not former archbishops, so please don't think it's just me. Monsignor Michael Lavelle, a rector here for over fifty years, and the venerable Pierre Toussaint are also buried in our crypt. I keep very good company these days, I admit."

"So this is why you are my new friend; it makes sense to me now. Saint Louis visited me because he has an altar here and now you are visiting me because you are buried here. I still don't get it but at least I've made the connection."

I stopped for a few seconds. "That being said, P.J., if next this folding chair starts talking to me, I'm done. I am out of here!"

Sheen grabbed a bright white handkerchief from his back pocket and wiped a few small beads of perspiration from his brow. "I'd probably run with you," he smiled.

"This may seem to be coming at you from left field," I resumed, "but may I tell you a story told to me by a friend recently? At the end, I hope, you'll understand why I bring it to your attention."

"Sure, go ahead."

"My buddy was talking about growing up in the 1960's like I did. He said a few years after he was born, his dad met a stranger who was new to their small town. From the beginning, the dad was fascinated with this stranger and soon invited him to live with the family. The stranger was accepted, even embraced.

"The stranger became the family's storyteller. He would keep the family spellbound for hours on end with adventures, mysteries and comedies. He took the family to their first major league baseball game. The stranger made family members laugh and cry. The stranger talked constantly but the dad never seemed to mind.

"Sometimes, my buddy said, the mom would get up quietly while the rest of the family was shushing one another to listen to what the stranger had to say. Looking back, my friend says he wonders if his mom was tired of the stranger and wished he would leave.

"The dad ruled the household with certain moral convictions. Many dads did back then. The stranger, however, never felt obligated to honor those convictions. The dad never insisted that the stranger follow his rules and guidelines as he did with all the others in the family. For example, profanity was never allowed in the household – not from the kids, not from visitors or friends

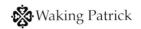

– but for some odd reason the stranger got away with four-letter words and innuendos that made even the dad squirm and the mom blush.

"The dad never allowed excessive use of alcohol in the home, but the stranger often encouraged us to drink heavily. The stranger talked about sex. His comments were sometimes blatant, sometimes suggestive, always embarrassing. My friend says that his early concepts about relationships were strongly influenced by the stranger. Often, the stranger opposed the values of the parents yet he was seldom rebuked. And he was never asked to leave.

"End of story." I looked directly at P.J. to ask him this question. "Do you know the name of this stranger in the house? Do you have a guess?"

"Tell me."

"The stranger was called… television."

He seemed unaffected. He remained calm and poised.

"Clever. What's your point?"

"Are you kidding me? Have you noticed what has become of your beloved television these days? Are you not able to watch anymore? It is filled with filth."

"And why, Bob, do you choose to tell *me* this specific story? Am I somehow to blame?"

"Heavens, no, I am not blaming you. I am only asking if you and the other pioneers of television ever imagined that it would one day be such a poor influence."

"We did not. In those early days, I cannot think of even one program which could have been considered obscene or objectionable. Our intent was to provide wholesome entertainment. To answer your earlier question, yes, I am well aware of the questionable content of too many of the television programs these days. Lucille Ball and I were talking about this just last month; we are mortified."

"What happened? Why and when did TV become such trash?" I asked.

"I would suggest it goes hand-in-hand with the moral decline of society as a whole. After all, trashy television shows are only produced because there is a large enough audience wanting them and watching them to make them profitable. So is it not a larger reflection on society itself?

"From my point of view, Bob, here's what I see in your current society: you've lost your spiritual equilibrium; your values have been reversed; you exploit the poor and call it the lottery; you reward laziness and call it welfare; you kill the unborn child and call it a choice; you neglect to discipline your children and call it building self-esteem; you abuse power and call it politics as usual; you covet your neighbor's possessions and call it ambition; you seek sex outside of marriage and call it an understandable weakness; you pollute the air and call it the price of progress; you backstab co-workers and call it job advancement; you fill the air with profanity and pornography and call it freedom of expression.

"Are those not the very things you see and hear on television and on talk-radio these days, Bob? Television reflects society. If you believe most of television is garbage, then are you not also horribly depressed with the condition of the world and the behavior of your fellow man?"

"Too often, yes, I am."

"And what do you do about it?"

"Excuse me?"

"It's not a complicated question, Bob. You are a father, correct?"

"I am. We have two daughters."

"And how many days of their lives have you had a television set in your home?"

I responded quietly. "Every single day."

"When they were in grade school and high school, how many television sets did you own?"

I had to think about it. "Three, I think."

"Did you ever walk in to find them watching a program which you would consider objectionable?"

"A few times. Probably."

"Did you ever turn off that program, no debate allowed? Did you ever tell them that any program first had to be approved by you?"

I became indignant. "Sometimes, I did, yes!"

"All times?"

"No."

"Then are you not like the dad in that clever little story of yours? You took the easy way out."

"This is just great, P.J. I am getting preached to about my parenting skills by a man who has never been a parent. I just love that."

"Hey, for one, you brought it up! And second, are you denying it?"

"Am I denying that I was not a perfect parent? No! Did I make mistakes? I most certainly did." I was trying, but failing, to hold back my temper. "The problem with being a parent, P.J., not that you'd know anything about this, is usually you don't know you made a mistake until well after the fact. It's a feel, P.J., it's an instinct, and there aren't any guidebooks one can use for reference every time a situation arises with one of your children. Frankly, I think our kids turned out pretty well, so we must have done *something* right, even if some of it was blind luck."

"That's my point, Bob. Forgive me for forcing you to get angry first before making my point. You were a good father. Your kids are well-grounded and responsible adults. Your wife and you worked very hard. And all because you *cared*! All because you *loved them*. All because you *refused to accept* anything less than your standards."

"Where are you going with this, P.J.?"

"You and so many others lament the state of society these days. You find it disturbing. It discourages you. You fear for the future. You believe the world is on the wrong track. You believe the world is nuts. There's terror and evil. Morality is a thing of the past. Selfishness rules. People are too often rude and impolite and inpatient and intolerant."

"I can't argue with any of that, P.J. It reminds me of what Will Rogers once said: 'God made man a little lower than the angels and he has been getting a little lower ever since.' I am indeed discouraged about what I witness in the world. And, by the way, if this is a pep talk, P.J., you are failing miserably."

"Here's the problem, Bob. You've given up! You believe you've lost. You don't fight the fight anymore. You don't think there's anything you can do about it. If you would have followed that same philosophy in your role as a father, how would your kids have turned out? You never gave up on raising your kids because you cared about them, because you loved them, because you knew it was in your power to properly teach them. It was your responsibility. You took it seriously.

"Do you not think that there were times when I got discouraged? Do you not think there were times I felt powerless to change the world? Do you not think that at times I felt like throwing up my arms and screaming, 'I cannot do this any more! It's not working! Nobody listens!' Do you not think the disciples and apostles and saints and all men and women of faith and strong character and principals ever felt like quitting?"

"I'm hardly in their category," I argued.

"You don't have to be a saint to make a difference. You don't even have to be a famous bishop with a radio and television show. You'll hear much more about this later..."

I interrupted. "What do you mean? What's going to happen later? I don't even know what's happening right now!"

He smiled. "Never mind. You and I have other things to chat about, but for now let's leave it at this: in the words of Anne Frank, 'How wonderful it is that nobody needs to wait a single moment before starting to improve the world.'"

❖❖❖❖❖❖❖

I stood up from my folding chair to stretch my lower back; as I've grown older it tightens up from time to time. P.J. seemed amused as he watched.

"I sure don't miss that," he stated.

"What?"

"Stretching. Exercising. Sore muscles. Getting old. All that disappears when you pass away."

"You look in good shape to me," I observed. "You also look

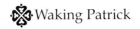

young. You were over eighty years old when you died; you sure don't look it right now."

"When you die, you get to pick an age at which to spend eternity. At least that's the rule in heaven. I have no idea if that's the case in that other place. I selected age forty-five. Its how most people remember me anyway; when I was on television all the time. It's funny, sometimes I'm just walking around heaven, minding my own business, and a total stranger will walk up to me and say, 'Hey, aren't you Fulton Sheen?' They recognize me from my TV days because I still look the same. Heaven is great, Bob. I recommend it."

He paused for a split second.

"Highly."

As he had previously, he laughed at his own joke. It seemed my friend was his own best audience.

"Tell me about heaven," I requested.

"I can't. It's not allowed. Besides, it's impossible to describe. I made a living by putting things into words and I won't even attempt to describe heaven. It's a waste of time, Bob, for you to even try to come up with a picture of it because heaven would hardly be heaven if you could imagine it. I will say this, however; whatever the cost, heaven is a bargain. Do whatever it takes to get there."

I contemplated his 'heaven would hardly be heaven if you could imagine it' remark. I think I understood. I sure wasn't going to ask him to repeat it.

"Bob, remember when we first started talking, I told you that I looked into your life because you first looked *my* life."

'Oh, no,' I thought to myself. 'Here it comes.'

"Yes." I said, aloud, hesitantly.

"Well, let's get to it then." He pulled up the sleeve on his grey cardigan and looked at a gold Timex watch on his left wrist. "I'm on the clock here. My time is short. I wish I could hang around with you for hours but there are a few other people who need to see you, too, and they are on very tight schedules."

I felt a knot in my stomach. I was hoping I could leave after Sheen. Obviously, that would not be the case. 'I don't have this many friends in real life,' I thought. 'Why in here am I suddenly so popular?'

"Do I have to?" I asked.

He stared at me.

"I take that as a 'yes'?" I said. "OK, then, what do you want to know."

"Oh, it's not that I don't already *know* it, it's just that I want to hear you tell it, or in some cases, explain it. Forget your upbringing, Bob, because I was listening in as you chatted with Louis; I am here to talk about your life as a husband and father."

"Gee, I can hardly wait."

"Later, I will ask you a very specific question. For you, it may be a difficult question. Let's begin, however, with this: tell me about your life from your wedding day to present day; whatever comes to mind from your role as a husband and father."

"I thought you said you were pressed for time! You're asking me to talk about nearly thirty years of my life."

"Bob, I'm not asking for a day-by-day account. Just give me whatever comes to mind. The highlights. The memories."

"Can we walk and talk? My legs are sore."

He nodded his head and walked slowly at my side down the right aisle of the cathedral.

"Start at the beginning," he prodded. "Tell me about your wedding day."

"OK. Beth and I were married in October, 1984. I wasn't as nervous as I expected; I knew I had chosen well and that I had fallen in love with the right woman."

"I bet *she* was a nervous wreck," P.J. wisecracked.

I ignored him, even though I understood: there are still times, nearly three decades later, when I wonder why she ever went through with it. I've hardly been a bargain.

"In the moment before we exchanged our vows," I resumed, "I remember the priest whispering to my best man, 'If Bob faints, it's your job to catch him.'

"We held our reception at the home of my in-laws. Everyone had a great time. We sang and danced and ate and drank. My in-laws worked very hard to pull it off. We couldn't afford a fancy reception in a hotel ballroom but we may not have gone that route even if we did have the money. The purpose of a wedding reception is to celebrate the new marriage, yet so many people spend money they don't have on things they don't need. Do you know, P.J., that many places have a 'corking fee' for wine and champagne; in other words, you buy the wine and champagne but then there is also a fee to remove the cork. Are you kidding me? There are examples like that throughout every fancy wedding reception. I see so many parents, well-intentioned most of them, who spend most of their life savings on the wedding reception of a child. I think it is sad. The bride and groom should insist they save some of that money for their retirement years; do they really need a reception like English royalty? I'll tell you, P.J., when our daughters get married we are not spending everything we've earned over the last thirty years. It will be nice and it will be respectful of the event and a good time will be had by all, but if you think I am paying the 'corking fees' of the world, you're crazy."

"Bob?" interjected P.J.

"Yes?"

"I think we are supposed to be talking about your life as a husband and father."

"Oh, yes. Sorry. Anyway, our wedding day was great; we honeymooned in Lake Geneva, Wisconsin, just over an hour away from our home, and our life as husband and wife began.

"Our first pregnancy ended in a miscarriage so our first daughter didn't arrive until two years into our marriage; our second daughter was born just 16 months later. We couldn't have children after that; too bad because we both would have enjoyed and welcomed at least one or two more.

"We embraced our roles as mother and father. We loved every stage of our daughter's lives.

"Christmas mornings were a joy as we watched them open far too many gifts while sitting cross-legged next to our lighted tree while still dressed in their snowman and reindeer long-john pajamas. Each new gift would result in several minutes of excited conversation and laughter. There were cookies and date-nut bread and coffee and egg nog on a table nearby. Christmas music was quietly playing on our Bose radio.

"Halloween was fun as we walked with them through the neighborhoods in search of homes with the king-sized candy bars; the 'good houses' is what we called them. The girls would sprint for about the first thirty minutes of trick or treat time, darting across driveways and front yards to get to the next home, but invariably by the end of the night we literally had to carry them for the final couple of streets. Every year there was a great debate about costumes; princess and Disney characters usually won out.

"Easter weekend was great. The girls would color hard-boiled eggs under Beth's supervision. They'd select a dress and a bonnet to wear for Sunday mass. Beth and I would spend a half an hour hiding plastic eggs, inside and out, and then watch the girls run around the yard or through every room of our house in search of the one 'prize' egg where inside they'd find a one dollar bill; they'd scream as if they'd just won the lottery. Later, they'd help their mom set the table and mash the potatoes while I carved our Easter ham as the *Easter Parade* movie played on our small kitchen television set."

I stopped for a second and looked at P.J.

"Are you bored yet? Is this really what you wanted to hear?"

"I want to hear only what you want to talk about," he replied. "You're doing fine. Continue."

"Now that I stand here and think about it," I went on, "I realize that so much of our married life revolved around our life as a mom and dad. Right or wrong, we prioritized our role as parent above our role as spouse. I would guess that's fairly common. We just loved our daughters so very much and we loved teaching them, guiding them, and spending time with them.

"Family vacations were always fun. It didn't matter where we traveled. A few times we went to Disney World where, when not standing in a long line or purchasing a seven dollar peanut butter and jelly sandwich, they smiled and blushed when they met Belle or The Little Mermaid or Mary Poppins.

"Once, we tried camping. We made it for about four hours until they got their first look at a bug the size of a Chevy Cavalier.

We had to pack up immediately. We laughed about it the entire way home where we proceeded to order Chinese take-out.

"Another year, we went to The Lake of the Ozarks in Missouri. We rented a small cabin that smelled like moth balls. The girls loved jumping off the pier in to the lake; until on day two they saw two dead fish float past the pier's ladder. That put an end to all lake activities. The remainder of the week we swam in the pool, we cooked on the cabin's outdoor charcoal grill which looked as if it had not been cleaned since the Truman administration, and we swept beetles out of our bedrooms. We laughed about all of that, too, as we made our way back home.

"Our favorite vacation destination was Door County, Wisconsin. We must have gone there over a dozen times. It's a beautiful part of the state tucked in between Lake Michigan and the bay of Green Bay. It is small, clean and quaint. There are biking and hiking trails in a gorgeous state park. There's our favorite cheeseburger place where the four of us could each eat the burger luncheon special for around twenty dollars; we'd play video trivia while waiting for our food. The county even has a drive-in theater with the old-time concession stand and the movie preview which featured the dancing hot dog bun and the singing bucket of popcorn. The four of us never failed to relax and bond during each of our Door County visits.

"We once took the girls to a local petting zoo. We left in ten minutes because our oldest daughter couldn't handle 'the stink.'

"We took them to many movies. They loved the big screen. When the scary Sea Witch first emerged from the water as we watched *The Little Mermaid*, our youngest daughter, then just three years old, jumped out of her seat and into my lap. She stayed there for the next ninety minutes.

"We once went to a Six Flags amusement park and only after paying about nine million dollars to gain entrance did we discover that none of us were brave enough to do most of the rides. Only the carousel and The Scrambler were appealing. We walked around the park for five hours and ate frozen lemonades. We took many pictures, pretending we really were having a good time. Years later when we saw those photos again, we realized that we *really did* have a good time, rides or no rides; we made the best of it. We always did.

"Often we'd keep the girls out of school in order for us to take a day trip or a long weekend to an historic site or a presidential library. Other parents thought we were irresponsible but we always believed there was far more to a good education than sitting in a classroom five days a week.

"Once I walked in to the living room to catch our oldest daughter throwing a book in a mild temper tantrum. She was four years old. 'We do not throw things in this house, young lady,' I said in my sternest 'dad voice.' All dads, I believe, have a fake 'mad voice' that they use when they want their kids to think they really are angry.

"I could see the wheels spinning in her head. Seconds later, she replied, 'But we throw balls.'

"My wife heard that from her position at the back of the room and immediately left for the kitchen so our daughter couldn't see her laughing. I had to pull the handkerchief out of my back pocket and place it over my mouth to hide my grin. We had just been trumped by a four year old; I mean, how does one argue with her logical comeback?

"On one of our visits back to my hometown of St. Louis, I decided to drive past the small home of my childhood. I wanted the girls to see where I came from. It reminded me of a song by Jackson Browne called *Looking Into You*:

> *Well, I looked into the house I once lived in*
> *Around the time I first went on my own.*
> *When the roads were as many as the places I had dreamed of*
> *And my friends and I were one.*
> *Now the distance is done and the search has begun*
> *I've come to see where my beginnings have gone.*

"The girls were ten and twelve years old at the time. They were accustomed to a nice life; not extravagant, but comfortable. My boyhood home, on the other hand, was very small. When I lived there from 1957 until college, it lovingly held seven people

in three tiny bedrooms, a living room and a kitchen.

"As we approached this home, I could see the faces of my two daughters in my rear-view mirror. I slowed the car to a crawl and pointed to the home to our right and I announced, 'There it is; that's where I grew up.'

"I was looking at my daughters when I said that. They didn't know I could see them. When they saw the home, they took it in and then quickly looked at each other with a look of surprise and sadness on their faces. 'Dad grew up in *that*?' they seemed to say.

"I think it may have made them appreciate my life although that was certainly not the intent of this drive-by.

"We experienced most everything, P.J., as our kids grew up: dance recitals, clarinet lessons, soccer and volleyball games, birthday parties, slumber parties, school field trips, good teachers, lazy teachers, good friends, bad friends, homecoming queens, Prom dates, honor rolls, family weddings and funerals.

"When we moved them to college, we cried as we said that first goodbye. And they did, too. That's when we knew that for the previous eighteen years that we must have done something right."

I stopped walking to rest against a pillar. I realized I had been talking non-stop for many minutes. I also realized that, for some reason, I was feeling sad.

P.J. sensed my mood. "You did well as a father, Bob. Your wife and you should be proud. It's very hard work. You took it seriously. You sacrificed. If more parents approached their role as responsibly as your wife and you, the world would be better off."

I don't take compliments well, including the few I happen to believe. "Thanks, P.J., I appreciate it," I said quietly.

"Do you want to know what's tough?" I continued. "You work so hard, you make your kids the focus of your life, you relish your time together and seemingly in a flash it's over. The years fly by. It's amazing how quickly they go from cradle to college. You drop them off at the university and they start their lives as responsible adults and at that precise moment your role as a parent changes dramatically. You are always their mom or dad, of course, but you are no longer their teacher and mentor and disciplinarian; instead, you are more their equal and their friend. And you realize that perhaps the most important phase of your life has ended. You look at your spouse and first you reintroduce yourself after eighteen years of being a parent, and then you ask, 'What now?'

Sheen had a puzzled look on his face. "It seems to me, Bob, that you just described the ideal situation. I don't understand your melancholy mood."

"There's a huge void in your life when your children are grown and gone. There's an emptiness knowing that your role as a parent is forever changed. Why do you not understand that?"

"I suggest you ask yourself this question: 'How else could it have turned out?'"

"Sorry, P.J., I don't follow you."

"Do you know how many parents *look forward* to getting their kids out of the house? Do you know how many parents don't have the great memories that you do? Do you know how many parents throw up their arms and give up on their kids at the first sign of trouble and challenge? Do you know how many parents do not love their children; they see their kids as a burden, not a blessing? Do you know how many parents refuse to sacrifice for their kids; instead, it is still all about themselves? Do you know how many parents have poor relationships with their kids in their adult years because they had no relationship with them in their childhood years?"

Finally, I got what he was driving at.

"Bob, look at the void and emptiness you feel as a good thing! The fact that you 'miss' something means it gave you great joy and contentment in the first place; why would anyone 'miss' something which brought sadness or heartache? You are one of the lucky ones! You loved your years as a father with your kids at home. You can look back at that stage of your life with pride and contentment and the feeling of satisfaction of a job well done. Your wife and you will always be close to your daughters because of that foundation you worked so hard to form. There are so many parents who would trade places with you in a heart

beat; parents who wish their kids still loved and respected them when they went off on their own."

He paused for a moment, waiting for me to make eye contact.

"Bob, there are too many times in life when one has every right to feel sad and depressed, so why look for sadness when there is no reason for it to be there? The worst thing one can do is to somehow find sadness in events and occasions which should bring one a feeling of great joy and peace. Embrace the joy of life, Bob, don't seek out the sadness."

I nodded my head at him to indicate I understood. "P.J., you are pretty good at this," I said.

"Thanks, but I'm just getting started," he replied.

I hate it when they things like that. My first friend Louis did the same thing. It means they still want me to talk. Like most men, I hate talking, unless it's about sports or politics or brands of Irish whiskey. But to talk about feelings or emotions, no thanks.

"What else, P.J.?"

"You did well in speaking of your role as a father; now tell me about your role as a husband."

"I have a better idea. Let's talk about Clint Eastwood movies."

"I'll make a deal with you. You can keep this short. That gives us more time for my final question."

"I may regret this, but I agree to that deal. Let's see, your instruction was; 'Tell me about your role as a husband'? Where do I possibly go with that? Am I supposed to say I have been the greatest husband in the world? I have not. Am I supposed to say I've been a horrible husband? I have not been that, either. Let's just say I fall somewhere in between. There, I'm done; let's move on to whatever it is you have for me next."

Sheen's stare told me it wasn't going to be that easy.

I relented. Let's get this over with.

"Ask a man to describe himself as a husband; he's likely to be more comfortable if you'd ask him to perform brain surgery, but here goes. I'll cut right to the chase because you told me to keep it brief.

"Bottom line: I think I could have been, should have been, a much better husband than what I was, than what I am. Did I fail miserably? No. Did I cheat, did I steal, did I abuse, did I break my wedding vows? No to all of the above. But there is nothing heroic or admirable about not doing things that none of us should do.

"But here are some other things I did not do. I didn't listen, respond or support as well and as often as I should have. Too often, I was needy. Too often, I was selfish. Too often, I was stubborn.

"I am hard to please. People disappoint me. I disappoint myself. I have a hard time being happy; does that make sense? Why choose *not* to be happy? There's a space somewhere between happy and sad and that's where I usually reside. For example, if I see a genuinely funny comedian at a live performance, I sometimes hold back my laughter even though I think the man is humorous; why do that? What sense does it make to restrict or inhibit one's own laughter? I can't figure myself out. Another example; whenever we are out socially with a group of people, I bend over backwards to make sure the others are having a good time; I try to be engaging and humorous and I want them to have a good time even though deep down I am usually *not* having a good time. That doesn't make sense, either. That inability or refusal to be joyful perplexes me and it must drive my wife nuts.

"I've changed jobs. In my nearly thirty years as a husband, I've held perhaps ten jobs. I've lost count. That probably introduced unnecessary stress to our marriage. I've left good jobs. I've never been fired, I just left them. I get bored very easily. I get frustrated with some of the co-workers. I need to be challenged; I don't want to punch a time clock and pretend I am working hard for the next eight hours. The incompetence and stupidity and laziness of bosses amaze me; how do many of them ever rise to that level? I often end up disliking, even hating, a specific job. So, I find a new one, figuring that you spend one-third of your life at work so you better make you sure you like it."

P.J. jumped in. "Only one thing in there, Bob, can I counter."

"What's that?"

"All bosses are incompetent."

"What about it?"

He lifted his head to the sky. "Mine isn't."

He stopped for a second for effect.

"In fact, my boss is the Greatest Ever. He is kind, caring, loving, compassionate, forgiving and generous. And you wouldn't believe his creativity skills; absolutely off the charts. I hope one day you get to work for Him. There's still time, you know."

I had no response. P.J. had a great skill to say things to which there was no adequate reply or argument. One had no choice but to agree. I bet he was like that decades ago, too.

"I can help you with one other thing, too, Bob. You told me you've had many jobs in your married life. You said that with a trace of embarrassment. You hinted it is not something a responsible husband should do."

"Yes?"

"I think we both know the reason behind that."

"Do we?"

"How old was your dad when he passed away?"

"51."

"At the time of his death, did he love his job or hate it?"

"He hated it."

"Why didn't he change jobs then?"

"He couldn't. Men of that generation were very limited in their options. Many men believed that once they found a good, steady job, they better hold on to it. They knew were lucky to have it. They had a family to support."

"And do you believe your dad's hatred of his job and his belief that he literally couldn't do anything about it was a factor in his early death?"

"I do indeed. On a scale of one-to-ten, I say a nine."

"Very well. Now, Bob, would you like to revisit and re-examine your job history; do you not think there is a deeper meaning to the fact that you often changed jobs?"

"The preacher is also a psychologist, is that it? You think that I equate hatred of a job or boredom with a job to an early death? You think that I refuse to get trapped in a job because I saw what those handcuffs did to my dad? Is that it, Doctor P.J.?"

"It's interesting, Bob, that I didn't say any of that; *you* did."

Again, my friend had given me something to think about.

"Look, P.J., you promised I could be brief when talking about my life as a husband. I'm going to call your bluff because I'm uncomfortable with this. I have so many flaws as a man, as a father, as a husband. I think you know that; why else would you have asked?

"I'll sum it up this way: I have never measured success by wealth or power or fame or popularity or possessions. Instead, I measure success by the ratio between what a man is and what he is capable of being. And in my opinion, my ratio is far too high. I think I am capable of so much more than what I've delivered. Time and time again, I disappoint myself. And that's hard to live with."

My friend didn't say a word; rather, he reached inside his pocket and pulled out a piece of scrap paper and an old Bic pen. He began to write something.

"What are you writing?" I asked.

"Success is measured by the ratio of what a man is and what he is capable of being," he responded. "I want to pass that along to a friend of mine. He can deal with that later."

❖❖❖❖❖❖❖

P.J. grabbed me by the elbow and ushered me over to the nearest pew at the right front corner of the cathedral, close to he shrine of the Sacred Heart.

"You may want to sit for this one, Bob," he stated. "It may take awhile."

I obeyed. I placed my feet on the top of the kneeler, draped my left arm over the back of the pew and waited for him to begin. This, I assumed, is why Sheen is with me tonight. All that other stuff was just the preliminary round; the game was about to begin. Just like everything else which had occurred since getting locked-in, I had no idea what was coming next.

P.J. pulled on the bottom of his grey cardigan sweater. He stood directly in front of me and leaned in, putting his hands on

the front of my pew.

"Tell me, Bob, about your prayer life."

Granted, I didn't know what to expect but I was not expecting that. "Excuse me?" I said.

"It's not a hard question, Bob; tell me about your prayer life."

"My prayer life? What do you mean?"

"What do you think I mean? I can see your defenses are up already. *When* do you pray? *What* do you pray? *How* do you pray? How often and how long every day do you pray?"

"Didn't you just hear me, P.J., talk about my life for the last nearly thirty years as a husband and father? Didn't I just tell you about those enormous responsibilities? Every minute of every day, or so it seems, is spoken for; career, kids, spouse, social obligations, volunteer work, responsibilities to your extended family. This is all-consuming, P.J. I'm sorry, but if you ask me 'How is your prayer life?' my answer may well be, '*What* prayer life?' I really don't have one."

"You *never* pray?"

"Well, I didn't go *that* far. You have a look on your face like I'm an atheist. Relax, P.J. Lighten up a bit. Of course I pray sometimes. I go to mass every week; there are plenty of prayers within a mass. Plus, we usually will pray at home before dinner. Sometimes before I ride on an airplane I will say a quick prayer. I will say a prayer if someone I love is sick or going through a tough time. And every now and then, just for the heck of it, I will throw in a quick 'Our Father' in the middle of the day."

I looked up at him. "There you have it. That's my prayer life. That wasn't as bad as I thought. Are you done? Can I go to my hotel now?"

"Bob, what you said about not having time to pray may well be your *explanation* but, pardon my candor, it's really more of an *excuse*. I don't doubt the time constraints placed upon a parent and spouse, but to say 'I don't have time to pray' doesn't cut it. We all have busy lives, Bob. We find time for dozens of things every day so we can certainly find time to pray. We make many choices every day on how to spend our time; somewhere in there, every day, we can choose to pray."

I decided to give in easily, hoping he'd drop it. "You're right. I'll try to do better," I said.

My strategy didn't work.

"Bob, I sense you have a problem with prayer. Or maybe an uncertainty or hesitation about prayer. Tell me."

"Oh, you *sense* that now, do you?" I responded somewhat sarcastically. "I didn't know 'mind reader' was one of your many talents, Archbishop."

"*Archbishop*? So it's 'Archbishop' now, is it? What happened to 'P.J.'? Are we no longer on friendly terms? Have I touched a nerve?"

I shot back quickly. "So you want to know if I have a 'problem' with prayer, correct? OK, you asked for it. Yes! I do have a problem with prayer. In fact, I have several. Here's one. Let's see how this sits with you. *I don't know how to pray.* Let me repeat that for you, Archbishop: *I don't know how to pray.*"

"Whatever do you mean?"

"See, I knew it! I knew you wouldn't understand even my most basic 'problem' with prayer. Just because prayer comes easily and naturally to people like you doesn't mean it does for all of us."

"Hold on! Who said prayer life comes easily and naturally? Do you really think that prayer is easy and natural just because we have a vocation? Are you kidding me? Ask anyone with a healthy prayer life and they will all tell you the same thing; it takes time, it takes effort, and it is not at all 'easy'. Nothing worthwhile is ever easy, Bob. One does not undertake prayer only when one has time; one must make time for the Lord with the firm determination to never give up, no matter what trials one may encounter. It takes dedication and hard work and patience. Prayer can be a battle. It always presupposes effort. Prayer is a battle against ourselves and against the pull of temptation to turn away from our union with God. We pray as we live; we live as we pray.

"To be human and to be relational means you must spend time with others; your children, your spouse, your close friends, your family. And in that time together, you must share your thoughts and emotions and fears. The same thing is true with your relationship with Jesus. There must be time together! That doesn't necessarily mean hours every day reciting the rosary or on your knees in silence; it does mean that even in our crazy life we have opportunities throughout the day to make time for the Lord, even if it is something short and simple like 'Lord, thank you for this' or 'God, I need your help right now.' Talk to Him during the day. Bring everything to the Lord, big and small, good and bad. Prayer is not something that only happens in a chapel; Jesus is with us every minute! We must spend time with Him every day! Do that and soon one begins to look at prayer not as a duty to be endured but as a privilege to be enjoyed. And when God finally breaks through to us, things suddenly disclose themselves with a depth we have never before perceived."

He spoke so enthusiastically. I knew he was sincere in his belief in prayer. I, however, wasn't sold. He must have realized that by the blank look on my face, a look so common for me I feel I was probably born with it.

"You are completely lost, aren't you, Bob?" he asked. "This is going to take longer than I thought. Move over. I need to get comfortable."

I moved in my pew to allow him a space to sit. "What are your questions, Bob?" he asked gently as he settled in.

"Well, it's not that I don't believe in the power of prayer. It's not that I don't respect or envy those with an effective prayer life. But, yes, I do have issues with it. I have questions. Let me throw them at you and we'll go from there. Are you ready?"

"I think so."

"Here goes. I don't know *how* to pray. I don't know *where* to pray. When I do pray, I feel I am not praying effectively. I wonder if there is a right way and a wrong way to pray. Often I feel that God isn't present when I pray. Sometimes I feel He is not listening, which brings me back to my belief that I must be praying improperly. It's my fault, not God's fault. I expect certain things from prayer but those expectations are never met. I don't even know the *purpose* of a prayer life. And finally, P.J., perhaps my biggest obstacle may be that I cannot grasp *why* we pray if we are supposed to believe in God's will. In other words, doesn't God's will, our destiny, trump prayer? My prayer is not going to change God's mind!"

Sheen remained silent for what seemed like several minutes. He ran his hand through his hair. He shifted his position in the pew. He stared at me with just the hint of a smile upon his lips.

"I should have let you return to your hotel," he finally said with a laugh. "You are indeed an interesting case, Robert Dolan. However, let's march on. You may be surprised that you are not alone. Many people ask those same questions. Not too many people ask *all* of them like you do, but these are issues and obstacles that we hear with some frequency. So, let's take them one-by-one, shall we?"

"Go ahead. You're in charge." I responded.

"Actually, I'm not. There is only one Person in charge, but let's stay on topic. You gave me so much, where do I begin?"

"Sorry to be so difficult," I smiled.

"Oh, I've had tougher cases than you, Bob. How about this? You said that you didn't know the 'purpose of a prayer life' so let's start with that. I'll bottom-line it. I'll keep it very basic. I'll give you the big picture. OK?"

"Sure."

"The purpose of a healthy prayer life is to maintain and strengthen our personal friendship with Jesus. He knows who we are but we remain a mystery to ourselves. We enter prayer with the admission that we are lost and prayer is discovering that the answer to our lives is not found within ourselves alone. God reveals the answer through our prayer life.

"Perhaps the most important understanding of prayer life is that it is a journey with Jesus. Saint Teresa put it very succinctly: 'Prayer is nothing else than an intimate sharing between friends; it means taking time frequently to be alone with Him who we know loves us.' There is no friend as good as Jesus. There is no one who desires our good as much as Jesus. We spend time with Him through prayer. We build that friendship through prayer.

"The essence of prayer does not consist in asking God for something specific; rather, it is opening our hearts to God and

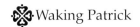

speaking with Him. It is the desire for God Himself. Prayer is a continual abandonment to God. It is not an effort to gain from God assistance in one or more aspects of our lives; it is the desire to *possess God*. Prayer is your personal relationship with the living and true God. Prayer is to enter more profoundly and more regularly into God's presence and to permit His love to claim more and more of whom we are. If, in prayer, we seek God for our own good and profit, then we are not seeking God.

"Some say prayer is a flight from the real world; I say the opposite! Prayer is not an escape from reality or a divorce from life. Prayer opens the door to the most important relationship of our life. Prayer is a life attitude."

"Wait a minute!" I said. "Go back to something you just said. You just told me that prayer is not asking God for something. That's my first mistake right there. I always ask God for something when I pray. I think most people do. I may pray for the improved health of a loved one or for someone who is unemployed to find a job or any number of specific requests; now you're telling me that's the wrong approach? Sorry, P.J., but that means *most* of us are praying improperly. I find that hard to believe."

"Let me clarify," Sheen replied. "I don't mean these things should not be a part of your prayer life. Of course, it is understandable and even worthy to ask God in prayer for His help in a specific burden you carry. However, there must also be a willingness and gentleness to let go of what we think we need. We must humbly present these burdens to God. His perspective far exceeds ours.

"My warning is that we cannot look to God as a genie-in-the-bottle. He is not our cash cow. You can't bargain with God like he is a street vendor. Our heart cannot be possessed with a small and finite notion of what it takes for us to be happy. It is perfectly normal to come to God in prayer with specific requests but our prayer life must be full and all-inclusive. Prayer is not a matter of me getting anything and everything I ask. Too often we view prayer as an act of self-assertion, a time when I define my needs to God, and if presented correctly then God will grant my wish. No! The value of consistent prayer is not just that He will hear us but that *we will hear Him*.  Prayer must involve the whole of our life and admitting how little we know regarding what truly is best and surrendering in faith and trust that God will never abandon us.  Pray with your eyes on God and not with your eyes only on your difficulties.

"Do not turn to prayer only when you are in trouble.  Do not turn to prayer only when you need help.  God is not a lawyer who is going to bail us out.  Prayer is not begging!  The Lord is calling us into a personal relationship through prayer.  He is not our Fix-It Man; he wants us to walk with Him as someone who loves us unconditionally.  Prayer is so much more than saying, 'Hey, Lord, give me this!'  As Saint Francis of Assisi said, 'When we pray to God, we must be seeking nothing.'"

"OK, this is good, this is actually helping!" I said earnestly.  "I like what you said about not turning to prayer only when you are in trouble.  For one, I think it is what most of us do.  Two, it reminds me of what Satchel Paige once said."

"Who is Satchel Paige?" Sheen inquired.

"Oh, P.J., you disappoint me.  Paige was a hugely talented pitcher in the old Negro baseball leagues.  It wasn't until he was over forty years old when he was allowed to play in the Major Leagues.  He is a member of the Hall of Fame.  He was well liked, too, because of his effervescent personality."

"And this man once talked about prayer?" Sheen asked hesitantly.

"He did.  Satchel said, 'Don't pray when it rains if you don't pray when the sun shines.'"

P.J. was speechless.

"Don't you see?  That's what *you* just said!  'Don't pray only when you need something' is what you just told me.  That sounds like Satchel Paige to me."

Sheen slowly shook his head.  "Bob?" he said.

"Yes?"

"You are living proof that we are all unique."

"Thanks!" I replied quickly before thinking that his comment may not have been intended for a compliment.

I thought it best to return him to the subject.

"You've told me what *not* to do in prayer; what about the other side? What *must* we do in prayer? What are the rules?"

"There aren't any rules, Bob. There aren't any guide books out there. We can all agree that prayer is a unique encounter with God so our prayer life is as unique as the individual. However, the two prerequisites are these: one must enter and continue prayer life with determination and trust."

"How about running that one by me again."

"We must have absolute *determination* to persevere in our prayer life. This is not a temporary endeavor. It must be life long. It must be consistent because only then can you grow accustomed to having Him present at your side; only then will He see that you wish to please Him; only then will you not be able to get away from Him. He will never fail you. He will never abandon you. You will find Him everywhere in your life. It is no small matter to have such a friend.

"Secondly, we must *trust* that someone we cannot see, someone we cannot hear, is there with us in prayer. You must never think that this is a one-way conversation. We must believe He is with us. Your faith puts you in the presence of God and He sees your effort as an act of love. Most of us trust in the Lord too little; realize that it is impossible to trust in Him too much."

"I'm glad you went there, P.J., because, frankly, sometimes I feel as if I am literally talking to the wall during the few times I've tried to establish a prayer life," I admitted. "Sometimes I wonder if God is really there. I mean, how can He really be listening to *just me* at this specific time? Aren't there millions of other people also praying to Him?"

I continued. "Let me try to explain. You've said that my prayer life is as simple as developing my relationship with Jesus, right?"

"Yes."

"Well, my difficulty comes when I compare that approach to how I develop and maintain my relationships here on earth with my loved ones and my friends. When I speak to them, I can look them in the eye. I can read their body language. I can see their reaction. I know if they are hearing me or not. They respond to me. They answer me. We have a real discussion. There is never any doubt about what our real meaning and message may be because we can talk and listen until we are all on the same page. And that's exactly how we strengthen our relationships. With God, however, I cannot do any of that! I don't know what He is thinking. I don't know what He is saying. I don't know how He is reacting to what I am saying. Sometimes I think, 'Give me something; show me something; give me a sign that this is really working; knock a book off my shelf or throw a lightning bolt outside my window; I need to know that you are really hearing me!' Do you understand what I am saying, P.J.?"

"Of course I do. It goes back to faith and determination. We desire God with flesh so we expect Him to be human even in our prayer life and when that doesn't occur we get impatient or distracted. It happens. Don't beat yourself up. My goodness, even Mother Teresa admitted she sometimes felt alone in her prayer life, that even she wondered if God was always present."

Suddenly, Sheen got a smile on his face and then continued. "Bob, I know Mother Teresa. I worked with Mother Teresa. Mother Teresa was a friend of mine. Bob, you're no Mother Teresa."

"Are you going nuts on me, P.J.? Why are you acting like Senator Lloyd Bentsen against Dan Quayle all of a sudden?"

"I couldn't resist. That was too easy. Nothing personal, I'm trying to show you that if even one of the most saintly women in history sometimes doubted the presence of God in her prayer life, then take it easy on yourself when you have the same questions. The Lord is not going to communicate in a way that knocks us to the floor; sorry, no lightning bolts. We must believe that He is listening and speaking but in a manner in which we are unfamiliar."

"That's a tough one, P.J. It might be easy for people like you but for sinners like me, that's tough. If I wonder if Jesus is really hearing me in prayer, I am very tempted to just give up. I have other things I can be doing."

"When Jesus said He is with us always, do you believe Him?" Sheen asked.

"No, P.J., Jesus was lying," I replied, dripping with sarcasm. "Of course I believe Him. What a silly question."

"Then put your money where your mouth is! Jesus is with you always, especially in your prayer life. Hey, sometimes even I felt God's presence in prayer and sometimes I did not. That's why faith and love are the surest means to God. It's our fault, not His. We are always so interested in the things that sparkle and make noise so when we experience the opposite we don't know what to make of it. We think there's nothing there. Often the Lord wants us to be still but we kick and scream. Prayer gives us time away from the chaos and noise and the meaningless activities. Silence is comforting. Silence is healing. We best hear God in total silence. It's like a father who looks at his kids at the dinner table; the father smiles and is comforted just by being in their presence; talking is not always necessary. That's a secure relationship. God's silence can be a good thing. He wants us in that quiet and reflective state-of- mind where He can best speak to our heart. God is not absent; you are not alone; often that place between promise and fulfillment is the perfect place to be.

"Is it all about *your* feelings, Bob? Does that describe your relationships with your wife and children? Does your spouse have to do a circus act for you every day for you to hear her? Good luck with that! It is not '*My* will be done', it is '*Thy* will be done.' Try any relationship using 'my will be done' as your criteria and see how far that gets you. God wants a relationship where we get to know Him as He really is and not as we wish He would be. It's not all about you in prayer; it's about God and what He asks of us.

"I know it can be frustrating. I know at times it will feel useless. Remain determined and persistent! It is very much like the stone cutter who hammers away at the rock one hundred times without so much of a crack showing in it, but on the next blow the rock splits. That stone cutter knows it was not because of that one final blow but because of all the ones before it.

"Stick with your prayer life and eventually there will be an enormous and overwhelming cry of recognition."

"What do you mean?" I asked.

"Let me use you as an example, Bob. Go back to your days in grade school and high school when you were playing sports. So many times you were completely absorbed in the game, shutting out all noise around you, correct?"

"Yes."

"Suddenly, inexplicably, you hear an encouraging and familiar voice rising above the rest of the crowd noise, perhaps the voice of your mom or dad or sibling; and you instantly realize that someone who loves you very much is present. You didn't even know that person was attending the game. That voice makes all the difference. That 'cry of recognition' is the consequence of a long and ever-deepening on-going relationship.

"That human intimacy only comes after sharing lots of time together, disclosing the mystery of one's self before the other and becoming vulnerable to that person. That same thing occurs in a consistent prayer life with Jesus."

Sheen was helping me a great deal. I still wasn't sure I was cut-out for a great prayer life but at least I was beginning to comprehend the concept of prayer. "OK then, let's get back to what I first said when this conversation began: *'I don't know how to pray!'* I don't know how to start, I don't know what to do or say."

He answered quickly. He was clearly in his comfort zone. "Many people have a great insecurity about their prayer life. We feel intimidated. We feel naked. So, like you, we avoid it. You say you don't know *what* to say and you don't know how to *present* it. Bob, why even go there? You seem intent on making your prayer life so complicated and so difficult. There's no need for that.

"Let me ask you this: When you are driving to a restaurant or a pub to meet a group of friends or family members, do you make a list of exactly everything you want to say that night?"

"Everything? Of course not! There may well be one or two items of importance that I feel need to be discussed, but most of the conversation will be ad-libbed and spur-of-the-moment."

"Then I suggest you use the same approach in your prayer life! Talk to God about anything and everything, big and small; that's how a friendship develops and matures. Start there; *just talk to Him*. Many people think that there are some things not

worthy of telling to God, but He wants to be a part of our entire life.

"Let's move on. A relationship becomes real and personal the moment you single a person out of the crowd; at that time the person ceases to become anonymous. A healthy prayer life begins at the moment when we no longer think of God in the third person way off in the distance somewhere. There is no effective prayer as long as there is a cautious, distant and cold relationship, as long as there is a ceremonial between us and God, as long as we feel we must go through a long and complex series of words and actions to approach Him. No! See God. Imagine God. Talk to God. Make it personal. You don't even need titles like The Almighty or The Redeemer; He is God, He is Jesus, He is your friend.

"Next, try this: select a prayer or a dialogue which makes sense to you; don't try to speak a language that you feel only God will understand. Speak on *your* level; God will understand! Why try to impress God with lofty phrases and intellect? Keep it simple. The words of your prayer must be completely true to who you are and how you feel. Don't use the words of others. This is *your* conversation with Jesus.

"Strange as it sounds, also do not lie in your prayer life!"

I jumped in. "Oh, come on, P.J.! Who would lie during prayer? Heck, not even I would think about doing that."

"You'd be surprised. *Bring to Christ as it really is*, not as you would want it or as you think He would prefer it, but as it is. Be completely honest in your prayer life. In our prayer, do not be ashamed. Be open.

"This, too, is important: pray with humility. Pray with a contrite heart. Humility is the foundation of prayer. Do not pray with pride. Part of the humility and truth that we are called to in prayer is to put everything on the table, almost as if to say, 'Here I am, Lord, warts and all; you know I am a sinner, you know I am troubled, and I also know that you love me.' Tell God your sins and then believe God's love is greater than whatever it is that we have done. We fall but we get back up for God's love. In prayer, hold nothing back.

"There is also no need to shout in prayer or even talk, for however softly we speak, He is near enough to hear us."

"You make it sound so easy," I stated.

"The most difficult part of a healthy prayer life is just sticking with it. Prayer itself, the part where you speak with Jesus, is the easy part. Have you heard the phrase, '90% of success is just showing up?'"

"I have."

"Well, Bob, remember this then: '100% of success in prayer life is just showing up.'"

"Not bad, P.J., not bad at all. Even I can just 'show up'!"

"I've noticed."

I stood in my pew. We'd been sitting for a long time. I looked down at my friend, still looking as poised and polished as he did when he first appeared to me. 'This guy is good,' I admitted to myself. 'It's no wonder millions of people listened to his every word.'

"I still have that one final problem or dilemma with prayer, P.J. This is a big one for me."

"Let's have it."

"I ask, 'If we believe in God's will then why do we pray?' If we believe that God has a plan for all of us, that we all have a destiny, then why pray? Even in Scripture you can read the apostle Matthew stating that 'Your Father knows what you need even before you ask Him.' So I see that and I ask, 'Then why do I pray? Why do I ask?' *Why pray if God's will is going to win anyway?* My prayer doesn't change God's mind, right? My prayer will not change His plan."

P.J. thought for a moment to gather his thoughts.

"I find it interesting that you indicate there is some sort of battle going on in prayer," he began. "You say it is your prayer versus God's will. That's not the point of prayer at all! In many ways, I've already covered this. Prayer, Bob, is not a battle; it is not you saying, 'God, give me this.' and then God decides whether or not to grant it. You are not looking to win something from God. He is way ahead of you. This is not a competition. God has already given you everything you need; he gave you His

Son to die on a cross for your salvation. You say, 'God is going to win anyway.' I say, 'You better *hope* He wins!' He wants your happiness. He wants you in His kingdom. In prayer, He does not coerce us; he moves us to choose what is good and right. The closer we get to Him in prayer, the more we choose what is right. When God hears our prayer we must trust that He will respond according to His wisdom and goodness; He is not subjected to our will.

"We pray to grow closer to Him. Prayer does not change God's mind, it does not change His will; rather, *prayer changes him who prays*. If we persevere long enough in a consistent and genuine prayer life, we will sense His overwhelming presence and we will be assured that God is working on His timeline, not ours, and He will set right the world and our hearts."

He stood above me before concluding. "Bob, you have asked sensible questions. Your doubts are far more common than you imagine. However, you no longer have any excuses not to begin a meaningful prayer life. You have time. We all do. Your kids are out of the house now. Your career is stable. No more excuses, no more doubts. Believe! Persevere! Be patient! And you will discover that he who has learned how to pray has learned the greatest secret to a happy life."

❖❖❖❖❖❖❖

"So what are your plans now, P.J.?"

My friend and I were standing at the base of the steps leading to the elevated pulpit on the left side of the main altar, the same pulpit where I had first seen and heard him. I'd come to like him. I felt comfortable with him. I understood him now, far more than I did when researching his life for the video documentary. You see someone on videotape, you watch someone on television, you listen to someone on the radio, and you come to believe you really know them. In this case, in most cases, that's not at all true.

"I hang around this cathedral most of my time," Sheen said. "And why wouldn't I? It is one of my great honors to be buried here. I get to pal around with some real giants. I get to listen in

My Second New Friend ❖

as people pray for my canonization. This place is my home-away-from-home.  I love it here."

"If this is your home-away-from-home," I asked, "where's your real home?"

"Up there."

"The pulpit?"

 He laughed.  "A little higher than that, Bob."

"Oh.  Of course."

"As much as I love it here, however," he continued, "I do need to get out for a few days every now and then.  We all need a change of scenery.  I usually go back to Peoria, see the old stomping grounds, and see where it all began.  I think it's time for another visit."

"What do you do there?"

"Always, I visit the Cathedral of St. Mary of the Immaculate Conception.  That's where I learned to serve mass.  That's where I was ordained as a priest.  It's a special place.

"Lately, though, I've also been eaves-dropping on a few board meetings."

"What do you mean?"

"Well, they have a Fulton J. Sheen Foundation now.  They are creating a museum for me; isn't that the coolest thing ever?  It will be right there in Peoria.  I am so humbled."

'I bet you are,' I said under my breath.

"So now when I return to my hometown," he went on, "I am literally the fly on the wall, listening in as the board members discuss their plans for the museum.  They always have such nice things to say about me.  They think I'm great.  They frequently call me one of the most important and influential Catholics in the last two centuries.  I burst with pride.  Often I am so tempted to just suddenly appear on the middle of their boardroom table and say, 'Thank you!  I appreciate your hard work!  Now, let's get this museum done!' and then just disappear again, but I'm not allowed to do that.

"After the board meeting, sometimes I check out my favorite diner and grab a piece of delicious cherry pie right out from under the nose of the waitress.  She freaks out every time!  She tells the boss that she must be losing her mind because she swears she just put a piece of pie on her tray, right next to the plate of meatloaf and gravy for the table by the door, and she looked away for just a second and the pie had disappeared. I know it's wrong but I can't help it; they serve the best pie in the world. Their pecan pie is good, too. I do miss that diner. I went there so often growing up; roast beef, carrots, a pile of mashed potatoes, a piece of pie and a small Coke, all for two dollars. Those were the good old days, Bob."

"Boy, P.J., I sure hope your little problem with pie-theft doesn't derail that whole canonization thing," I said. "You could be the first person worthy of sainthood ever to be denied because of habitual lifting of a slice of cherry pie from the diner of his boyhood. That sainthood committee might call you The Pie Pilferer. Or, The Cherry Kleptomaniac. Or…"

"Bob?"

"Yes?"

"Drop it."

"OK."

"Besides," he resumed. "Even saints weren't perfect."

Sheen placed his right foot on the first step of the staircase. It was almost time to say goodbye.

"Another thing I often do when I go back home is catch a baseball game. I love watching the Peoria Chiefs. It's minor league baseball. It's good quality."

"What do you steal there, a couple of hot dogs?"

He let that comment pass with a smile. "Did you ever see the movie, Bob, called *Angels in the Outfield*?"

"I did! I liked it. I think Danny Glover was the star. An angel helps a losing baseball team become a winner. Why do you ask?"

"Well, I went to a Chiefs game last summer and I sat on second base for the entire game. Players were running right through me for all nine innings and they never once noticed me. It was a better seat for the game than even the first row behind the dugout. So, instead of *Angels in the Outfield*, I refer to that game as *Sheen on the Infield*."

He extended his right arm and offered a final handshake.

"Bob, this has been fun. It's been nice to talk to you."

"And it's been nice to meet you, too, Archbishop," I replied as I firmly grasped his hand. "Thank you for your help."

With that, he smiled, nodded his head, and turned to walk up the staircase. I watched him as he took his place in front of the microphone, once again looking out to the main floor of the cathedral, just as he was when I first saw him.

I walked the few steps around the communion rail to the walkway in front of the first pew, directly underneath the pulpit. I looked up to wave one final goodbye to my most recent new friend, to tell him 'Thank you!' one final time.

And no one was there. He was already gone.

'How did he get away without me seeing him? Where did he go?' I wondered.

And then it hit me.

He's probably still climbing.

Photo: Chris Danielson

The Altar of the Holy Face, which features an image of a man's face that believers say is the true face of Christ, is one of the side altars inside the Cathedral of Saint Patrick.

The side altar honoring Our Lady of Guadalupe is the cathedral's most frequently visited side altar.

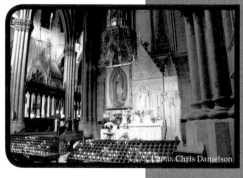
Photo: Chris Danielson

Photo: Chris Danielson

There are several side altars inside the Cathedral which honor two saints, including this altar named after saints Louis and Michael.

Saint Joseph is honored with a side altar inside the Cathedral of Saint Patrick. The altar is intentionally simple and humble, much like the man it honors.

Photo: Chris Danielson

The life of Pope John Paul II is remembered and saluted by this bust located inside the main entrance of the Cathedral.

The former archbishops of New York are buried in the crypt, located underneath the High Altar. The crypt also includes the remains of Fulton J. Sheen.

Photo: John Glover

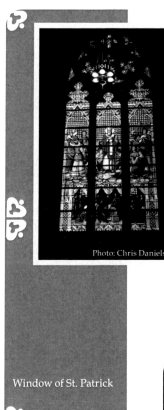

Photo: Chris Danielson

Window of St. Patrick

St. Patrick is honored inside the Cathedral in both a stained-glass window and a statue.

Photo: Chris Danielson

Photo: John Glover

This view from the upper choir loft of the interior of the cathedral includes both the Main Altar and the High Altar.

The pulpit.

Photo: Chris Danielson

The Cathedral of Saint Patrick is located on Fifth Avenue in the heart of Manhattan.

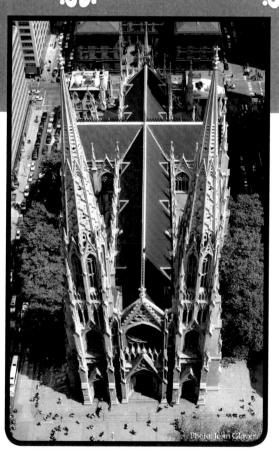

Photo: John Glover

Chapter

# V
# *My Third New Friend*

I'm not as dumb as I look, although many who know me may wish to debate that. After I said goodbye to my first new friend, Saint Louis, I mistakenly thought my night inside the cathedral was finished and I would be allowed to walk out the door and back to my hotel.

That did not happen. Soon, I encountered Fulton Sheen.

Now that he, too, has left, I'm not going anywhere. I knew it'd be useless for me to walk to the exit. I knew the doors would remain locked. Several times during our conversation, Sheen had implied that I'd have other visitors before the night was through, so instead of walking to a door like I had after Louis's departure, this time I took a seat in a pew and waited to see what, or more accurately, *who* would happen next.

The events of the evening thus far had already had an impact. Louis and Sheen were good guys. True, each had frustrated me at times with their candor and perspective but they had been helpful. Somehow, I felt more at peace than I had just moments ago, hours ago, whenever it was when I had first entered this building. I also had the strange sensation that both were still present, even though I couldn't see them or hear them anymore.

At this moment, I was also very much puzzled and confused. I'm a Catholic; I don't think we are supposed to believe in spirits or ghosts. It's not that I recall a specific lesson in grade school or a particular paragraph in my catechism book about not believing in ghosts, but somewhere along the line someone must have told me not to believe in them; for why else would I assume I shouldn't? Yet, I'd just come to know two men who have been

159

dead for over eight hundred years combined. They sure looked and sounded real to me. They talked to me. I talked to them. Our conversations made sense.

I've wavered on this ghost thing for several years now. Initially, no, I didn't believe in ghosts; my Catholic upbringing may or may not have had anything to do with that. I just couldn't comprehend the idea of this place after death where people go to be ghosts; why wouldn't *every* place be haunted then? Why wouldn't there be *billions* of ghosts then? Why wouldn't *everyone* have a 'ghost story'? Doesn't it have to be one way or the other, with no middle ground; shouldn't it be that there are *no ghosts at all* or *we all* become ghosts after death? Why some ghosts but not others? Why do we hear just a few ghost stories? If ghosts were real, wouldn't there be ghost stories all the time? Wouldn't we all see a ghost in our lifetime? For a long time, I concluded ghosts did not, could not, exist.

In recent years, however, I find myself allowing for the possibility. In fact, it's probably more than that. My new position has been influenced by two men I know and respect. Both men told me they not only believe in spirits but they have experienced them! They'd *seen* them! These are two men who are very sensible and intelligent. They wouldn't fabricate a ghost story in order to gain attention. They live normal lives. They are respected in their professions.

One man told me he saw spirits often following his wife; once he saw a ghost standing at the foot of their bed. He also said ghosts were prevalent on or around very old furniture in some homes he'd visited. He wasn't scared at all; for him, it was all very matter-of-fact.

The second man told me his boyhood home was haunted although he didn't realize it until he purchased the house after he got married. He noticed strange sounds and sights and incidents. When he finally mentioned it to his wife, she confessed that she, too, had noticed many of the same things. Again, these are two very smart and sensible adults; they'd have no reason to make this up. If nothing else, *they* believed it completely, unequivocally.

I grabbed my backpack, retrieved my I-Pad and began

searching the internet for what, if anything, my church instructs on the existence of ghosts. I couldn't find an 'official teaching'. I discovered that the church certainly offers a caveat not to subscribe to superstition and sorcery but nothing definite about the existence of spirits. As Catholics, we believe in life after death, sometimes even very soon after death. And we most certainly accept as fact a few, but definitely not all, apparitions of Mary and some others we know are long deceased.

I sense a grey area. My limited research tells me that even our religions concede that ghosts may indeed exist. I'm still not convinced, but I'm close to admitting that, yes, I believe in ghosts.

'Somehow,' I think to myself with a smile, "I bet Saint Louis and Fulton Sheen would agree with me.'

Suddenly I noticed movement off to my left. I stood up in my pew and saw a man sitting on the front step of the communion rail, with his back leaning against the rail. He was looking down and appeared to be writing on a pad of paper placed upon his knee.

I walked over slowly. 'There he is,' I whispered. 'There is my next new friend.'

Never once did the man look up as I approached. Not only that but once I arrived and stood immediately in front of him, he still did not acknowledge my presence. I stood in silence for a few seconds expecting him to finally introduce himself. He did not.

I looked to where he was writing and saw that it wasn't a pad of paper on his knee after all; instead, it was a pile of postcards, all of them featuring a photograph of either the exterior of Saint Peter's Basilica in Rome or Saint Peter's Square, the huge area in front of the basilica which can hold hundreds of thousands of tourists and pilgrims. The man was carefully writing on the back of each postcard, one-by-one, as if he was going to soon mail them to friends and family back home.

Still, he never looked up and he never said a word.

He looked to be in his early twenties. He had black hair and a black thick beard.

He looked to be of Middle Eastern descent but I've never

really been very good at correctly guessing these things. He was wearing a navy blue sweatshirt, black jeans and sneakers. He looked thin with a small frame.

I shuffled my feet. I cleared my throat. I faked a cough. I was trying to get him to notice me. He never did, so I finally gave in and said a cheerful, 'Hello!'

He continued writing on the postcards until, several seconds later, he looked up and made eye contact.

He didn't respond. He didn't smile. He didn't nod his head. He did nothing one would normally do to indicate the presence of another person. He simply looked at me.

And it scared me. *He* scared me. His demeanor scared me.

And his eyes, jet black, unfeeling, icy, even evil, certainly scared me.

Immediately, I took a step back. He made me very uncomfortable.

He continued to stare at me, appearing angry that I had interrupted his postcard duties. I couldn't get beyond his eyes; unlike any I'd ever seen before.

Finally, he turned his attention back to his writing, without ever saying a word.

'Well, what am I supposed to do with this guy?' I wondered to myself. 'If I try to leave, obviously that won't work because he was certainly sent here for a reason and, judging from his foul mood, apparently without his approval. So what am I to do?'

I continued to look down at him. Strangely, as I did when I first saw Fulton Sheen, a feeling of vague familiarity swept over me. Somewhere, I had seen this guy before. I just couldn't place him.

I stepped in closer and bent down to get a better look at his face. He didn't seem to mind; he never once stopped his writing.

Soon, not only did *how he looked* ring a bell but also *what he was doing*; a picture was beginning to form in my head of this man with the evil eyes and the heavy beard writing on postcards of Saint Peter's Square.

And this time I didn't step back, I jumped. And not one step, but several. This time, I really did feel like leaving. 'This can't be!' I thought. 'Why would *he* be here? It doesn't make sense. It's one thing for Saint Louis and Fulton Sheen to be in this cathedral, but not this guy!'

I remained very much afraid. Now, though, I was also intrigued. I had to make sense of this.

I gathered my thoughts. 'If he is who I think he is, then what were the facts?' I asked myself.

The event in question came back to me quickly and clearly. It occurred in 1981. I was in my early twenties at the time, about the same age as this man sitting at the communion rail. I paid total attention to that event; I watched news coverage; I read magazines and newspapers about it. Most everyone did. This event had worldwide impact.

'It cannot be,' I repeated to myself. 'But nothing else makes sense. It looks like him. And he's writing postcards! What other explanation is there?'

I thought about how best to approach him; how best to determine if what I now believed could really be true.

Clearly, he is not going to offer anything to me. He is not going to stand up and shake my hand and begin a pleasant conversation. This man wanted nothing to do with me. I had no choice but to take the most direct route. I decided to confront him directly. I moved in closer.

"On May 13, 1981, were you in Rome?"

He continued to work on the postcards.

"You had arrived in Rome just three days before on a train from Milan. Before Milan, you were in Bulgaria. Am I right?"

No reaction.

"You were twenty-three years old. I remember that because I recall thinking at the time, 'My goodness; he is my age! Why would he do something like this?' Then all the news reporters would soon tell me that in your earlier years you were a petty thief, a gang member, a smuggler, and finally a killer; you murdered a journalist just two years before that date in Rome. You had escaped from prison."

The man below me put his pen down on the step.

"Are you from Turkey?" I asked.

He removed the pile of postcards from his knee and placed them, too, upon the step.

"That day in Rome, you sat on the cobblestones of Saint Peter's square, writing on postcards so you would blend in with all the other tourists, so as not to draw attention to yourself."

He ran his fingers through his thick hair.

"You are Mehmet Ali Agca, aren't you?"  I couldn't believe I was asking that question.

He looked up at me.  He showed no emotion whatsoever.

"You tried to kill Pope John Paul II.  When his Pope-mobile drove by, you jumped up and fired several shots.  He was critically injured.  You had more bullets to fire but you were quickly tackled by security and bystanders."

He stared at me.  He never made an attempt to respond.  Again, I was frightened just by the way he looked.

"Later, you told many stories.  You told many lies.  You said there was a second gunman but he bailed out when the Pope approached.  You said you were acting on orders from the Bulgarian Secret Service; later you blamed the Soviet K-G-B; later again you said you acted alone as a protest against imperialism; yet another story was that you had been paid by the Turkish mafia to assassinate the Pope; and finally your best fabrication of all was that Vatican Secretary Agostino Cardinal Casaroli was behind the attempt on John Paul's life."

He stared me down with his black, evil eyes.  His facial expression never changed.

"You were sentenced to life in prison in Italy but after nineteen years they sent you back to Turkey; and there, just a few years later, they released you.  Unbelievable.

"Since then, you have predicted the end of the world.  You sign your statements, 'The Christ Eternal.'  You've said you will write the perfect Gospel because the ones we have from Matthew, Mark, Luke and John are horribly flawed.  You're a crazy man, aren't you, Mehmet?"

I surprised myself with my forcefulness.  My voice was strong and confident.  I was no longer intimidated by this terrorist.

He stood up and walked towards me.  He looked mean and

menacing. His eyes pierced right through me. He stood just inches away from me.

"And the most remarkable thing about this entire episode," I continued, returning his icy glare, "is that the Pope, the man you wanted to kill, visited you in prison and offered his forgiveness. He forgave you! If that was me, I would have gone into that cell and killed you. When John Paul left the prison he asked all of us; 'Pray for my brother, who I have sincerely forgiven.'"

I stepped back so that I could see him more clearly when I asked him this final question. "Why on earth, Agca, would John Paul II forgive a monster like you? I don't understand at all."

He paused for a few seconds, and then leaned in to whisper in to my right ear: "Ask him yourself, smart ass."

❖❖❖❖❖❖❖

I quickly pushed away from this maniac and noticed he was looking over my shoulder to the area near the entrance of the cathedral. I turned and saw the back of a man standing near the large doors at the entrance. He was at least two hundred feet away and facing the opposite direction but there was no mistaking his identity; solid build, broad shoulders, wearing a white papal vestment and, rather oddly, a ski jacket.

'People here sure do dress strangely,' I thought to myself. Then, snapping back to the enormity of this situation, I wondered: 'What am I ever going to say to *him*?'

I turned back in Agca's direction. I had no plans to say goodbye; I just wanted to see his reaction to the presence of the man he once tried to murder.

He was gone. He was just there seconds ago. His pile of postcards remained on the communion rail step but there was no sign of the man himself. This was fine by me; I didn't care where he had gone, I only hoped he'd never come back.

I turned my attention back to my new friend, still standing motionless way up the aisle. From where I stood he seemed to be staring at something placed immediately in front of him.

I began to walk up the center aisle, very slowly because I

still wasn't sure what I was going to say once I got to him. I've been way out-of-my-league ever since the minute I walked into this place but John Paul II was on a higher level, for me at least, than even Louis and Sheen because here was a man who made his enormous contributions during my lifetime. I could relate to him far better than the two men who visited me earlier. I lived through his papacy. I followed his life. I knew his story. I felt his impact. I admired his example.

I easily remembered where I was when I heard of his death in 2005. My wife and daughters were visiting my sister and her daughter in Chicago. We were enjoying lunch in a crowded pub and when the television set screamed out the news of John Paul's death, a hush came across the huge room. For minutes, no one spoke. Some even made the sign-of-the-cross.

The days which followed his death were remarkable, unlike anything I had ever seen before. I watched from my home in Milwaukee as an estimated four million pilgrims, young and old, Catholic and non-Catholic, made their way to Rome to attend the funeral. They came from most everywhere in the world. They arrived on trains and busses and crowded mini-vans. They slept in the streets of Rome. They lined up for many miles just to get a quick glimpse of him in death inside Saint Peter's Basilica.

Four million people and, in his memory, they behaved. There were no riots or crime. They shared water and bread. They recited the rosary and broke into song. It was called the largest single pilgrimage of Christianity ever. It was a perfect tribute to this man's life.

For all these reasons, yes, I was very apprehensive, even nervous, as I got close. What am I doing here? What do I say? What does he want with me?

I recalled an opportunity about a decade ago when I had a chance to meet him. 'How ironic,' I thought to myself now as I stopped about twenty feel away from him. 'I turned down a chance to meet him when he was alive and here I am about to meet him after he has died.'

My family and I were with hundreds of pilgrims touring Vatican City. Our busy itinerary included the weekly general audience with the Pope.  The night before, one of the priests in our group disclosed that four people from our pilgrimage would be allowed to meet John Paul II during the public audience.  Kindly, he offered to me one of those four spots.

Of course, I was honored and humbled.  However, I believed I was also undeserving.  As a result, with the permission of the man making the offer, I gave my spot to my wife.  The next day, she met the Pope and I happily watched from the middle row.

Others described my gesture as 'unselfish' or 'generous' or some kind of great sign of a husband's love and respect for his wife.  Nonsense!  I didn't deserve it and she did; simple as that.  Besides, I was too frightened to meet that man.  I was afraid I'd throw-up as I was climbing the steps to his chair.

Now, about ten years removed from that opportunity in Rome, there would be no escape or no excuse.  This time, I would meet him.  I had no choice.

I walked up beside him and noticed he'd been staring at his own bust located very close to the main entrance of Saint Patrick's Cathedral.  The small plaque underneath read: 'His Holiness John Paul II visited this cathedral on October 2-3, 1978.'  The bust, I decided, would at least present to me a logical beginning to whatever dialogue was to follow.

"Do you approve?" I asked.  "Do you think it looks like you?"

"I do.  I like it very much," he replied in a thick Polish accent.

"Do you like this cathedral?" I continued, hesitantly.

"I do."

He paused, probably expecting me to come up with something else to continue this conversation.  I didn't, so he resumed.

"I visited New York City on two occasions but only once did I come to this cathedral.  I regret that.  Now, I come here often."

"Do you come here now just to stare at your bust?" I wondered.

He chuckled.  "Not at all.  There are memorials to a few Polish saints in this cathedral so I come here for them.  In addition, a shrine to Our Lady of Czsestochowa is in here, so I sometimes visit in order to pray there.  In fact, right before I died I blessed the icon now located in that shrine.  You see, I have many reasons to visit this wonderful cathedral.  My own likeness on this bust has

little to do with it."

I turned to face him and extended my right hand. "My name is Bob."

"I know," he said.

He took my hand and nearly crushed it with his strong handshake. "And my name is Karol," he continued.

"I know."

"Do you? I am impressed," he said. "Most people only know me by my professional name, John Paul. Some are prone to abbreviate that to just JP2. Honestly, I'm not too crazy about that nickname but at least they remember me. At least they are usually speaking well of me so why worry about the name they may use."

"Would you like me to call you John Paul or Karol?", I asked with sincerity. I remained unsure about how best to proceed with this intimidating man.

"I prefer Karol. It reminds me of who I was and where I came from; Poland."

For the first time, I looked at him closely. This was not the Pope I remembered from his final days. The man standing with me at this moment was not a sick old man dominated by Parkinson's disease. Instead, this man I saw was young and attractive with an athletic build. His face was chiseled, his jaw was firm, and his eyes a bright baby blue.

I remembered that he was an excellent athlete in his day and worked hard to remain physically fit; he was a goaltender in soccer, he hiked mountain trails, he was a downhill skier, he swam, he ran, he kayaked. The man who did all of that was the man I saw in front of me; ruggedly handsome. This was hardly the very sick man we all saw in those painful years before his death. I assumed his current very healthy and fit appearance was the reason for his bright red ski jacket; for now he was not only dressed as a Pope with the white full-body length vestment but he was also dressed as the athlete he once was.

"Well, Karol, it is very good to meet you," I resumed. "I am honored."

He smiled and said. "Well then, you should have met me ten

years ago. Do you know that you are one of the few people to turn down the chance to meet me?"

"How do you know that?" I said.

"I didn't until just a few minutes ago when I heard what you were thinking as you were walking up the aisle. I'm just giving you a hard time. Besides, I enjoyed meeting your wife in your place. I recall she was very pretty and kind."

"You remember her?"

He didn't respond; he just smiled again. It was the most disarming smile I'd ever seen. Whatever tight spot in which he ever may have found himself, I bet that smile helped get him out of it.

He changed the subject. "So, Bob, you know my birth name is Karol; what else do you know about me?"

"Honestly, Karol, until you were elected as Pope in 1978, I didn't know *anything* about you. I remember the dramatic announcement in Latin from the balcony of Saint Peter's Basilica on that crisp October evening: 'Habemus Papam, Cardinale Wojtyla'. ('We have a Pope; Cardinal Wojtyla.') First, the huge crowd gather below cheered and screamed; but seconds later most of them asked, 'Who?' Very few people knew of you at that time, Karol."

"I was just as surprised as everyone else, Bob," he said. "There were two strong contenders on the early ballots of the conclave, Cardinals Siri and Benelli, both from Italy. However, neither man was able to win a majority, so I emerged as the compromise candidate. I was stunned. I was also reluctant. I did not want this responsibility. But, one must always trust in the Lord's plan. I recited His words, 'Be not afraid.'"

"You were only fifty-eight years old, shockingly young for a Pope. Plus, you were from Poland! For nearly five hundred years an Italian had held the papacy. It was an historical moment. You'll probably think I'm strange but every now and then I will watch the video of that announcement on You Tube. It still makes me smile so many years later.

"Your fellow Cardinals clearly knew what they were doing," I continued. "Do you realize your impact on the world? You were instrumental in ending communism in Europe. You consistently denounced the evil of the excesses of capitalism. You improved the Catholic Church's relations with Judaism, Islam and so many others. Your courageous visit to Poland in 1979 sparked the formation of the Solidarity movement. I could go on and on."

Karol flashed that famous smile again. "Why don't you?"

"What don't I what?"

"Go on and on."

I knew he was kidding. I'd read enough about him to know he had a very playful sense of humor.

"Why did you travel so often?" I inquired. "If I recall correctly, you visited one hundred and thirty countries during your pontificate."

"I like airplane food."

I smiled. "Was there any other reason?"

"It was just part of my effort to emphasize a universal call to holiness."

"And millions of people turned out to see and hear you; it was remarkable to watch. For example, an estimated five-to-seven million people attended your Manila World Youth Day visit. That's hard to fathom!"

"I remember what I said to my security staff on that Manila trip," Karol said. "While standing on stage looking at the millions of people, I told them that I wanted to run on the beach. They became alarmed and warned me; 'Your Holiness, the beach will be much too dangerous; it will be crowded.' And I immediately shot back: 'Too crowded? Everyone is here. The beach will be empty.' They only realized I was joking when I added: 'I will leave for the beach right after communion.'

This guy would be fun in a pub, I thought to myself.

I went on. I think he was surprised that I knew so much about him. "Why did you name so many new saints? There were almost five hundred men and women so honored during your term, by far the most in history."

"I believe it remains very possible to live a saintly life, even now. As proof, I presented those hundreds of people. The world is in very bad shape; we needed those saints as an inspiration."

"How many foreign languages were you able to speak? I think I remember it being some ridiculous number."

He looked embarrassed. "Dodici. That's Italian for twelve. I can get by in twelve languages; I am fluent, however in nine. Dziewiec; that's the number nine in Polish."

"I understand. By the way, Karol, in English that's 'I understand.'"

John Paul laughed. I think he liked me.

"I don't mean to sound like the president of your fan club, Karol. I do know a lot about you. I was an adult for your entire pontificate. I saw you in-person several times. I watched the news coverage of many of your trips and was always amazed at the outpouring of love. Yes, I admired and respected you. So many people did; don't act like you don't know that. If you could have seen your own funeral…"

"I did."

"Oh. I see." I paused briefly to see if he was smiling again. He was not.

"Well, then, you understand the impact you had," I resumed. "You changed lives. For me, maybe it comes down to this: you made a huge impression because you were making a difference during the same period of time when I realized that I could not. I'm a very common man; what can I possibly do to change the world? Thus, I am always fascinated by the actions of the few *uncommon* men and women who happen to be alive during my lifetime and who are able to make a significant contribution. There are way-too-many like me; there are far-too-few like you."

He looked me in the eye. "Why do you insist on believing that you are too common to make a difference? Just tonight, I've heard you say something to that effect to both Fulton Sheen and Saint Louis. I don't understand."

I deflected his comment. "Do you know them? Do you pal around with them in here?"

"Of course I know them. Heck, I knew Sheen when we were both alive. He visited me in the Vatican. I publicly praised his service. Nowadays when I see him, I joke that I will be a saint before him; I'm on the fast track. He acts like he thinks it's funny but deep down I think it bugs him. I do it to keep him modest. He was a big TV star, you know; sometimes you have to put them in their place."

"Yeah, I know. I was on TV for a long time, too, Karol."

"I'm aware of that. You didn't have an ego like Sheen, though."

"Thanks."

He slapped me on my shoulder. "Of course, you didn't have his talent, either."

Ouch.

"I see," I mumbled.

"I know your other new friend, too; Saint Louis. He's a good guy. He's from France and I'm from Poland, so sometimes we will watch the World Cup soccer games together. I take it more seriously than he does because I played soccer in my youth; when he was young, all he did was sit around and be king. He's been a saint for centuries, so he's always ribbing me about my status. For example, on his cell phone contact list he has me saved under 'saint2B.' He shows me all the time. It never fails to make him laugh. He's a fine fellow. You made two good friends tonight so far, Bob."

"So far? You mean…"

"The night is still young, Bob."

Finally, we began to walk away from his bronze bust at the entrance of the cathedral. He led the way down the left aisle.

"By the way, that was a worthy effort a few minutes ago; ignoring my comment about your belief that you are a common man."

"I'm just stating the obvious."

"Well, I find that interesting and even a bit troubling, but that is not my jurisdiction. That will be dealt with. I am with you on another matter."

"Now that you brought it up, Karol, I assumed you weren't here to talk about the World Cup. Let's get on with it then. What do you want to ask?"

"I don't want to ask anything."

"What do you want then?"

"Apparently, Bob, it is *you* who has a question to ask, remember?"

I couldn't grasp what he was getting at.  I thought about it.  Clearly, he wasn't going to offer any assistance or hints for he remained quiet.

Within a minute we had arrived at the communion rail in front of the main altar; it was there I saw the pile of postcards left behind by the terrorist Agca.  Now I recalled what I wanted to ask; now I remembered my final words to that killer.

"Why on earth would John Paul II forgive a monster like you?"

❖❖❖❖❖❖❖

Judging by the small smirk on his face, I suspected that John Paul had guessed or read my mind that I now knew what it was I wanted to ask.  His next comment proved I had guessed correctly.

"So, Bob, I understand you have a problem with my forgiveness of Mehmet Ali Agca.  Is that correct?"

"How do you know that?"

"What does it matter?  I know things.  Sheen knew things.  Louis knew things.  Move beyond that.  Stop stalling.  Let's cut to the chase: what is your hang-up with Agca and me?"

"I'm not sure I'd call it a 'hang-up' or a 'problem'.  It's just that I don't get it.  I don't understand how one man can truly forgive another man for an act so hideous.  In fact, I'd find that to be impossible.  I'm just being honest with you, Karol.  If someone ever tried to kill me there is no way I'd offer forgiveness.  *No way*!  I wouldn't even consider it.  I'm not even ashamed to admit that.  In fact, I'd take the opposite approach; I'd be the first man in line to push for the most severe punishment possible.  Wouldn't most of us feel that way?  So it's not that I have a 'problem' with what you did, it is simply that I cannot *comprehend* it.  Granted, you were a Pope and I'm just a regular guy, but even for a Pope this seems to be a hard-to-believe gesture.  In fact, a cynic might say…"

I stopped mid-sentence because I thought I shouldn't go

there. I'd probably already said too much.

"A cynic might say *what*, Bob?" he pressed.

"Never mind."

His glare turned cold. "A cynic might say what, Bob? Please finish your thought."

I took a deep breath.

"A cynic, Karol, might say that it was insincere. One might say it was a public relations stunt. And they'd say that because of what I mentioned earlier; we cannot comprehend forgiving a man who tried to kill us. We literally *cannot believe it* which then makes the cynic search for some other explanation."

"I see," he responded softly.

I tried to back peddle. "I'm not saying I agree with the cynic, Karol."

"Of course not."

"I'm just telling you what *some* people might say."

"Of course."

I'm not sure he believed me. He looked hurt. He looked surprised. 'You were a very bright man, John Paul,' I thought to myself. 'How could you not know that some people questioned your motives?'

I continued in an attempt to clean-up my mess. "I probably wasn't very clear, Karol. Sometimes I speak before I put together my thoughts. Here's what I mean: this single act of forgiveness was considered so extreme because most of the rest of us wouldn't do it ourselves. We wouldn't even *think of* doing it. We simply cannot understand such a gracious act.

"I mean, most of us won't even forgive a guy who way back in high school tried to hit on our girlfriend. Most of us won't forgive our spouse for something he or she said five years ago. Most of us won't forgive a former co-worker who got the job promotion we thought we deserved. And then we see *you* forgiving an attempted assassin? Are you kidding me? We don't get that! So, because it is something we would never do, we look for explanations or motives when someone like you does it."

Karol walked away from the communion rail and sat in the front pew. I stayed where I was.

"Bob, let me ask you something," he started.

'Here it comes,' I thought.

"Go ahead," I said to him.

"Do you have the time?"

That was the last thing I expected to hear. The question was so out-of-the-blue it even took a few seconds to register.

"Excuse me?" I responded.

He repeated it, very calmly. "Do you have the time?"

I had no idea where this was going.

"I'm sorry, Karol. I don't know the time. The time has gotten away from me since I entered this cathedral just before closing time."

"You *usually* know the time; am I correct? Do you not have a rather unusual sense of time-of-day?"

"I do. How do you know that?"

"Will you please stop asking me why I know things? It matters little. Please return to what I just inquired; your uncanny sense of time."

"Karol, are you trying to change the subject? I mean, I am really sorry if I offended you with my statements about forgiving Agca."

"I am *not* changing the subject, Bob. Once and for all, tell me about this interesting skill of yours concerning time-of-day."

I was completely lost. 'What does this have to do with anything?' I wondered to myself. I decided to play along. Obviously I didn't have a choice.

"Well, Karol, you are right; I always seem to know the time-of-day. I am always within about five minutes of the actual time. I can go hours without seeing a clock and then I can announce to either myself or those with me what time I believe it to be and, sure enough, moments later when we see a clock or someone checks their wrist watch we discover that my guess was dead-on. I'm not reading the sun or anything like that; I just have a sense. I think back on all I've done since the last time I saw the time-of-day and somehow I can determine how much time has passed.

"I own one wrist watch. I love it. It's beautiful. I bought it a few years ago as a silent auction item at a fundraiser. I wear it

on special occasions only because it's a great looking wrist watch; however, I never need it to tell me the time-of-day.

"There's more. I never have to set an alarm clock for an early-morning appointment because I always wake up about two minutes before I must. For example, if I need to be awake at five o'clock in the morning, I will unfailingly wake up out of a deep sleep at four-fifty-eight. Somehow, I just *sense* it is time to wake up.

"It gets stranger, Karol. Sometimes I play a little game with myself. As I get older, I am usually up several times a night to use the restroom."

"I know the feeling well," he smiled.

"I suppose it does come with the territory! Anyway, after I wake up but before I get out of bed to go to the restroom, I will quietly guess to myself about the time-of-day. Mind you, this is the middle-of-the-night; I may have been asleep for minutes or hours, how would I know? I'll guess, I'll look at my bedside clock, and nearly 100% of the time I am within just a few minutes of the actual time. It is so weird."

"You seem quite pleased with yourself," Karol observed.

"Well, look, I know it's silly, I know it means nothing but it's just one of those weird things we all seem to possess. And because it is unique to us, we take pride in it. For example, my dad had a toenail that grew straight *up*; it didn't grow *out*. Very weird. We called it his 'funny toenail', as in, 'Dad, show us your funny toenail.' And each time, he patiently removed his shoe and sock and showed us. It was almost as if he was proud of it! It's the same thing with me and my ability to know the time; it's a talent that means absolutely nothing, but it is *my* talent."

"I can relate to that," John Paul admitted. "My talent was ending communism, your dad's talent was a funny toenail; same thing."

I laughed out loud. "Exactly! I knew you'd understand."

I made my way over to the pew and sat with him.

"Bob, are you ever late for an appointment or a social engagement or a work project?" he asked.

"Never! I am always on time. In fact, usually I arrive ten or fifteen minutes early because I don't want anyone to wait for me. I take pride in that. I am very punctual. I am very orderly. I like to know when things begin and when things end."

"That's what I thought. Then let me ask you this: how do you feel when others are late, when you are waiting on them?"

"I hate it. I know it's a fault of mine. I am very impatient. My window is about ten minutes; if the agreed-upon time is six o'clock and the other party arrives at six-ten, I can live with that. I'm not mad. However, if you arrive at six-twelve, my patience is gone and I am angry. I think it is rude. I think it's a sign of disrespect.

"I don't like any type of wait or delay," I continued. "I hate traffic jams. I hate a longer-than-usual red light at an intersection. I don't like waiting for a table at a restaurant. I don't like a long line at the grocery store. I hate slow play during a round of golf. Mine is a strange mentality; when I am ready for something, I want it *now*. I am very impatient, I admit."

"It's a good thing I was on time tonight," John Paul stated. "God forbid a Pope to keep the great Bob waiting. You would have been upset with me."

He smiled at that last comment and then placed his chin upon his right fist. For a moment, he looked like that famous bronze and marble sculpture, The Thinker, by Rodin.

Clearly, he wasn't sure where to go next.

'Leave it to me,' I thought. 'Even a Pope can't figure me out.'

I spoke again just to break the silence. "Karol, it's been enjoyable to fill you in on my time-telling talent and my dad's toenail and how much I hate it when people are late; but I really don't know how or why we got here. How did we go from killers and forgiveness to the games I play with my alarm clock?"

"I will get there in just a moment. Let me think. You provide to me an interesting challenge."

Gee, thanks, Karol.

We sat for what seemed to be several minutes. On occasion, I noticed him looking at me briefly and nodding his head with a trace of a smile on his lips. I think he was enjoying this. To him, I must have been a human Rubik's cube and he was having great

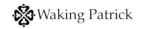 

fun solving this puzzle that only I could provide.

Just to kill the time, I reached into my backpack and pulled out a bag of red licorice bites. I might as make myself comfortable while the great John Paul dissected me like a frog in biology class.

It bothered me that it was taking him so long. He probably didn't think this long and hard over his last papal encyclical. Why was I such a challenge? Were my questions and doubts really that far removed from the norm? I've long thought I was confused, even lost, but now Karol seemed to be confirming it; why else did he need so much time to offer guidance?

I jumped in; I couldn't take the silence any longer. "Look, Karol, buddy, we can sure do this some other time if you wish. I'm sure you must have other things to do; go ski Ghost Mountain, perhaps?"

He said nothing but he did unzip his red ski vest and cracked his knuckles. I took it as a sign he was finally ready to continue.

I extended my bag of licorice and said, "Want some?"

"No, thanks," he said. "I've never been much of a candy guy myself. You don't happen to have a juicy polish sausage in that bag, do you?"

I shook my head. "No. Sorry."

I looked away and stared at the row of candles to my left near the baptismal font. Suddenly I regretted bringing up the concept of forgiveness. I wished I had never met that terrorist Agca. I wished I had never burdened John Paul with my dilemma. I was reluctant to hear whatever it was he had to offer. He must have thought me to be either horribly misguided when it comes to forgiveness or, even worse, just a horrible person period.

He may have been right on both counts.

Karol shifted in the pew beside me. He turned his shoulders in my direction.

"Bob, I checked out your life's resume before I came here tonight. I listened in during your visits with P.J. and Louis. And what you have told me face-to-face so far has also filled in a few blanks. I am now ready to proceed."

I sat up straight in the pew and folded my arms across my chest. "Let's have it, then," I responded.

"I believe that your problem with the concept of forgiveness, and it *is* a problem, Bob, despite your earlier objection to that specific word, coincides with your fear of Judgment Day."

That confused me. "How and why did you jump to Judgment Day?"

Karol responded quickly, as if he anticipated my question. "You do not fear death, is that correct?"

"I would say that is true. Don't get me wrong, I don't look forward to it, I want to live for many more years, but I'm not afraid of death. I certainly don't spend a lot of time contemplating it other than to frequently acknowledge that it is coming, and no matter when it comes it'll be far sooner than I wish. However, I've just told you that I hate wasting time; and what greater waste of time is there than to worry or stress over something that is as absolutely inevitable as one's own death? So, to get back to your question, Karol, you are correct, I do not fear death."

"Now let me ask you the same question but replace the word 'death' with 'Judgment Day': Do you fear Judgment Day?"

"I haven't really thought about it."

He responded forcefully. "Bob, do not tap dance with your friend John Paul! I know things! I know how you feel and what you think! It is far from the truth when you say to me, 'I haven't really thought of Judgment Day.' In fact, you *do* think about it; you may even be afraid of it. Let's get to the bottom of it and at the same time we can probe your problem with forgiveness. You say you hate to waste time; then stop wasting mine."

For the first time since we met, my new friend was angry at me. I knew immediately he wasn't a man to be messed with.

"OK, I'll cooperate, sorry. There's no need to get all worked up about it. I'm confused, Karol. I thought we were going to talk about how you found it in your heart to forgive the man who wanted you dead; instead we're talking about my alleged fear of judgment day. But, I should know by now that tonight of all nights I need to trust completely those who are with me. So, what do you want to know, Karol?"

"First, can you admit that you fear judgment day?"

I considered the question for a few seconds.

"Sure. I have no problem with that. But so what? Who cares? I hardly think that makes me unusual. I bet most people are afraid of judgment day."

"That may well be true, Bob, but what may make you different than many of the others is that you are expecting the worst. Most people will look at judgment day and think that although they certainly didn't live a life anything near perfect, they still lived a *good enough* life. Most people believe that although they probably won't enter heaven immediately after death, they will enter one day. However, with you, Bob, I get the sense that you don't believe any of that."

"That depends," I responded.

"That depends on what?"

"It depends on if heaven is more inclusive or exclusive? I think if heaven is inclusive, then I have a chance. However, if heaven is exclusive, I have no chance."

Karol nodded his head. "That's an interesting viewpoint, Bob. We shall come back to that in a few minutes."

"In other words…" I started.

He finished the thought for me. "In other words, let's tackle one dilemma at a time. For now, let's get back to judgment day and forgiveness. We've established the fact that you do indeed fear judgment day. What else?"

"Can you blame me, Karol, for feeling that way? I mean, all my life I've been told that we will all be judged at the gates of heaven; of course I am going to wonder and worry about my past sins and faults and failings; of course I wonder about how I will be judged. In fact, I'll go deeper than that: I spend more time worrying about all the times I've hurt or disappointed people than I do feeling happy or proud about the times I've pleased them. That's a trait I don't like. Even if my ratio of good-to-bad was off-the-charts, I'd still first feel disappointment and sadness over the times I failed instead of feeling gratified and joy over the times I did not."

"That's a tough standard, Bob. Why reject joy?"

"I don't think I reject it; most times it's just that I feel I haven't earned it."

Karol shook his head slowly and said: "You are reminding me of an old Latin proverb: 'Forgive others often, but yourself never.'"

"What's that got to do with anything," I asked?

He explained. "You rarely forgive yourself for the times you've sinned and failed and disappointed people. You are your own worst critic. You are your own harshest judge. And because of that, you keep joy at arm's length."

"I'm not saying I agree with you, but continue on with that thought. You might be on to something." I stated.

"I'd rather it'd be *you* to continue. Go ahead."

"That could be one reason why I fear judgment day. If I have a hard time forgiving *myself*, then why would *God* forgive me? And if God won't forgive me, and I wouldn't blame Him if he doesn't, then what hope do I have on judgment day? Is that what you are trying to get me to say, Karol?"

He said nothing. I hate it when they do that. Louis and Sheen at times also said nothing to a direct question. What do they want me to do, think for myself?

"Karol, did you ever see the movie *Unforgiven*?"

I could see the look of surprise on his face.

"No, I can't say that I ever did," he replied haltingly. "Why do you ask?"

"It is one of my favorite movies. It won the Academy Award for Best Picture in 1992."

"Well, that explains then why I missed it. I was kind of busy, Bob, in 1992. Just a little thing called *being the Pope*!"

"Yes, I suppose you did have a few other things to do. Anyway, it's a western starring Clint Eastwood. He plays an aging outlaw and ex-gunslinger who takes up one final job years after hanging up his holster. There's a big reward for the capture, dead or alive, of a couple of thugs who cut up a prostitute, so Clint's character, William Munny, takes the job because he needs the money."

I stopped mid-story.

"Can I say that word, Karol?"

"What word?"

"Prostitute."

"You just did. Twice."

He had me there. Nothing gets by this guy.

I continued. "Anyway, there are two others who ride along with Munny: one is his longtime friend, played by Morgan Freeman, and the other is a brash teenager who constantly boasts about all the men he's previously shot and killed. He calls himself 'The Schofield Kid.'

"After a long and difficult ride, Clint and his two friends finally reach the small town where the two wanted men are hiding. The Kid shoots and kills one of them but then, because they were out-numbered, they had to retreat back into the hills for the night.

"As they drank whiskey out of a bottle around the campfire, The Kid comes clean; he had never before killed a man. He's very upset. Munny, who has killed so many men that he's lost count, tells the boy: 'It's a hell of a thing, killing a man; you take away all he's got and all he's ever gonna have.'"

John Paul jumped in again. "Bob?"

"Yes?"

"Is there a conclusion in our immediate future?"

"Oh. Sorry, Karol. OK, here it is. The Kid tries to make sense of it; after all, the man he just gunned down was a very bad man. So he says, 'Well, I guess he had it coming.'

"And Clint, looking out from under his cowboy hat off into the horizon, growls: 'We all got it coming', Kid.'"

I paused and smiled and said enthusiastically, "That's one of my favorite movie lines of all time!"

Karol looked at me, still perplexed.

"Don't you see? That's exactly how I feel! *We all got it coming, kid*. Well, maybe *you* didn't have 'it coming', Karol, but *I* got it coming. Most of us have 'it coming'. And that's how I feel about judgment day; I got it coming and that's the day it comes. Of course I fear it; who wouldn't? I'm a sinner, I have failed too often, I have disappointed others too often, I haven't been the man I am capable of being, so my outlook about judgment day is that, to quote Clint once again, 'I got it coming.'

"And while we're on this same subject," I went on, "here is

something else I don't like about judgment day: I don't know *when* it's coming!"

"What do you mean?" John Paul asked

"What's that quote in Scripture? 'Death comes like a thief in the night'? I just told you, Karol, how good I am at the concept of time. I always know the time. I am very organized. I love schedules. Yet I have no idea when death will come; thus, I have no idea when I am scheduled to appear for judgment day. Nobody does, I get that; but it bothers me. I know if my judgment day arrives tomorrow, I am not ready: and I fear that whenever judgment day arrives that still I won't be ready to be judged."

Karol rubbed his chin for a moment before responding.

"Yours is a healthy fear, Bob. It's also quite common. Many of us worry that we will fail that final test on judgment day. When one is a person of faith, when one is a believer in God, then it makes perfect sense to dread judgment day. As we get older, we begin to think about and worry about that day more frequently. Of course we do, for we know that day may not be too far off in the future. We realize that most of our life is behind us. What we trust is that the mercy of God on judgment day will be stronger than our fear of judgment day.

"I am also intrigued by your belief that you 'have it coming'. I'm not sure where to even begin on that one!"

He paused for a few seconds to gather his thoughts.

"First," he resumed, "I believe the very fact that you feel you 'have it coming' is a cause for hope."

I jumped in, surprised at that statement.

"Hope? Where do you come up with that? How do you find hope in the fact that I will get exactly what I deserve on judgment day?"

He offered a comforting smile.

"I find hope because it means you are close enough to God to realize exactly who God is and exactly who you are and the big difference between the two."

"You've lost me."

"You recognize that God is the judge. You recognize that you are a sinner. You know you need to ask for His mercy. It is good and encouraging for you to acknowledge all these things. I believe it is the person who lived as if they did not need God who may be in serious trouble on judgment day. It's the person who never feared God who risks severe judgment. However, people like you, Bob, who think you 'have it coming' who may well fare better in that final judgment."

I still didn't quite grasp it. I think Karol knew that.

He continued. "I have a suggestion, Bob. Walk with me to the back corner of the cathedral, near where we first met at my bust, and I'll explain."

I rose from the pew and followed close behind him as we walked up the main aisle.

"I think we need to regroup," he said in a calm voice. "Let's start over. You are curious and questioning some serious issues; forgiveness and judgment day. And, if I may be so bold to suggest, next-in-line in that progression may even be eternal life and heaven itself."

He had me there. The validity of the concept of heaven, and especially hell, had been on my mind recently. How did he know that? It's hard to keep secrets in this place, I thought to myself. Do these ghosts in here, Louis and P.J. and now Karol and anyone else who may be next, know *everything* about me? Do they know about old girlfriends and bad grades and driving too fast and too many wagers on horses? Do they know I don't count penalty shots in golf? Do they know I still owe my oldest daughter ten dollars from her First Communion haul? My questions about heaven and hell are one thing, but if these new friends knew I once seriously considered liposuction I would truly be humiliated. Or if they knew I once ate at a hotel's complimentary breakfast buffet even though I hadn't stayed at that hotel the previous night; what would they think of me then? Or that I had once cheated during a game of *Clue* by showing *all* of my cards to the person on my left and not just the Conservatory card that he had asked to see. Suddenly, I felt like an awful person, stripped bare naked in the presence of these friendly ghosts.

Karol briefly turned his head in my direction and motioned to me to pick up the pace. He wanted me at his side as he continued.

"We need to take our time. We need to relax. The conversation will come quite naturally. We've gone from Agca to Eastwood in just a few moments. We've been all over the map. We need an honest but casual exchange. We need to focus. Are you good with that?"

"Sure," I replied, quietly acknowledging that I didn't have a choice. He's a Pope and I'm just a regular guy. He helped to change the world; all I ever change is the oil and my socks. What was I going to do, disagree? Tell him I had a better idea?

We reached the entrance area of the cathedral and as we turned toward his bust I saw two chairs and a dining room table dressed in a white tablecloth upon which were platters of food, napkins and silverware.

"Are you hungry?" Karol asked.

I stopped mid-stride and stared at the feast before me. I had no idea how many minutes or, more likely, hours had passed since my last meal of Irish stew in a pub on Fifth Avenue.

"I am starving," I answered excitedly.

I was also very much confused. "Where did all of this come from; the table, the chairs, the food? It wasn't here when I first met you."

"Never mind with all of that," he replied. "Consider it as my gift to you. I thought we'd have a much more fruitful conversation while relaxing around a dinner table. I've been told that you do your best talking and thinking while enjoying great food and drink."

"That's probably true," I concurred.

I arrived at the table and looked at the generous portions of food. Who knew the Cathedral of Saint Patrick offered room service?

There seemed to be more than a dozen varieties of food in front of me. "What do we have here?" I asked my host. "And why so much of it? Are there others who will join us?"

I asked that last question because I hate it when unexpected guests show up for dinner. Come to think of it, I usually also hate it when *expected* guests show up.

"No, there will be just the two of us. Let us eat, drink and be

merry!  And perhaps by the time we are finished we will have reached some conclusions about your doubts and fears.

"I have arranged for us samples of delicious items from my two favorite countries, Poland, where I was born and raised, and Italy, where I was able to make my greatest contributions and eventually where I died."

I nodded in approval and said, "Good idea!"

"Allow me to tell you about your selections," Karol said as he motioned for me to sit down in one of the high-backed chairs.

"First, from my beloved homeland, we have several sausage samples; parowki, kabonosy and kielbasa.  I love all three.  They make a man strong."

'I hope there are some Tums or a bottle of Mylanta somewhere on this table,' I thought to myself as I grabbed a fork and reached for one of each of the sausages.  "They look terrific," I said out loud.

"In the large bowl next to the kielbasa," Karol resumed, "is our tasty potato soup, called kartoflanka."

I grabbed the ladle and filled my bowl.  "I love soup!  My wife makes great soup; her specialties are pumpkin, squash, and broccoli and cheese."

He didn't seem to care about my soups back home for he moved right on.  "You may also try a prerogi, which is a large dumpling filled with cheese and sauerkraut," John Paul said as he pointed at the next plate.  "And next to that I have provided roasted lamb, which in Poland is called baranina.

"And our Polish desert will be pudding, which we refer to as budyn."

I was already enjoying my first few bites of the lamb and prerogi as Karol moved on to the samples from Italy. "You will join me, correct?" I asked.

"Of course I will!" he replied quickly.  "Ever since my death, I never have to worry about my weight or high cholesterol or fatty acids or starches or glutton or any of those silly things you humans stress about.  Wherever I am, all of us are able to eat and drink anything, anytime."

"You never get indigestion?  You never gain weight?  You

never have a hangover?"

I winced at that last comment. I am so sure I just asked a Pope if he has ever had too much to drink.

"I'm sorry, Karol; that was probably a bit too personal and out-of-line."

"Not to worry, Bob," he said with a chuckle. "You and I will be fine. Eat and drink as much as you like. Enjoy all of it! There will not be any repercussions. In my company, all will be well."

He pulled back his chair from the table, allowing him room to finally sit down, and he grabbed an empty plate.

"Let me continue. Many of these Italian foods are my favorites. You probably recognize many of them because you've been to Italy several times, correct?"

"Yes. I've been there three times. I love that country. I see some of my favorites, too!"

Karol pointed first at the plate immediately in front of him. "Spaghetti alla carbonara."

"My all-time favorite Italian dish," I remarked.

"We also have some Cotoletta alla Bolognese; veal with ham, mozzarella and tomato sauce. And next to that is our Saltimbocca alla Romano; a veal rump with ham, butter and sage."

I reached in. "You can't beat a good piece of rump," I mumbled.

"Bob?" said Karol.

"Yes?"

"Watch yourself."

"Sorry."

"I have also ordered Prosciutto e Melone, ham with melons; and fried olives stuffed with ground meat, which is a fine appetizer we call Olive Ascolana."

"Karol, you are too kind. Everything looks and smells fantastic. I am very hungry. Are you sure I can eat as much as I wish without soon feeling the effects?"

"Eat up!" he encouraged.

"Oh, I nearly forgot," John Paul went on. "To help wash it down, you may have a cold Tyskie, a popular beer in Poland; or a glass of Brunello di Montalcino, one of our many very fine Italian wines. And as there always is on every Italian dinner table, we have bottles of San Pellegrino mineral water."

"May I have some of all three?" I asked sheepishly.

"You may."

I grabbed a bottle of beer, poured a glass of the wine and the water for each of us and took dead aim at the food in front of me. We ate in silence for several minutes. I was famished. Everything on my plates tasted delicious. It had been a long, strange and stressful night but during these moments at the table, everything seemed normal again, eating and drinking with a friend.

"Bob, as we continue to eat, let's also return to our discussion," started Karol, as I lunged for a second kielbasa. "You are curious about the concept of forgiveness; you are fearful of judgment day; and even though you have not yet verbalized this to me, I also know you have questions about heaven and hell. So, with your permission, let us begin."

"Are you sure you don't mind if I continue with my meal?" I asked.

"Not at all. I want you to be relaxed and comfortable. I want our conversation to be open and free-wheeling, as if you were with a group of family or friends in a casual restaurant talking about sports or movies. We eat, we drink, we talk; OK?"

"Sure," I answered. "And can you pass the carbonara, please?"

Karol handed over the platter and began. "Let's first establish the foundation and perhaps from there everything else falls into place."

"A foundation on…?"

"Forgiveness. After all, that's where all of this began, when you met the man who tried to kill me."

"You are right," I said as I remembered my brief but frightening encounter at the communion rail with Ali Agca. "I still cannot believe you forgave him."

Karol ignored that.

"Are you familiar, Bob, with the parable of the prodigal son?"

"Well, J.P., I am hardly an expert on scripture, but yes, that one I know."

"Good!  It is in that parable where I find my foundation.  As I just mentioned, it is commonly referred to as the story of the prodigal son but I see it instead as the lesson of the merciful father.

"I compare the life of every Christian to that of the prodigal son.  Remember the story; the son squandered the riches provided by his father, who obviously represents God the Father.

"This man loves his son very much and he anxiously waits for the young man to return home from a life of loose living and squalor, which obviously represent the misery of sin."

"Obviously," I interjected.  Frankly, it really wasn't all that obvious to me but at this point it was the best I could do.

"The Gospel story describes the exuberant joy felt by the father when the son finally returns.  He embraces the son and orders the staff to prepare a fabulous meal.  He arranges for music and a lively celebration.

"There is also another brother.  I am sure you remember him, Bob."

"I do indeed.  I always felt sorry for the other brother.  He never caused his father any grief.  He was always the loyal son.  And yet, dear old dad never threw a huge party for him."

"And what did this brother do at the party?" asked Karol.

"What did he do?  He did nothing!  If I recall correctly, he didn't even attend the celebration.  His father begged him to join in but he stubbornly refused."

"You are correct, Bob.  And that is where I find my foundation for the concept of forgiveness.  Let no one behave like the elder brother in that parable.  May the joy of forgiveness be stronger and greater than any resentment."

I thought about that as I took a long drink from my bottle of Tyskie.  "I'm sorry, Karol, but I fail to see your foundation.  My fault, not yours."

"Bottom-line, it is this: Offering forgiveness and even accepting forgiveness are essential conditions for authentic peace.  I admit that both asking for and granting forgiveness may seem contrary to human instinct in which revenge often prevails, but forgiveness is inspired by the logic of love; that love which God has for every woman, every man, every nation.  God forgives us,

we must forgive each other, it's that simple."

I considered that as I finished a bite of prosciutto. "You make it sound so easy, Karol, but I'm sorry, it is *not* that simple. It might be for you, but believe me for most of the rest of us, it is very hard and sometimes even impossible."

He placed his elbows on the table and leaned in.

"Like me forgiving Agca; that would be impossible for you?"

"Absolutely," I said forcefully. "I would not forgive him. I wouldn't even think about it. I'd wish him to be miserable for every minute of the rest of his life."

Karol leaned back into his chair and took a sip of his wine, never once removing his eyes from mine.

"And just where does that get you, Bob?"

"Where does that *get* me?" I asked incredulously. "It gets me the satisfaction of not forgiving the man who shot me. There's nothing more to it than that."

He did not reply. He picked at his food with his fork.

I resumed. "That probably disappoints you, Karol, that a man can be so cold and vengeful. I'm sorry for that but we're not all like you, don't you understand? You are going to be a saint one day. I'm not."

I raised my left arm and pointed to the cathedral's main door. "Most of the people out there, Karol, are not saints, either. They're exactly like me. They are sinners. They wouldn't forgive a man who tried to kill them. That's so extreme it seems ludicrous to even talk about. I hardly think that makes me a monster. The monster in this circumstance is the man with the gun. Forgiving Agca makes you a great human being, even a saint; but *not* forgiving him does not make me a horrible man. It makes me a common man."

Karol put down his fork and stared at me. "To hear you talk tonight, Bob, I thought you didn't like being common."

I had to admit, he had me there. I hate it when that happens.

"Bob, what's so difficult to grasp about my forgiveness of the man who shot me?"

"Are you kidding me with that?" I shot back. "Let me begin with this: *he tried to kill you!* Isn't that enough? However, there is also this: don't you desire justice? Or do you believe we only need to tell all killers and rapists and terrorists, 'Hey, it's OK, we all forgive you, we all understand, please just don't do it again, you can go free now. Keep in touch. Maybe we'll grab lunch sometime.'"

"What does one have to do with the other? What does forgiveness have to do with justice? Yet again, you disappoint me, Bob."

"Don't go there, please. I *despise it* when someone tells me that," I protested.

"I know that. I heard your conversation with Saint Louis. Thus, I use that phrase intentionally. Your ignorance disappoints me and surprises me. There is no peace without justice and there is no justice without forgiveness. This is true in circumstances great and small, at a personal level or a wider, even international level. Forgiveness is in no way opposed to justice, as if to forgive meant the need to right the wrong done. Nonsense! Rather, forgiveness is the fullness of justice, leading to a tranquility of order which is much more than a fragile and temporary cessation of hostilities, involving as it does the deepest healing of the wounds which fester in the human heart. Justice and forgiveness are *both* essential to such healing!"

I had nothing to say in reply. Much of it was way over my head. I'm sure it all made perfect sense to him but I was lost. He had already cited my 'ignorance' once and that little explanation of his just proved it. I think somewhere in there was his logic in forgiving his would-be assassin but I sure wasn't going to ask him to repeat it.

Karol must have sensed I had little to offer in return so he kindly moved on.

"Look, Bob, forget about Agca," he said in a soft voice. "You say you could not forgive a man like that; I believe you. I accept that. I don't agree, but I get it. But we need to talk about the bigger picture."

"Which is…?"

"You seem to have trouble with forgiveness, period!"

I considered that comment for a few seconds.

"I think you are wrong," I said with a smile, "but I forgive you for believing that."

Inwardly, I thought that was funny, but judging by the serious look on my friend's face, he disagreed. Too soon, perhaps, for forgiveness jokes?

"Seriously, John Paul, I don't think I have any more of a problem with forgiveness than most others, present company excluded," I stated as I reached for a second bottle of beer. "Do you mind, by the way, if I have another Tyskie? I like it! If I ever visit Poland, I'll have a head start on what to drink. Besides, if you want me to really open up about this forgiveness and judgment day stuff, this second beer will help."

"I do not mind at all," he responded.

He fidgeted with his napkin before he continued.

"So, you do not believe you have a problem or a difficulty with offering forgiveness, is that correct?"

"Can you prove otherwise?"

"Mehmet Ali Agca."

"I thought we were through with *him*," I responded angrily. "Can you please stop holding me to your high standards? Give me something a bit more realistic. What other examples do you have for me?"

"Fair enough. What about the person who blamed you for your dad's death; have you ever offered forgiveness?"

"No. Why would I? I was a teenager, my father has just dropped dead at an early age, I am understandably very sad and bitter, and now I am getting blamed for causing his death because I supposedly had given him more stress than he could handle. I should have strangled that person right there on the spot; what the hell, let's just have *two* funerals that weekend, you know what I mean? Forgive *that*? Not going to happen, sorry. I mean, Karol, can you imagine the impact of such an accusation?"

"As a matter of fact, yes I can. Do you not think I was not falsely and unfairly accused of many things in my life?"

I considered his life, from hiding from the Nazi's as a teenager to being placed in the world's bulls-eye as head of the Catholic Church.

"I suppose so," I conceded.

"Bob, the weak never forgive. Forgiveness is an attribute of the strong. Which are you? And which do you want to be? Forgiveness is, above all, a personal choice, a decision of the heart to go against the natural instinct to pay back evil with evil, pettiness with pettiness, anger with anger."

"Will you please stop using against me these impossible examples?" I pleaded. "You seem to think I'm a super-hero, capable of forgiving what I consider to be horrific acts. I wouldn't forgive Agca and I wouldn't forgive the person who insanely blamed me for my father's death. If you can forgive these acts, good for you! I can't. I won't."

"It isn't just me, Bob. When I forgave the man who shot me, I was only acting in the image of Jesus."

Bringing Christ into the discussion nearly made me choke on my bite of veal. "Oh, this is just great, Karol. Now you're going to compare me to the actions and standards of *Jesus*? First, you point out that it's *your* high standards that I fail to meet and now it's *His*? Can you just once fight fair?"

"And how can I do that?" he asked.

"You can compare me to everybody *out there*," I said, motioning to the world outside. "Compare me to all the regular people."

"You've already done that, Bob, many times tonight. And, if I may add, you've done it so effectively that I'm beginning to believe you. You believe that you are a common man but then in the next breath you maintain that you *don't want to be* a common man. Next I present to you an opportunity to rise above the actions of a common man and you argue that I am not being fair. Which way is it? Are you common or not? Do you want to be common or do you want to be better?"

Damn. He had me again. I waited for him to move on.

"As I was saying about acting in the image of Jesus; as our Lord neared death on the cross, he said…"

I jumped in and quietly finished his thought. "He said, 'Forgive them, Father, for they know not what they do.' Or something close to that."

I reached for a fried olive and rolled it in the palm of my hand.

"Very good." Karol continued. "Not only that but when teaching us how best to pray, Jesus gave us the very first *Our Father*, which of course includes the phrase…"

Once again, I jumped in to finish. "It includes the phrase, 'Forgive us our trespasses as we forgive those who trespass against us.'"

I popped the olive in my mouth. I thought about what Karol was trying to convey. Truth be told, I also thought about how much I loved these appetizers, this Olive Ascolana!

"I understand your point but I still maintain that this is not a fair fight," I said emphatically. "First, you compare my capacity for forgiveness, or lack of, to you in your dealings with Agca and now you toss Christ on the cross at me and Christ teaching all of us how to pray? You are expecting me to be like *Jesus*? And failing that, you are at least expecting me to be like *you*? I don't measure up to Jesus and I don't measure up to you! I can easily admit that. Is that what you want to hear?"

He shook his head. I sensed he was getting impatient with me.

"You are making forgiveness far too difficult, Bob. Don't you see, it is what we are called to do? It is part of our deal with God."

"What do you mean?"

"In life, we all ask to be forgiven. True?"

"Yes."

"Even you, Bob, have done many things for which you desire forgiveness from others, correct?"

"Again, yes."

"Then how can one genuinely *ask* to be forgiven if that same person refuses to *offer* forgiveness when asked by others?"

I nodded my head. "I get that. But how does 'It is part of our deal with God' fit in?"

Karol smiled. I think he realized he had finally broken through to me.

"Because he who cannot forgive others breaks the bridge over which he himself must one day pass; for at the gates of heaven everyone has the need for forgiveness. Jesus said, 'For if you forgive men when they sin against you, your heavenly Father will also forgive you.' No part of Jesus' teaching is clearer. When we forgive others here on earth, God forgives us at our final judgment."

"That seems to be a giant leap, Karol. If I forgive others now, then I am forgiven by God later? It doesn't matter what kind of life I live in between? That seems to be a stretch."

"But that 'life you live in between' is going to be a wonderful and loving life, don't you see that? That is why it is not a leap at all; it is a promise!"

"Go on," I encouraged.

"In a sense, Bob, forgiveness is Christianity at its highest level. It sets love in motion. It unleashes joy and peace which means that 'life you live in between' must be a good and fruitful life; how could it not be? Once you realize that, then one can even view the act of forgiveness as a *selfish* act. And acting selfishly comes naturally and easily for all of us."

"Oh, come on!" I protested. "Forgiving someone is selfish? I don't see that at all."

"I'm serious. Forgiveness, in its truest and highest form, is a free act of love. Forgiveness always involves an apparent short-term loss for a real and genuine long-term gain for it opens wide the heart of the forgiver. The worst prison of all is a closed heart; and with a closed heart one cannot experience true joy and love. And that is why to every person of good will and eager to work tirelessly in the building of a new civilization of love, I say offer forgiveness and receive peace and joy in return!"

'Is this guy for real?' I wondered. How can someone be this *good*? I have never in my life felt so inferior.

He wasn't done yet either. "There is also the bigger picture. Indeed, forgiveness is good and even necessary for the individual, but it expands from there like a ripple in the water. Forgiveness demonstrates the presence in the world of a love which is far more powerful than sin. A world from which forgiveness was eliminated would be nothing but a world of cold and unfeeling justice."

"This is pretty deep for a simple guy like me, Karol," I confessed. "I need a few minutes to think about that. How about passing over another piece of baranina in the meantime?"

My friend graciously did as requested. He seemed amused by the size of my appetite.

"I am glad to see you are enjoying the meal," he said.

"Oh, it is terrific! I like all of it! Thanks for providing it." I paused for a second before adding; "Now I know why they call you 'John Paul the *Great*!'"

Karol laughed heartily while reaching for a second bowl of potato soup. Then he said, "Well, I hope and trust there were other reasons as well but if my list of contributions also includes the ability to offer a superb meal, then so be it!"

We ate in silence for a few moments; I needed the time to digest not only the food but the intimidating lecture on forgiveness.

"I understand what you say about forgiveness, John Paul. I'm not saying it's going to be an easy thing for me to do from now on, but I do understand. It's a good thing for me to at least *try* to do it. I think I get it when you tell me that it is for my own good. At least you have me *thinking* now, and that's something I don't do often or well."

He smiled at my self-criticism.

"And the more I think about it, perhaps my problem is not, at least in most cases, in forgiving people; rather, it is in *forgetting*. Honestly, I think I have a pretty good track record of forgiving. The huge offenses, maybe not, and I will try to work on that; but most things, yes. Earlier tonight I told my friend Louis about an obnoxious soccer coach from my youth and about a high school friend who hit on a girl I liked. Well, if they walked in to this cathedral right now, of course I'd forgive them; their offenses were very minor and, not only that, it's been about forty years! I've forgiven a man who back-stabbed me during my career. I've forgiven friends and family members for all the silly and thoughtless things all of us say or do during a lifetime. I make the same mistakes that they do; probably more. Of course I forgive them. I know they forgive me for all of the same offenses. In the grand scheme of things, these are all so very trivial. And I do agree with you; when you forgive, it opens your heart, which in turn opens the door to a much more joyful life."

"Very good," John Paul acknowledged. "Assuming that is all true, then what's your hang-up?"

"Well, even though most times I do forgive, I do not *forget*! And now that I think about it, that may be the reason for my great fear of judgment day."

"What do you mean?"

"Let me use a hypothetical: let's say I once said something unkind or inappropriate to a friend. I hurt his feelings. He is angry. I apologize. He accepts. We move on. Our friendship endures."

Karol looked confused. "So what's the problem?"

I answered forcefully. "The problem is that *I still did it*! He may forgive my act but he cannot *erase* my act. Does that make sense to you?"

"I'm not sure. Please, go on."

"That act is forever on my resume, forever on my lifetime ledger sheet. Do you understand? I thank my friend for his forgiveness but there's no 'delete' button in life; I still committed that act of unkindness. It's done. And I did it."

"Yes?"

"So I worry about the length of my ledger sheet when it is rolled out in front of me on judgment day! Can you imagine? If on that sheet there is written every sin, every act or word of selfishness or thoughtlessness or anger or carelessness, every moment of weakness, every poor decision, then how long is my rap sheet? How can that possibly be ignored when it comes time for God to judge my life?"

"I see," Karol said quietly.

"I'm afraid because that's what I do when I forgive someone; I don't forget the act. When someone wrongs me, of course I forgive them because I'm just as guilty as they are; but I don't forget the fact that they committed that act in the first place. It's as if I keep a running tab, good and bad, on how everyone treats me in my countless relationships. It's almost as if I am keeping score. So, using that same logic, I tell myself, 'If *God* is keeping score on *my* life, I lose.'

"Do you understand my dilemma? On one hand I have the

fact that I've been forgiven; on the other hand, I have the fact that I did all those bad things, I committed all those sins. My offenses may be forgiven but they have not been forgotten; it is impossible to forget them because it's human nature to remember the times we feel we've been treated poorly.

"Now, fast forward to judgment day; our generous God may well forgive me but how can He forget all the bad I've done for it is right there on my lifetime ledger sheet! After all, that's what judgment day is all about; we are *to be judged*! Correct?"

Karol sipped on his wine as he contemplated his response. To fill the dead air, I grabbed another slice of veal. Of course I did. Eating is what I do best.

Finally, he set down his wine glass and shifted forward in his chair.

"When God pardons, Bob, He consigns the offense to everlasting forgetfulness."

That one took some time to sink in. "Run that by me again, please," I said.

John Paul repeated it, slightly louder this second time. "When God pardons, He consigns the offense to everlasting forgetfulness."

"You are going to have to simplify; I'm not the brightest bulb in the box."

"As you wish," he responded. "God is God. You are you. Is that simple enough for you?"

Now I was completely confused. "Apparently not because I have no idea what you are talking about." I paused. "God is God and you are you. And I needed a *Pope* to tell me that? I think even a first-grader could have given me that much."

"Perhaps that was too simplistic; let me try once more," he went on. "You apply your actions to God's actions and your standards to God's standards. You say you 'keep score' so you assume God does the same. You say that while you may forgive others you do not forget, so you assume God does not forget, either.

"God is God. The rest of us are sinners. On judgment day, each and every one of us appears before God wearing the residue of sin."

"That's hardly comforting, Karol."

"Bob?"

"Yes?"

"You have a small piece of kabonosy stuck in your teeth."

"Oh. Sorry."

"Now, let's move on, shall we? Where was I?"

"You mean before you embarrassed me? Something about 'God is God' and the rest of us are sinners."

"Good. Thanks. We all fear judgment day, Bob, because we make the mistake of comparing ourselves to God. It is no wonder you feel great despair because you assume God will act and judge as you would if you were in that same position. If presented with your own 'ledger sheet', you may well judge that person as unworthy of eternal life in heaven. That is what scares you. But you are applying to this situation your very limited human standards.

"That's what I mean when I say, 'God is God'. He doesn't act as we would. He forgives and He forgets. We trust in His powerful mercy that He welcomes into his kingdom even a sinner like you and me. Only God is capable of such goodness.

"Remember this: *Our entrance in to heaven has little to do with how good we were; it has everything to do with how good God is*! Truth be told, none of us are truly worthy of heaven. We are all sinners. It is only though God's mercy and forgiveness that we are granted eternal life in His company."

I thought about that for a few moments. "Hey, that's pretty good, Karol. Even I can understand that."

He reached in to the middle of the table for the bowl of Polish pudding. "Dessert?" he asked.

"Sure, why not! After all the meat and pasta I just ate, pudding will fill in the cracks," I responded.

"You know, buddy, since we are talking about judgment, I've got an unusual admission for you," I said.

"And what might that be?" he wondered.

"It's probably more of a pet peeve than anything else, but it is my reaction anytime someone advises me or reprimands me,

'Don't judge!' which by the way one hears all the time."

"And you reaction is what?" he asked.

"Let me give you a few examples first: I might say to someone, 'Bill has really let himself go these past few years; he has put on weight.' And the person is likely to respond, 'Well, I try not to judge.'

"Or I may say, 'Betty is sure crabby and petty; I wonder how her husband puts up with her.' And someone in my group may respond, 'Well, I always feel it is best not to judge.'

"Or I may say to my wife…"

Karol interrupted. "Bob?"

"Yes?"

"I get it. I don't need examples."

"Oh. Now, where was I? Oh yes; do you know my reaction whenever I hear someone tell me not to judge?"

"I think we've covered this. No, I do not know your reaction when you hear that. You haven't told me yet. The suspense is killing me. It's a good thing I am already dead. Please, tell me."

I looked beyond his condescending tone.

"I think, 'Well, right now, *you are judging me*! You are guilty of the very same thing just by telling me not to judge. That statement is so hypocritical and I find it so annoying. The person who admonishes me not to judge is at that precise moment *judging me* as being too judgmental! They are judging me as being too harsh, too critical, too petty, whatever. Do you understand, Karol?"

"I suppose so."

"It is what we do. All of us. We make judgments hundreds of times a day, every day. This includes judgments both good and bad, by the way. For example, if I were to say, 'Betty did a great job on her proposal' why do I never hear in reply, 'Don't judge!'

"We judge a co-worker's ability or attitude; we judge our children's study habits or group of friends, we judge our neighbor's effectiveness as parents, we judge the singer at church, we judge the priest's homily, we judge the manners of the clerk at the grocery store, we judge the clothing choice of the teenage girl across the street, we judge the cook at the local restaurant, we judge the actors in a movie, we judge politicians when we vote, we judge during a business meeting, we judge during a job interview. Why, dare I say, even *you* 'judge'."

"How so?"

"Well, just moments ago you judged me as 'ignorant'. The fact that you were probably correct has nothing to do with it; it was still a judgment. As Pope, you declared abortions to be immoral; you judged hundreds of believers who lived decades or centuries before you to be worthy of sainthood; you judged communism to be a crime against freedom; you judged many people as having turned away from Christ, so on and so on. Believe me, I'm not disagreeing with those viewpoints but many people did so they were judging you as 'out of touch' or 'ultra-conservative' or numerous other labels just as you were judging them. We *all* judge. So please, everyone, stop telling me, 'Don't judge.'"

"What's your point?"

"Well, I'm not sure I have a point other than I find it horribly hypocritical, insincere and unrealistic. Even God judges. And it is only His judgment which matters."

"Good ending," my friend commented.

"What do you mean?"

"My head was spinning until that final summation. I had no clue just where your little rant was going, but if in your unique and unusual way you have arrived at the conclusion that it is only God's judgment which should be our concern, then you have done well."

I think he just gave me a compliment. "Thank you," I said. The other very real possibility, of course, was that he just wanted me to be done with it.

"If you are quite finished, Bob, with your most interesting dissertation, may we please continue our discussion about *God's* judgment?"

I followed his obvious lead and returned to the topic at hand. "Is it true, Karol, that on judgment day we are shown a movie of our life; I don't mean that literally, of course, not to suggest we sit in a heavenly theater with buckets of buttered popcorn and on the big-screen we see our life from birth to death; but somehow our life is revealed to us, it is re-played and reviewed. You've had your judgment day, is that what happens?"

"I cannot say.  Perhaps that is true for some and not true for others.  The Judge runs judgment day; it's His call as to what transpires."

"Well, if He shows me a movie about *my* life, I think I already know the title," I said.

Karol played along.  "And what is that?"

"The Good, The Bad and The Ugly.  And I fear probably far too much of those last two."

"Bob, I know you are attempting to be light and funny but I can't help to think that you seem to believe that you are doomed. Once again, I am reminded of your previous story about the line from a movie: 'We all got it coming, kid.'  And now the statement just seconds ago about there being too much bad and ugly in your life.  From where I stand, you are being far too harsh in your self-critique.  Why do you have such a fear of your final judgment?"

"Why?  Because only I know the life I have led."

"Not true," he interjected.  "God knows, too!"

"Exactly!  God knows completely the life I've led and so do I; and that's why I dread His judgment.  I am the only person on earth who knows precisely the life He is going to judge."

"Bob, you are hardly a horrible human being.  I am reminded of what you thought earlier today as you were sitting on the bench in Central Park."

"How do you know what I was thinking ten hours ago?"

"Never mind how I know; I just do. As you were contemplating your current status in life, you thought to yourself, 'I love my wife and kids and for some reason they love me.'  It's that specific phrase 'and for some reason' that intrigues me.  Do you not believe you are worthy of being loved?  If true, then the next logical step would be that you'd also believe you are not worthy of the kingdom of heaven."

"Perhaps," I replied.

Karol forged ahead.  "I see before me a decent and kind man. I see a good husband and father.  I see a charitable man.  I see one who volunteers.  Why do you not believe that God approves of your life?"

"I appreciate all of that, Karol, but here's the problem: I should have been so much more. I should have made a much bigger difference. Somehow, I think God disapproves of those who fail to do all they can do.

"Plus, I am a sinner. That seems to be the one thing I do well. And I can't shake the feeling that if I can't forgive myself for my sins and failings, then why will God?"

Karol rose from his chair and raised his voice. "*Because He is God*! It's that simple! God sees within each of us His image. He sees something stunningly beautiful."

He walked over to stand at the side of my chair.

"Bob, you continue to insist that judgment day is all about 'keeping score', that God will look at your ledger sheet and add up the two columns; the 'Bob Did Well' column and the 'Bob Did Poorly" column. Then perhaps you think that He will announce the final score: 'Bob Did Well, 5498. Bob Did Poorly, 7323. Bob Did Poorly wins, so Bob loses. Goodbye Bob, you may not enter my kingdom. Have a nice time in Hell.'"

"Well, that may be a bit over the top, but something like that, yes," I responded rather meekly.

"My good man," he responded with exasperation. "You've got it all wrong. Your fear of judgment day is a healthy one and I commend you for that; again, it tells me that your belief in God is so solid that you understand and accept His role as your Creator and ultimately as your final judge. However, you seem to have an image of God as someone who can't wait to knock you over with a lightning bolt and then laughs as he condemns you to damnation because you were a sinner.

"Take it from me. I've been there. In the end, all we will be judged on is how much did we love God and how much did we love God's people. God is the King of love and therefore His final judgment will be one of love and mercy. As He determines our final destination, He will ask first and foremost whether or not you have loved."

John Paul slowly walked back to his chair and sat down. He poured into his glass a few ounces of the wine and took a sip.

I looked at him. "So you're saying that I've got a chance?"

His eyes locked with mine. "It is not my judgment that matters, but if you are asking for my opinion: Yes, Bob, you have a chance. We all do."

❖❖❖❖❖❖❖

I reached for my third cold bottle of Tyskie. It was quickly becoming one of my new favorite brands.

"If what you say is true, Karol, and I have no reason to doubt you, then that brings me to a whole new line of questioning."

"I expected it would," he smiled.

"You said, 'I have a chance.'"

"Yes."

"Then you added, 'We all have a chance.'"

"Again, yes. We all have a chance of entering heaven, the Kingdom of God. He doesn't keep anyone out; we keep ourselves out by the lives we choose to lead. He gave us the freedom to turn away from Him just as we have a choice to turn to Him. God doesn't force. He doesn't bang on the door. He calls us. He invites us, but He respects our ability to reject him. If we fail in our quest for heaven, it's on us, not Him."

"Got it. But that brings me to this: is heaven *exclusive* or *inclusive*?"

He took another sip from his glass before responding.

"What do you mean?"

"Well, you just told me that we all have a chance, so it makes me think that if even people like me have a chance at heaven then it must be very inclusive; the more, the merrier! However, common sense tells me that heaven should be very exclusive, reserved for only the very good. Heaven should be *special*. Heaven should be a reward. If most everyone gets in, however, well, what's so special about that? To paraphrase Woody Allen, 'What's so special about a club that would accept me as a member?'

"For example, there are approximately seven billion people in the world at this moment. Seven billion, imagine that! And that's just right now, that's just a current snapshot of human history. On top of that, think about the astronomical number of people, literally impossible to calculate, who have *ever* been alive. I find it hard to believe that most of those people are in heaven. Further, I find it hard to believe that most of the seven billion alive right now will end up in heaven; there are a lot of nasty people out there, we all know that. Too many people today, it seems, don't follow God, some even don't believe in Him, but you are telling me that God is a merciful judge who will rule on the side of compassion and love, so I ask again; is heaven more inclusive or exclusive?"

"I can't answer that with certainty, Bob, but I can offer a fairly strong opinion because, after all, I've been hanging around that neighborhood for almost a decade now."

"Nice!" I said.

He paused and closed his eyes. "It sure is."

I had never in my life seen a man who looked so at peace than John Paul at this precise moment.

In a few moments, he resumed. "Keep in mind, I am still the new kid on the block, I certainly haven't seen it all, but from what little I know, to answer your question, I would say that heaven is more inclusive than exclusive."

"Honestly? I must admit, I am surprised."

"Of this, at least, I am certain: that heaven is inclusive in terms of God's desire to accept us. He wants every one of us.

"Now, on the other hand, it may be more exclusive if looked at by the number of people who have intentionally rejected God, those who completely shut out God, those who choose early in life not to attend that party. These days, it seems, it is common to believe, 'God is a nice guy, He wants me in heaven, so it doesn't really matter what I do with my life because God is going to let me in anyway, so I'm just going to life my life without God and when I see Him at the pearly gates I will apologize and He'll let me enter heaven; I don't need God until then.' But where is the foundation for that belief? Jesus said more than once that the road to heaven is a rough one, that the gates are narrow, and how few there are who will find everlasting life. So, for those who lock God out of their lives, heaven would indeed be exclusive."

"I'm sorry, Karol, maybe all of this food and drink has clogged up my hearing but it sounds like you are talking out of both sides of your mouth," I said. "It's inclusive in one example, it's exclusive in another. What gives?"

"Let me put it this way. God's salvation is for everyone; thus, obviously, heaven is inclusive. However, we all have the freedom to choose for God or against God dozens of times every day of our lives; each and every day we make decisions which contribute to the big picture and will answer the critical question, 'Am I moving closer to God or moving away from God?' Thus, salvation is for everyone, heaven is for everyone, but we can lose salvation and heaven by the way we live, by how much or how little we love. Anyone who searches for God with a sincere heart will, I believe, discover that heaven is inclusive.

"Plus, Bob, there is this: In my relatively brief time in heaven, I have already come across several people who represent, at least to me, undeniable proof of God's immeasurable love and mercy."

"What do you mean?"

"When I saw them, I couldn't believe it! To one I almost said, 'What are *you* doing here?' And to another, I literally did say, 'Well, this is the last place I ever thought I'd run into you!'"

"If I ever get there, that's probably what many of them up there will say to me," I offered. "Can you tell me their names, these people whose presence surprised you? You're not telling me saw Hitler walking around up there, are you?"

He let out with a hearty laugh. "I can't say. We're all sworn to secrecy, sorry. I guess, Bob, if you are truly curious, there's only one way to find out." He paused. "Come up and see for yourself!"

"What's it like?" I asked.

"What's *what* like?"

"Heaven, you old ghost, what did you think I meant? That's what we're talking about, isn't it? Describe it."

"I can't."

"That's what my buddy P.J. Sheen told me, too. He told me, 'heaven would hardly be heaven if you could imagine it.'"

Karol smiled. "I agree with him. One literally cannot describe heaven. If you think you have a picture of heaven, trust me, it's not heaven."

"When attempting to imagine heaven, I don't even know where to begin," I admitted. "Is it like a celestial country club? Is it a divine Disney World? Are there angels playing harps on every corner?"

"You are wasting you time, Bob."

"I'm good at that, Karol."

I reached for yet another fried olive, wondering if one could actually become addicted to these things. There's probably an F-O-A support system somewhere; Fried Olives Anonymous. I better look into it.

"Speaking of heaven, Karol," I finally resumed, "did you know that according to a recent poll only 85% believe in such a place?"

"Is that all? That saddens me."

"Some of those who do not believe in heaven, however, don't see any harm in the belief. For example, they acknowledge the concept of heaven is worthy because if heaven is seen as life's ultimate reward then it will certainly have an impact on the type of life one lives. Others point out that the concept of heaven offers powerful comfort in the days after the loss of a loved one. So, of those 15% who do not believe in heaven, at least some of them grudgingly concede that it's not a bad idea to believe in it."

Suddenly, Karol had a look of shock on his handsome face.

"Bob, it *almost* sounds as if you understand or sympathize with their point-of-view; please don't tell me that *you* are among those who don't believe in heaven."

I nearly spit out my olive. "Oh my gosh, no! I'm sorry to have somehow misled you. Of course, I believe in heaven. If not, why am I so anguished and fearful about judgment day?"

"Good point."

"However…" I stopped there, uncertain if I wanted to go there.

"However… *what*?" Karol asked curiously.

"You probably know this anyway, you seem to know many things I do and think, so why not? Is there a heaven? Sure. However, John Paul, I'm not convinced there is a *hell*."

"No hell?" he replied. "How can that be? After all, you just

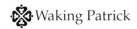 

asked, intelligently I might add, if heaven was more inclusive or exclusive, so just by the very nature of that question you admit that not everyone enters heaven. So, for those who do not, where do they go if there is no hell?"

"Well… maybe they don't go anywhere. Maybe they just die and that's it. *Maybe not getting into heaven is hell.* Maybe hell is just being dead with no place to go. Ever."

John Paul failed to respond. Instead, he played with his cloth napkin. So, since he offered no resistance, I continued.

"I mean, how can a loving and merciful and compassionate God send anyone to an eternity in flames? Maybe God's one and only limitation is His wrath. Maybe the extent of His wrath is sentencing all those unworthy of heaven to just be dead, forever, with no hope of heaven."

Even with that, there was still nothing from my friend Karol.

"Have I surprised you? Have I alarmed you that I could have such thoughts? I'm sorry but I can't help it. If you've listened at all tonight you've heard me say that as I get older I have more doubts and more questions than at any other time of my life. And if this one about hell-or-no-hell scares you, Karol, just wait until I tell you about relics and angels and all these other things about my faith that I wonder about."

Finally, he made a move to speak. He leaned in and placed his elbows on the table.

"Those items are best left for someone else. Our time together is nearly finished. I have just one thing for you about your theory on perhaps there not being an actual place called hell."

"Yes?"

"In your remaining years on earth, live well, love God, love God's people; for if not your death will be a lousy time to discover that you were mistaken."

❖ ❖ ❖ ❖ ❖ ❖ ❖

Karol stood from the table and motioned for me to join him. He turned to look down the main aisle of the cathedral. It seemed he was looking at the crucifix hanging above the altar. I think he was quietly praying. It even appeared as if his eyes were moist.

Obviously, I didn't intrude. I'm not *that* stupid.

After several minutes, his glance left the altar and returned to me at his side. "So, my friend, what did you think of our meal?"

"Oh, it was fantastic! I liked your idea of showing off samples from both Italy and Poland. At first, I thought that was a strange combination but they complemented one another very nicely. I liked the Tyskie. The Italian wine, as usual, was excellent. And you were right; I don't at all feel full or sick even though I ate far too much. If I ate that much back home I'd be swallowing a bottle of Tums right now. Thank you so much for all of it!"

Then I remembered something. "I am sorry, how rude of me! I didn't even offer to help with the clean-up."

"What clean-up?" he said.

"You know, the dinner table, the leftover food, the empty bottles, the dirty knives and forks and napkins."

He repeated. "Again I ask, what clean-up?"

I turned to look to where we had just dined. Nothing was there. All evidence of our meal was gone. The space was exactly as it appeared when I first entered the cathedral hours ago.

I looked at John Paul and smiled. "Can I hire your kitchen staff?"

He laughed and said, "They only work my private parties."

As we stood near the back pews, I couldn't help but wonder where and how my new friend was going to exit. I remembered Louis somehow disappearing through the back of his altar. Sheen, I recalled, left by climbing the steps to the pulpit and magically kept climbing. How would John Paul leave?

"When we first met, Bob, did you get a good look at my bust?" he asked.

"Honestly, I barely noticed it. I couldn't take my eyes off of you; the *real you*, not your bust. I couldn't believe I was about to meet Pope John Paul II. It still seems hard to believe."

"Well, let's look at it now," he suggested. "And when we get there please give to me your honest opinion."

The bust was just a few steps away and I studied it as we approached and even more once we arrived. It showed the very familiar features of the face of John Paul II, including even a small mound of curly hair on the top of his head. I thought it captured the man perfectly and I told him so.

"I think it is an excellent likeness," I said. Then, without thinking, I added, "Your Holiness."

I could tell that he liked that. "Bob, that's the only time tonight you have used that title. I don't hear that too often these days, if at all. Where I am now, titles don't mean very much."

He put his right hand on my left shoulder. "Bob, you ask many interesting questions. You are blessed with a natural curiosity. You don't take things at face-value and you rarely believe things just because you've been told to believe them. Your search for answers is a good one! I commend your search for the truth and may I say, I think you will be very pleased when you find it.

"And always remember: Be not afraid!"

I was so humbled by his encouragement that I stared down at the floor just to gather my thoughts. John Paul II seemed to be giving me his personal stamp-of-approval that maybe I wasn't so far off the path after all. Imagine that!

"Well, Karol, I cannot find the words to thank you enough for all that you…"

I stopped cold in mid-sentence because as I looked up from the floor to look him in the eye and say goodbye, he wasn't there. In a split-second, he had vanished, just like my two friends earlier in the night. How do they do that? Where do they go? Why must they always leave so quickly? It made me sad that I couldn't talk to him one final time.

I looked again at his bust. The sculpted smile on it was a reassuring one. The eyes were comforting. Strange, but somehow it looked just a bit more lifelike than it did just seconds ago.

And as I turned to leave it, a thought came over me: if I can somehow manage to follow the advice he had offered earlier, to love God and to love God's people, that maybe one day I will be talking to Karol again.

# VI
## *My Final Friends*

I stood just a few steps away from the main exit. The Cathedral was still. It appeared to be empty, other than me. Moments ago, Karol had indicated that more friends would soon be visiting but perhaps he was joking. Perhaps, even, he was wrong. He may have been infallible as Pope but in his new life, in his new residence, I doubt it.

I didn't move for about a minute. I was listening for a sound, any sound, which would tell me I was no longer alone.

Nothing.

And that exit was tantalizingly close.

I looked around the interior one final time, starting with the gift shop on my immediate left, then down the right wall of side altars and stained-glass windows to the main altar in the front-center of the cathedral, then to the huge baptismal font in the front corner, up the left aisle of still more altars, statues and windows, and finally back to where I stood near the bust of John Paul II.

I didn't see anyone. I didn't hear anything. 'Maybe,' I thought to myself, 'I can finally leave.'

I took tiny steps to the exit door being very careful not to make any noise. With both hands, I tightly grabbed the silver bar attached waist-level on the door, took a deep breath, closed my eyes, and pushed down on the bar hoping that the next thing I'd see would be the front steps leading down to Fifth Avenue.

I should have known better.

The door remained locked. I was still stuck inside. Karol had not been joking nor had he been wrong.

Now what? Or, more accurately, now *who*? Who, I wondered

as I turned back from the door and returned to the back pew, would visit me next?

Funny, but I wasn't afraid anymore. Certainly my first few meetings with my new and unexpected friends had frightened me; Louis and Sheen in particular. At that time I wasn't convinced it was all real. Why would I? They were dead, of that I was quite certain; and yet here they seemed to be, living, breathing, laughing, reacting, walking and talking, engaging me in long and complicated conversations. At that time, I thought this could not be happening, that it must be a dream; an interesting and even an entertaining dream, yes, but still just a dream that frightened me because it seemed so lifelike.

By the time I met the killer Agca I was no longer scared; I believed it really was him. I was most certainly afraid of who he was, a murderer; but I no longer feared for my safety and I wasn't afraid of the experience. I felt the same when moments later I met the Pope; I knew it was him. I couldn't explain it, of course, I had no idea how it was happening or how they were able to visit with me but I accepted it as fact and I was no longer afraid.

Now, I was curious, even anxious, to find out who would be next. Clearly, this person was in no hurry to reveal his or her identity because I stood at that back pew for what seemed to be at least five minutes, waiting for *something* to happen.

My mind drifted back to the friends I'd already encountered. Louis was nice man who walked me through some of the episodes of my childhood and teenage years. He taught me about the folly of revenge; and of the need to let-go both the good and bad of one's past; and the enormous impact a parent has on the life of a child.

Sheen was dynamic and intimidating, at times a bit too arrogant for my taste but very helpful and wise when it came to dissecting my prayer life. He was able to get me to understand prayer, finally, after over fifty years of doing it.

Agca was evil and mean; I was grateful our time together had been short.

And Karol, my most recent new friend, was as intriguing and engaging as any person I'd ever met. He not only assisted me with things like forgiveness and judgment day but he also provided me with one of the great meals of my life. He was my favorite. Of course, *anybody* who feeds me so well usually becomes my favorite.

I had no idea who would follow. Further, I had no clue as to what we'd talk about. What other help did I need? What other problems were there? I'm a normal guy, I know, but I'm not completely helpless, am I? Did I really need yet another new friend to talk me through yet another issue? And who could it be? If I deleted Agca, something I was more than willing to do, then the line-up thus far tonight had been Saint Louis, Fulton Sheen and Pope John Paul II. Who could possibly hit clean-up in an all-star line-up like that? Who is next; Christ Himself?

Now *that*, I quickly determined, *would* indeed frighten me! In fact, pun intended, it would scare the hell out of me. A face-to-face with Jesus? What would I possibly say to Him? Would that mean my judgment day was already here?

I hurriedly looked at the large cross at the front of the cathedral to see if the figure of the crucified Christ was still in place. What if the figure was instead walking down the center aisle, wearing sandals and holding a fishing pole, maybe followed closely by a burning bush, heading in my direction? I am *so afraid* right now. I am so…stupid.

I looked. Christ was still on the cross. Of course He is. He's there for us always. That much, even I knew.

My melt down was over. Christ was not hitting clean-up tonight for me. How ignorant of me to even think it.

But, *who was*?

Then, suddenly, I sensed movement off to my right and before I could turn to look I heard a man's voice. "Last call!"

I turned in that direction.

"Last call! Do you want one or not?"

For now, I looked beyond the man because I was more interested in his surroundings. Seconds ago, this area was the cathedral's gift shop but somehow it had become an Irish pub. I've been in enough of them to immediately know the look and feel of one: dimly lit, dark wood, a snug in each corner, a

Kilkenny flagstone floor, and hanging on the walls were grainy black and white photographs of soccer, rugby and hurling glory days. There were other photos as well; an empty fishing canoe on a rocky beach, an Irish cottage with a thatched roof, and John Wayne and Maureen O'Hara in a scene from the movie *The Quiet Man*. And off in the corner of the pub stood the green, white and orange flag of Ireland.

As I walked closer I saw three empty stools placed in front of a beautiful mahogany bar. There were coasters and clean glasses resting on top of the bar. The beer taps featured Guinness, Harp and Smithwicks; and on the shelf behind the bar were bottles of Irish whiskeys including Jameson, Powers, Black Bush, Redbreast and Tullamore Dew.

I smiled and thought to myself, 'John Paul was right: there is a heaven.'

I heard music quietly playing from a small sound system on a shelf below the bottles. I recognized the current song as *Wild Rover* as performed by The Clancy Brothers. And in the nearby pile of compact discs were other Irish musical stars such as The Cranberries, Thin Lizzy, Clannad, The Chieftains, The Irish Tenors and, my personal favorite, The Saw Doctors.

Oh, could I ever get used to this place!

It wasn't until this moment that I finally concentrated on the bartender. My heart raced because I recognized him immediately. Other than his clothes, he looked exactly like the statue at the front of the cathedral.

❖❖❖❖❖❖

"You're Patrick, aren't you?" I asked, taking a seat on the middle bar stool.

"Yes, I am."

"As in *Saint* Patrick, right?"

"The one and only," he responded. His voice had a distinct brogue but strangely, I thought, not your typical Irish brogue. I know what an Irish brogue sounds like from my frequent trips to the Emerald Isle; plus, I have friends in this country that grew up in Ireland and they still have that great Irish sound when they speak.

Patrick was tall and thin with a thick beard which was brown with streaks of grey. However, he was not wearing a long robe or vestment as was depicted on his statue; rather, he looked very fashionable in a white woolly Aran sweater and a grey and brown tweed Irish flat cap. And in his left hand he grasped a Blackthorn walking stick.

"You don't look like your statue," I noted.

He shrugged. "Ah, that's just my official pose. One has to be very serious and business-like when one poses for a statue or a stained-glass window. Heck, often the artist doesn't have the slightest clue what we really looked like so they just make it up. Then we see from above what they've done and we shout out, 'Is that supposed to be *me*?' It can be quite annoying, frankly. However, in my case, the artist did quite well. That statue up front is pretty much how I looked in my later years in Ireland but what you see in front of you is how I appeared in my forties when I went back to Ireland to convert the country. And now that I get to hang around you for awhile, I get to select the clothes. All very stylish, don't you think?"

I had to agree. "Yes, you look good," I admitted.

"Now, back to my initial question," he continued.

"Which was…?"

"Do you want one or not? This is last call. Do you want a drink?"

"This is last call for *whom*? I'm the only guy in here. What are you going to do if I tell you I don't want a drink? Is our visit over?"

"Do you really want to find out?"

He had me there. It's not that I ever needed to have my arm twisted to accept a drink offer but I had to concede his technique was very effective.

"Good point. Sure, I'll have a drink." I took several seconds to again look over my options. "A Guinness sounds good. I'll have a pint; thanks!"

Patrick grabbed a glass and placed it under the tap. He knew what he was doing; there is a trick to pouring a proper pint of Guinness. It takes several minutes to do it the right way. It's a two-part pour. First, one must hold the glass at a 45-degree angle under the tap and fill it to about three-quarters full. Next, the bartender must set down the glass and allow the surge to settle before taking the second step which is filling the glass to the top. The creamy white head, about three inches thick, is proof of the proper pour. I watched in silence, my thirst growing with every second, as he followed the procedure perfectly.

I liked this guy already.

"Here you go, Bob," he said as he handed over the pint.

"You know my name?" I asked.

"In here, doesn't everybody?"

'This guy is good,' I thought.

I lifted my glass in his direction. "Slainte," I offered as a Gaelic toast and raised the glass to my lips.

That first taste of a Guinness is one of life's simple pleasures. At this stage of my life this has become my favorite alcoholic drink, at least it is while out for an evening in a restaurant or pub. At home, with a good book and in front of a warm fire, or with a few friends in a lively conversation, my drink of choice is an Irish whiskey on the rocks. However, in a setting such as this then give me a Guinness. Please.

"This tastes terrific," I told my bartender. "Even here."

"What do you mean, 'even here'?"

"Here, as in the United States. I've been to Ireland several times and for some reason the Guinness there tastes better. That's not to knock it over here because I still love it but you just can't beat a Guinness while in Ireland."

"Whatever you say, Bob."

I felt bad. Obviously the poor guy had never enjoyed one. "Sorry, Patrick, that's a little insensitive of me to be bragging about my Guinness when you've never had one."

"Why would you think that?" he wondered.

I reached into my memory. "Well, because this wonderful drink in front of me wasn't created until the late seventeen hundreds. You were long dead by then."

"Yes?"

Why couldn't he grasp this? "Thus, you've never tasted one."

"That's not true."

I didn't get it. "But how can that be?" I asked.

He paused and smiled. "Why do you think they call it 'heaven'?"

Score another point for Pat. Good thing we weren't playing cribbage; he'd be way ahead. I took another long drink before I continued.

"So, Saint Patrick, you probably know by now that I'm a little uncomfortable addressing you by that name and title. I assume you were watching and listening earlier tonight."

"I was."

"So then you know that I need a nickname for you. It'll help to put me at ease. For example, King Louis was 'Lou' to me. Archbishop Fulton Sheen was simply 'P.J.' Pope John Paul II was, more often than not, just 'Karol' to me. It's less intimidating. Do you mind?"

"Well, that depends on what you come up with."

I took a quick sip to think about it. "Well, how about 'Paddy'? It's a common nickname in Ireland for anyone named 'Patrick.' We can leave that whole Saint thing out of it and you can just be my friendly neighborhood bartender."

Quickly another thought came to me. "And this place can be called 'Paddy's Pub'; how's that sit with you?"

"I like it," he replied sincerely.

"Good! Then that settles it! I'm just regular guy Bob sitting in a typical Irish pub, 'Paddy's Pub', short for Public House which is where the term 'pub' comes from, talking to my Irish bartender, Paddy. There is nothing imposing about that at all. Now I am comfortable."

"It's all grande. Except for the Irish part," he said.

"What do you mean?"

"I'm not Irish."

I stared at him, waiting for him to crack a smile, waiting perhaps for a punch line. He knew I was stumped.

"I converted Ireland," he resumed. "And after so many years

I certainly consider myself to be Irish. However, I was born in Scotland."

"Scotland?" I nearly shouted.

"Yes. Delicious irony, isn't it? I was born in tiny Kilpatrick, near what is today Glascow. Later, I once again spent many years in Great Britain."

"So that explains your brogue," I stated. "I thought it didn't sound specifically Irish."

"You have a good ear. My accent is probably a mixture of Irish, Scottish and English. Plus, I also speak Gaelic," he explained.

"My goodness," I said with a smile. "It's amazing anybody could understand you well enough to be converted!"

I put both hands around my half-empty pint. "I just realized, Paddy, how little I know about you. I mean, I thought you were born in Ireland, a natural assumption if I may offer a weak excuse, and even that is incorrect. Come to think about it, other than converting an entire country to Christianity and something about the legend of chasing away snakes, I don't know anything else other than on your feast day of March 17th I drink green beer and I eat corned beef and cabbage. I am sorry to say, Paddy, and even a bit embarrassed to admit that I know so little about you.

"I *do* know, however, why you are here with me right now. I know that we are 'connected', just like my other friends earlier tonight."

"Connected? What do you mean?" he asked as he leaned in against the back of the bar.

"Well, I met Louis because he is the patron saint of my hometown; and he is in this cathedral because he has an altar here. Right?"

Paddy nodded his head.

"And I met Sheen because I once worked on a documentary about his life; and he is buried here in the crypt."

"Yes."

"And then I encountered John Paul because I once presented to my wife the opportunity to meet him; and we met here because he has a bust in the cathedral. You see, we are all connected to each other."

"Interesting choice of words," he said. "But more about that later."

What, I wondered, was so 'interesting' about that particular phrase? As had occurred several times earlier tonight with my previous friends, I had no idea what he meant by that. So much of my life, I live in a fog.

He continued. "Now, what about *me*, Bob; what is our so-called connection?"

"That's easy, Paddy," I replied. "First, you converted Ireland; and I am of Irish ancestry. That may be a very loose connection, but a connection nonetheless.

"The second one is much better. I have visited your grave."

He interrupted. "Have you? You've been to Downpatrick in County Down? I am honored." He seemed genuinely surprised.

"I worked a project at the Saint Patrick Centre," I explained. "I believe it is the only museum in the country, perhaps the world, dedicated solely to you. It's a great place to visit; very informative and state-of-the-art. Your grave sits on top of a hill overlooking the museum and that small town. I saw your grave. I said a prayer at it. I remember it very clearly because I had just received word from back home that my wonderful mother-in-law had just passed away. Frankly, I found it to be a moving experience, to be standing at the gravesite of the famous Saint Patrick and praying for a deceased loved one."

I stopped for a second to soak in the magnitude of this coincidence. "And here we are, several years later, face-to-face. Amazing! Who could ever imagine such a thing?"

I took a drink from my pint before resuming.

"And our third connection, Paddy, is that my grade school back in tiny Ballwin, Missouri holds its annual fundraiser *in your honor*! It is Holy Infant's largest event of the year. Our nuns are from Ireland and when they arrived about fifty years ago they set aside every March 17th, St. Patrick's Day, for this money-making celebration. It includes corned beef dinners, green beer and Irish dancers and music. There are carnival games and cake walks for the kids. Back in the day, we even had an old-time parishioner dress up as a leprechaun. The men of the parish always ended

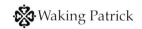 

up in the one classroom that had been transformed into a pub. They'd drink pitchers of beer and sing Irish songs and buy raffle tickets. It was a great time. And it raised loads of money for the school. And it's all in your name, Paddy."

"I know," he said. "Every year, I am touched."

"You know about it?"

"*Know* about it? Heck, I *go there* every year. I watch from above the stage or from the back table in the cafeteria. One year, Bob, I even went *as myself*. I walked around the festival *as me*; I didn't try to hide at all. It was a blast!"

"Are you kidding me? How did you get away with that?"

"It was easy. Everybody thought I was just some guy from the parish pretending to be Saint Patrick; just like that man dressed up as a leprechaun. It gets better. I played a trick on the crowd; I made a snake appear in the middle of the bingo room and I ran in and chased it away. It was perfectly symbolic. I laughed for hours over that one!"

I looked at him as if he was nuts. Leave it to me to get connected to a practical-joker saint. I had nothing to offer as a suitable response so I just moved on.

"So those are the three reasons, Paddy, of how you and I are connected."

I raised my glass in his direction and added, "And here we are, in your cathedral, at your pub, in the first stages of a friendship. Life can sure be interesting, can't it?"

And with that, I emptied my Guinness.

The alcohol was not having any impact. I remembered just a short time ago enjoying several Polish beers with Karol, plus some Italian wine, and now I had just finished a pint with Paddy. If I had done this much drinking back home with friends or family, by now I'd be either leading a sing-along or sleeping on the floor. I'd certainly be handing over my car keys to my wife. Yet, here in this cathedral, with this new group of friends, I felt fine; perfectly normal. I don't understand. What is it about these *people?* What is it about this *place?*

"Would you like another?" my bartender asked, stopping my train-of-thought.

Straight-faced, I responded. "Paddy, that's the first stupid thing you've said so far."

He laughed. "I'll take that as a 'yes'!"

Paddy grabbed a clean glass and began to draw my second pint. He adjusted the volume on the music and then ran a wet wash rag over the top of the bar. If I didn't know any better I would have sworn that this guy really was a bartender. Maybe it was one of his gigs before starting that little Christianity-Conversion career of his.

"By the way, Pat, I absolutely love your country," I said as he placed my pint in front of me. "Ireland is my favorite country to visit."

"Bob, Ireland is not my country!" he said firmly. "I've told you that."

"What are you getting so worked up about? You must get over that 'I wasn't born in Ireland' thing. You seem to take that so personally. So what? You couldn't help where you were born. Big deal!

"You converted that country! You are Ireland's patron saint. Arguably, you are Ireland's most famous historical figure. So, yes, Pat, Ireland *is* your country. And to return to where this started, I happen to love it."

I waited for a reply but didn't get one. Instead, he placed in front of me a basket of pretzels and cashews and a plate of freshly-baked Irish brown bread. Where did *that* come from? I sure didn't see a kitchen or oven in this small pub. Maybe Paddy was using the same caterers used by Karol; maybe they stuck around for a little overtime. In this place, who knows? By now, I'd stop trying to figure it out.

He finally broke the silence. "Where have you visited in Ireland?" he inquired.

"Well, Paddy, I've seen a lot but not nearly enough. I can't wait to return. But let me rack my brain to see how much I can remember from my previous trips."

I stopped to spread whipped butter on a slice of the bread.

"Let me begin with what many think is the most unlikely place to visit in Ireland; and that would be Belfast."

"I thought we were talking about Ireland," he stated.

"We are," I replied, somewhat confused.

"Belfast is in *Northern* Ireland, Bob. That's a different country." That caught me off-guard for a moment.

"Well, you're right, Paddy; I knew that, but since it's all on the same island don't most of us just consider it all one country?"

"No, I don't think they do. That'd be like tourists from Europe believing that New York City is in Pennsylvania."

"Point taken," I grudgingly conceded.

"Furthermore, why would you say 'let's begin with the most *unlikely* place to visit'?"

I responded candidly. "Because most people think you'll get killed if you go to Belfast! In fact, that's the most common reaction anytime I tell people I visited Belfast; they'll jokingly ask if I had a death wish."

"Oh, come on, Bob! It's not like that anymore. I concede that it was a bad place to be during The Troubles but Belfast is a peaceful city now. You know that."

"Yes, I do; but it's hard to shake such a poor reputation, which, by the way, is true of people, too. But you are right; I found Belfast to be a wonderful city! They have that huge Ferris wheel on the grounds of City Hall. Bill Clinton gave a speech there."

"Clinton gave a speech at the Ferris wheel?"

I laughed. "No! He spoke from the dome at City Hall. He probably went to the Ferris wheel *after* the speech." Pause. "Because that's where all the babes hang out."

"I'm sure he did," agreed Paddy.

I continued on about Belfast. "Their Grand Opera House is impressive. The streets were clean. I felt very safe just wandering around. And I found a great pub…"

"Gee, what a shock."

"…called The Crown Liquor Saloon. All things considered, I was impressed with Belfast. I am glad I visited."

"Where else have you been?" he urged.

"Well, you will like this, Paddy: I've been to Armagh."

"Oh, so we're still talking *Northern* Ireland, are we?"

"Oh, still nit-picking, are we? Yes, Paddy, Armagh is in

*Northern* Ireland."

"As is, by the way, my grave and the Saint Patrick Centre you mentioned earlier; you neglected to make that clarification at the time."

I answered sarcastically. "Well, considering I was talking to the man who is *in* that grave, I didn't think a clarification was needed but thanks ever so much for pointing out my error. Now, may I please continue?"

"Please do. I believe you were in Armagh? I have a cathedral there."

"I saw it. It's beautiful. Although, I must say, *this* Saint Patrick's cathedral, where the two of us are sitting at this very moment, is much better in my opinion."

"Is that your American bias, perhaps?"

"And if you disagree, could that not be your Irish bias, perhaps?"

Reluctantly, he nodded in agreement.

"That's about it for my experiences in Northern Ireland, Paddy; Belfast and Armagh and Downpatrick. The large majority of my time in your country has been spent in the *Republic* of Ireland.

"By the way, did I make the proper clarification this time?"

I can be a cocky wise guy when I want to be. It comes easy to me. Of course, why I'd *want* to be is a whole different matter. Not even saints can help me with that one.

Paddy placed a few more pretzels in the bowl and poured for himself a large glass of ice water. He passed over that last comment.

"You've been to Dublin, our country's capital city, I assume?" he asked.

"I have. Honestly, though, it's not at all my favorite. Don't get me wrong because I certainly enjoyed seeing the brightly-colored doors on all the townhouses; and the Book of Kells at Trinity College; and walking across the River Liffey on the Ha'penny Bridge; and browsing the shops on Grafton Street; and relaxing in beautiful St. Stephen's Green; and a cool pint at the famous Temple Bar. I had a good time in Dublin; it's just that it is a bit too crowded and busy for my tastes. I mean, I go to Ireland to *get*

*away* from big cities and crowds and Dublin to me is just another big city.

"Really, the only big city in Ireland I like is Galway and at times even that can seem imposing. I enjoy Eyre Square and the maze of shops and pubs on the surrounding streets. There's a terrific bowl of Irish stew at O'Connell's Pub. And obviously one has to walk to the waterfront and sing a verse of Galway Bay. It's a neat town but, like Dublin, a one-day visit is all I want or need. For me, the charm and beauty of Ireland is found when one gets away from the bigger cities; find the towns and villages off the beaten path, the smaller, the better. That's where Ireland is at her best!"

"Such as?" inquired Paddy.

I shrugged my shoulders. "Where do I start?"

I had to think about it for a few seconds. "I love the stunning beauty of nature found in Connemara National Park. From there, I always have to walk through the Kylemore Abbey and Garden. Of course, in this area of the country you are also close to the famous and magnificent Ashford Castle; and from there you can walk or bike ride to the village of Cong where my favorite movie *The Quiet Man* was filmed.

"I think the small towns along the Ring of Kerry are wonderful; Sneem and Carragh are my two favorites. I golfed once at Waterville; visually breathtaking but it absolutely destroyed my golf game. I haven't been the same since!"

I stopped long enough for a quick sip from my Guinness.

"I love the small town of Adare in County Limerick. I adore Dingle; if I could ever afford a vacation home it might be there. We once had Irish tea and blueberry scones at a farmhouse restaurant in tiny Athy. I love Ennis and Kilkee and Westport and Ballyvaughan. And the small town of Liscannor in County Clare is yet another gem.

"Am I boring you yet?"

"Not at all. I am fascinated always by how so many people love my country," replied Paddy.

"Even some of the 'tourist traps' are worth a one-time visit," I resumed. "I refer to places like the Waterford Crystal factory;

or attending one of those god-awful medieval entertainment programs at the Knappogue Castle; or the silly tradition of kissing the Blarney Stone; or the gardens and mansion at the Mucross House; or an overpriced pint at Durty Nelly's Tavern; or buying Irish marble in Moycullen or Nicholas Mosse pottery in Bennettsbridge. Even the places or things I find to be most unbearable are worth the experience; as I always say, 'If it's in Ireland, it's worth it.'"

"In my day, I didn't have such things to see or do; all I encountered were pagans and Druids!" laughed my bartender friend.

"However, I find it interesting, Bob, that you didn't mention visiting Knock in County Mayo," he remarked.

"There's a good reason for that, Paddy; I didn't mention Knock because I've never been there. I just never found the time."

"Really? That's surprising," he responded. "This is the site of Ireland's greatest miracle. Mary appeared there, as did St. Joseph and St. John the Evangelist. There were at least fifteen witnesses who also saw an altar with a cross, a lamb and angels."

"I am well aware of the story," I managed.

"You found the time for what you admit were disappointing activities like medieval feasts but you never found the time for Knock," he said as he jotted something on a small pad of paper off to the side of the bar. It was the second time I'd seen him writing something on that pad. "Interesting," he said again, quietly.

I could tell he was perplexed; not angry, certainly, just confused or surprised. Clearly, he didn't approve of what I had just told him but I couldn't grasp what could be so wrong with never visiting Knock.

I decided to quickly get him off subject and return him to the things I loved about his country.

"There are other things, Paddy, which I like about Ireland, some small observances I've made through the years. For example, whenever possible, I notice the Irish leave things alone. Many of the roads are narrow; they only make them as wide as they need to be. The same is true, too, with many of their homes; they are only as large as necessary to provide a comfortable home for the family.

"In my opinion, life is simple and relaxed in Ireland; and I mean that as a compliment. I never saw a fancy or expensive 15-speed bike; instead, the bicycles are very basic. And so many people ride bikes, even the elderly; heck, in Kilkenny I saw the postman delivering the mail while on bicycle! When one goes golfing, you walk; there are few courses which feature riding carts. On Lake Killarney, boats cannot have engines or motors; no noise or fumes are accepted; you row or you don't go. There are stone fences everywhere because the stone is already there in the ground, so they dig it up and use that for their fence and border; why buy and ship wood?

"I like their terminology. The Irish may say 'It is a soft day' when it is raining; a shop owner may ask 'Are you being looked after?' instead of 'What do you want?'; that same business owner may also say as you enter, 'You are very welcome' rather than 'hello'; and in a small village the pub is referred to as 'The Local', as in 'I will meet you at The Local in an hour.'

"I remember having to stop our car on a country road for about fifteen minutes to allow dozens of sheep to wander across. In America, I am very angry and impatient if I am in a fifteen minute delay on the roads but in Ireland I found it charming! It's a different pace there. It's a beautiful country visually; there seems to be a postcard moment around every bend."

"It was gorgeous even in my day," Paddy commented. "In fact, it was probably even more stunning than it is today simply because the landscape was uninterrupted with buildings and businesses and highways and the like."

I popped a cashew in my mouth. "I saved the best for last, Paddy; do you know what I like most about Ireland?"

"What's that?"

"The *people*! I think so many of them are genuine and friendly and warm. They are great story-tellers and conversationalists. May I share two examples which prove my point?"

I went on without even waiting for his permission.

"Example number one: my wife and I were in Ireland during the terrorist attacks on our country on September 11, 2001. And in those days immediately after the tragedy we found great strength and comfort in the kindness and compassion shown to us and the other Americans in our group. People opened their homes to us, they prayed with us, restaurant meals or pints at the pub suddenly were complimentary just because we were Americans. In fact, many Irish thanked us for everything America had done in the past to assist Ireland; they, too, were angry at such a vicious attack. They took it very personally. They were a great help to us in those difficult days."

"I am not at all surprised," said Paddy. "The Irish can be a very loyal friend."

"Example number two: my wife and I were traveling Ireland with four family members. We rented a mini-van so all six of us could ride together comfortably. On our second day we stopped to fill up the gas tank. We were unaware that most cars in Ireland only run on diesel fuel; understandably but mistakenly we filled the tank with regular gasoline. About twenty miles later, on a dot on the map somewhere in County Westmeath between tiny Horseleap and Kilbeggan, the van broke down.

"It was early on a Sunday morning and we were stranded. We didn't have cell phones. We didn't know anyone. We didn't even know exactly where we were.

"Three of us stayed with the van and three of us went out in search for help. Soon we came across a small cottage, the only home we could see in any direction.

"We walked up the gravel driveway. We came across a beat-up car parked very close to the front door; we thought it odd that the driver's side door was open! We continued to the home just a few steps away. We knocked. We had no choice. We had nowhere else to turn for help.

"It was 7:30am. The sun had just risen over the distant green hills. The cottage was still. For several minutes we heard nothing from inside. Finally, we turned to leave.

"After just a few steps we heard the front door open behind us. We turned and saw a man about thirty years of age. He was wearing only boxer shorts. His hair was a mess. Clearly, he just woke up. Our persistent knocking had ended his sleep.

"He had every right to be upset; three complete strangers waking him early on a Sunday morning.

"He called out to us with a groggy but cheerful 'Top of the morning!' He asked how he can help.

"We explained our situation. We told him about our stranded mini-van. We said there were three others in our group waiting for us to return.

"Once he understood our dilemma, he smiled at me and said the following in his thick Irish brogue: 'Well, I just rolled in from a long night at The Local with the lads a few hours ago. You see my car; I stopped just short of the porch and I even forgot to close the door. My head is pounding. Do you understand?'"

"We did. We've all been there before. This man was hung-over. We expected him to slam shut the door and send us on our way."

"'So, I may not be the best host in the world at this particular time, but please do come in. I will put on a pot of coffee. I will warm a few stale scones. And I will ring-up my friend who just happens to be a car mechanic. Now, go fetch the others in your group and bring them here with you.'"

"I still remember his name; Danny Tuohy. For the next hour, this very tired man fed us and entertained us with stories. We learned that his brother was a boxer who was training for the Olympics. Danny's repairman friend showed up within twenty minutes and drained the van's gas tank and poured diesel fuel in to it. Soon, we were on our way with a story to tell for the rest of our lives: what could have been a hugely frustrating experience turned out to be a wonderful one because of this man's kindness and hospitality. In our moment of distress and difficulty and trouble in Ireland we knocked on one door, purely by chance, and we found a Good Samaritan."

I paused and added with a small smile: "A *hung-over* Samaritan but still a good one!"

I looked at Patrick and noticed a tiny trace of a tear in his eye. "Thanks for sharing that with me, Bob. I am proud. You found a *Christian*. My work there endures."

❖❖❖❖❖❖❖

I think we bonded at that moment. I had no idea that my simple story would have such an impact on my new friend. I didn't think he'd be so touched. Even though I did it completely innocently and unintentionally, I felt good to have helped him in a very small way. After all, he was here to *help me*, we both knew that, but for a few brief seconds I had turned the tables.

"Pat, I'm sorry that I've been doing all the talking," I said. "I probably bored you to death."

"Too late for that, Bob," he replied. "I died over fifteen hundred years ago."

I pushed aside my empty pint of Guinness. "So, your era was in the fourth century? I didn't realize that, which reminds me again of how little I know about you. I'm ashamed. As I told you earlier, all I know for sure is that you converted Ireland to Christianity, plus something about a legend of chasing away snakes, and most obviously that your feast day is March 17th. So, if you don't mind, can you fill me in? How does a man who was born in Scotland and who later spent years in Great Britain end up as one of Ireland's greatest figures?"

"Do you want the long version or the short version?" he wondered.

"Hey, your schedule tonight is my schedule, your timetable is mine; I have absolutely no control over the concept of time tonight. Tell me whatever you wish; whatever it is will be more than I currently know."

"Would you like another Guinness before I begin?"

I thought about it. "I'm going to surprise you with this; no!"

"You're kidding?"

I laughed. "I'd rather have a Coca-Cola. I love a Coke every now and then. You don't happen to have an ice-cold bottle of Coke, do you? It always tastes best out of a bottle."

Sure enough, Paddy reached underneath the back of the bar and produced a sixteen-ounce bottle of Coke. Of course he did. He'd already produced for me, like magic, brown bread and real Guinness, so why not a Coke? He grabbed a bottle-opener from a drawer and removed the cap, then handed over the bottle and a coaster. This was quickly becoming my favorite pub in the whole wide world.

I took a long drink and then repeated my request: "So, Paddy, what's your story?"

"Well, I wasn't born in Ireland…"

"I know that."

"But I first went to Ireland at around the age of sixteen because I was kidnapped."

"I did *not* know that. Kidnapped! Really?"

"No, Bob, I'm joking." Pause. "Yes, Bob, *really*! Do you think I'm just going to *fabricate* my life story?"

"Sorry. Please go on."

"The word 'kidnap' may not be the most accurate word; I mean, I was never held for ransom or anything like that; they never threatened to kill me. Let's just say I was 'taken against my will' to Ireland to serve as a slave to herd and tend to sheep and cattle. The conditions were atrocious. I lived and worked often in nakedness and hunger."

"Boy, that's hardly the ideal way to see Ireland for the first time," I absent-mindedly commented. "I remember my first time to Ireland; I was…"

He jumped in. "Bob?"

"Yes?"

"Is this *my* story or *yours*?"

"Oh. Sorry."

He started up again. "As I was saying, I lived as a slave for about six years. One night I had a dream during which God told me how to escape."

"**God** told you?"

"He sure did. And guess what? I escaped the next day. I eventually found my family who were living in Britain but that experience of the Irish pagan life left an indelible mark. I knew one-day I would return as a missionary for Christ."

"How'd you know that?"

"God told me to do it."

"Oh. In that same dream?"

"Yes."

I sure have boring dreams compared to this guy, I thought to myself. I dream often of tornados or talking lions or of my teeth falling out but never once has God appeared in a dream. I wish He would. It would probably be less frightening than a talking lion.

"Many years later, I went back to Ireland," continued Paddy. "I gave my life to Christ. I was determined to educate and convert the largely pagan population. Before I arrived they worshipped the sun and idols. I had my work cut out for me."

"How'd you do it?"

"Well, for one, I could speak Gaelic. I learned that language when I was a slave. It was a big help to be able to talk to them in their own language. Plus, I've been told I had a commanding presence; I was very hard to ignore; I was very persuasive.

"I also used symbols to effectively convey my message. For example, one Easter eve I started a large bonfire on the hill of Slane. It was in defiance of a High King who had ruled against any other fires while a festival fire was burning on the nearby Hill of Tara, which was about ten miles away. I told the people that the folks in Tara could see our fire on Slane but that we could not see their fire; then I told them to imagine our bonfire as the power and glory of the 'Light of Christ'; the light of Christ is far brighter than any other one imaginable. They immediately grasped my message.

"Also, more famously, I used a shamrock to explain the mystery of the Trinity; and now centuries later the shamrock is one of the famous symbols of Ireland."

"What about the snakes?" I wondered.

"Oh yes, the snakes. I once used my staff to chase away a snake that a slave had carried with him from another country. The legend was born; Saint Patrick had expelled all the snakes from Ireland; to this very day one cannot find a snake there."

"Can you please do me a favor?" I asked. "Can you sneak down to Washington, D.C. soon and chase away the snakes there?"

"That may be more than a one-man job, Bob; but I'll think

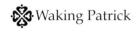 

about it!"

He returned to his story. "In fact, because of that legend about the snakes, I am the patron saint for snake bites and for the fear of snakes."

"Honest?"

"Indeed! I am also, of course, the patron saint for Ireland, for Nigeria, and for those who feel excluded or left-out from the rest of society."

I thought about that. "So, if I am a Nigerian who lives in Ireland and I'm an outcast who hates snakes…"

"I'm your man!"

I reflected for a moment during my next drink of Coke. "Let me get back to that snake story: in some way it sounds similar to God's banishment of the serpent from the Garden of Eden."

"Yes, that is a comparison I have heard before," he agreed.

"Or, the snake could also symbolize all things pagan and all things contrary to the message of God; and those things are what you really expelled."

"That, too, makes some sense."

He adjusted his white sweater before concluding his story.

"For the rest of my days, Bob, I preached the Gospel. That was my life for about forty years. One by one, I converted the pagans to Christianity. It was fascinating to watch it spread, like a wave in the ocean. I founded religious houses and educated the children. I once spent forty days in retreat on Cruachan Aigli in County Mayo, which today you may know as Croagh Patrick, also called The Reek by locals."

I jumped in enthusiastically. "Of course! That's where the pilgrims gather every year to walk barefoot up the rocky hill. So *that's* how it started; I didn't know that! I want to do that one day; I want to walk that pilgrimage."

"I think you should. When you do, remember me; and that you are literally following in my footsteps.

"And there you have it, Bob; that is my life in a nut-shell. I persevered. I prevailed. I gave my life to Christ. And I'd do it all over again if given the opportunity."

He looked so comfortable and full of joy as he said that. Here was a man who was happy with the life he led. No regrets. No doubts. No questions asked.

And, like I had previously with Lou, P.J., and Karol, I felt completely out of place and I wondered just what I was doing in his company.

❖❖❖❖❖❖

"How's your Coca-Cola?" Pat asked as he removed the empty plate of brown bread.

"It's great!" I replied. "Thanks. I'll probably need another one soon if you don't mind."

"And how is everything else? Are you comfortable? Are you happy?"

"I'm doing well! I've been well fed. My two pints of Guinness tasted very good. My Coke is very refreshing. I have a nice bartender. Yes, I'm very comfortable and happy; thanks for asking. I love Paddy's Pub."

He shook his head. "That's not exactly what I meant, Bob. I didn't mean to ask if you were comfortable and happy *here*; I am asking if you are comfortable and happy, *period*."

I stared him down for a few seconds. "Oh, I get it. Here it comes, right? The small talk is ending, is that it? It's time for the great and legendary Saint Patrick to come to the rescue of this poor miserable peon taking up space at his bar. Is that what you mean?"

"And is there a reason why you are so nasty all of a sudden?" he asked. He looked sad. He looked as if I had hurt his feelings. Come to think of it, he was right; why did I turn nasty? Wasn't he just offering to help, just as the others had before him?

I took a big drink from my Coke and then responded. "Pat, you are right. I got sarcastic with you with no cause. I'm sorry. You've been a good guy so far. I like you. And I know you are only looking out for me. Again, I am sorry.

"Maybe I'm just getting tired of feeling so helpless. Am I really that lost? Am I really that confused? Am I so incapable of figuring things out on my own? I must be; why else would guys like Saint Louis and Fulton Sheen and Pope John Paul II and now you feel the need to be my friend? I doubt if the four of you make a habit of this. I guess I should feel honored to be your special case but it also makes me feel like a loser; again, am I so lost and helpless that I need four people like you to set me straight?"

Paddy pulled up a stool from his side of the bar and sat down directly across from me.

"Bob, what's eating at you? Let's talk, man to man."

"Man to ghost, you mean?"

"Whatever. Let's get to the bottom of it, whatever it is. I'll open for you another Coke; I'll make for me a cup of Irish coffee; and let's talk."

"Talk?" I nearly shouted at him. "Do you mean talk about *feelings*? Come on, Paddy, you know better than that! Guys don't like to talk about feelings or emotions.

"Do you want to talk about baseball? Do you want to talk about movies or politics or my new three-wood? Do you want to talk about politicians and how adept they are at screwing up the country? Do you want to talk about the cute waitress? Do you want to talk about the bait I used last weekend out on the lake? Do you want to talk about the boss at work who doesn't know what he's doing? That's what guys talk about, Pat! So if that's what you want to chat about, great! Let's talk. Where shall we begin?"

"You know what I mean, Bob," he said firmly. "Let's talk about you. Let's talk about your future in whatever time you may have left. Let's talk about your role in the world. Let's talk about Bob the common man as you so often refer to yourself. Let's talk about God. Let's talk about all of those doubts and questions you have about all of it."

"And how are you going to get me to do that? Are you dropping truth serum in my Coke?"

He smiled. "If that's what it takes."

There were a few moments of uncomfortable silence as we each thought of where to go next. To fill the gap, Pat filled his coffee mug and handed to me a second soda.

He was the first to break. "Have your other friends helped

you tonight?" he asked quietly.

"Do you mean Lou and P.J. and Karol? Oh, they've been a great help. Each of them took a very specific dilemma or problem and talked me through it in a way I could understand."

"I am happy to hear that. And now it's my turn. That's why I'm here; you have to know that by now."

"Help me with *what*?"

"Whatever it is that's bothering you."

"There's nothing bothering me. I'm fine!"

Now it was his turn to get sarcastic. "Nah, there's nothing bothering you, of course not! The great Bob has it all figured out on his own and the insignificant Saint Patrick has been sent here by mistake. Sorry to take up your time, Bob; glad to hear you are good-to-go from here on out."

Next, he lost the sarcasm and once again turned serious. "Bob, it's time. Our time tonight is nearly done. Your time *on earth* may be nearly done; you may have thirty days or thirty years, I don't pretend to know, but I do know that most of your life is over. It's time, Bob. It's time to figure out what's wrong."

"And why do you assume there is still something wrong?" I asked. "Those other guys helped me figure it out already."

"But there's more," he said.

"And why are you so sure of that?"

"Because I was sent here for you! If all you needed was a cold Coke, you could have gotten that anywhere. I am here for a reason; I am here with a purpose; the Man who sent me does not make mistakes. He sent me to you. Now can we please stop playing games and get on with it?"

By this stage of the night you would have thought I had learned my lesson; these new friends are, if nothing else, persistent. They were sent on a mission and they won't leave until it is mission accomplished. I realized I had no other choice but to give in.

"You're right. Let's talk. But I have a problem right off the top; I'm not at all sure what you want me to talk about. You ask, 'What's eating you?' Frankly, I don't know if anything is eating me. I think I'm fine. So how do we begin?"

Then I remembered that small pad of paper at Paddy's side.

Earlier tonight I'd seen him writing on that pad as we talked.

"Let's do this," I suggested. "Let's start with that pad of paper. You wrote on it as we were chatting. You were taking notes. What about?"

"That's a grande idea! I forgot about that. Let's see what I have here."

He reached down the bar and grabbed the small pad of yellow paper. Then, reading from it, he continued. "I wrote two things. One was a direct quote from something you said: 'We are all connected to each other.' And the other was a reminder that John Paul II had left for me to have a discussion with you about relics and angels and the like; do you remember that?"

I thought about my previous conversation with Karol. We had discussed many things.

Soon, it hit me.

"Oh yes. I told him that I had questions about the concept of hell. I told him I also wondered about such things as angels and relics. And he said to me, 'Those items are best left for someone else.' I suppose he was talking about you."

"He was. I already had that piece of information written on my pad of paper but then later I added something to it as you were telling me about your trips to Ireland."

"And what was that?"

"That you never found the time to visit Knock."

I got quiet for a few seconds. "I could tell at the time that it bothered you. Shall we start there?"

"It's as good a place to start as any other," he replied.

Once again, neither one of us knew what to say next. And once again, he was the first to break the uncomfortable silence.

"So…?"

I played dumb. It comes easy to me. "So… *what*?"

This time Paddy jumped on quickly. "So, why didn't you go to Knock?"

"I just never got around to it, I guess."

"Don't give me that, Bob! If I am going to help you then you at least have to play by the rules; and the first rule is that you have to be candid with me. So let me ask again, 'Why, in your many trips to Ireland, did you never go to Knock?'"

"Obviously, Paddy, it was never very high on my list."

His tone became stern. "Do you not believe?"

I took a deep breath. "You demand my candor, correct?"

"Yes."

"Well, Paddy, it's somewhere between believing and not believing; does that make any sense? It's just so hard for a man of my limited intelligence to comprehend. If you ask me if I believe that the Virgin Mary appeared in Lourdes and Fatima and Guadalupe, I'd respond, truthfully, that I believe it about 99.9%, using 100% as an absolute certainty. If you ask me if I believe that not only Mary appeared in Knock but at the same time so did Saint Joseph and Saint John the Evangelist and some angels and doves, well, now I start asking a few questions. On this journey why did Mary travel with friends? So if it is specifically Knock on which you are asking me to comment then I'm at about 90%.

"Recently, I read that the Vatican declared a site in Wisconsin to be 'worthy of belief'; it is an officially-sanctioned site of an apparition, the first and only one in the United States. It's called the Shrine of Our Lady of Good Help. It's near Green Bay. Again, I ask more questions. When did Mary start appearing in America? And why Wisconsin? So for this site I'm probably at about 75%.

"Truthfully, though, Pat, it's far more than that. I have doubts and questions about many things. That's one reason I often feel so lost. I don't believe things only because I am told by others to believe them. I'm not necessarily proud of that; it's just the way I am.

"I walked by a stained-glass window in this cathedral earlier tonight and I saw the apostle Thomas. I stopped and looked at him. I recalled his story. He doubted the word of the other apostles that Christ had risen from the dead. He wouldn't believe it until he saw it with his own eyes. And I understood! I can relate! If I was Thomas at that precise time and place, I probably wouldn't have believed their story either. When it comes to believing or not believing, I am very much like Thomas."

"What other things do you question?" Paddy asked. His voice was no longer stern. He sounded compassionate. He was trying very hard to understand where I was coming from.

So was I. And I always have been.

"Well, some things fall far down on my 'believability meter'. If Lourdes is 99.9%, then the Holy Stairs in Rome are about 50%."

"How do you figure?"

"It just doesn't make sense to me! These Holy Stairs, or Scala Sancta, are said to be the same steps upon which Jesus stood in front of Pontius Pilate. They are located next to the Basilica of Saint John Lateran. Obviously, they are an enormously popular site for pilgrims. Many people ascend the steps on their knees. It is an emotional experience for many of them. I understand all of that but what I don't get is how they got to Rome. It is said that they were brought to Rome in the fourth century by Saint Helena. And just how did she happen to pull *that* off? Did she hire a moving van? Did she carry them by camel from Jerusalem to Rome?

"I feel bad about doubting this story, I really do. I respect those people who have such a strong faith that they can believe it. It's not me, though. And it makes me feel bad about myself and the strength of my faith life.

"There are many others, also. We are told that portions of the one-and-only manger from Bethlehem are located inside the Basilica of Saint Mary Major in Rome. Really? The manger where Jesus was born, *the real manger*, somehow made it to Rome? Wouldn't someone have kept it or sold it or destroyed it? Or did Helena pack that up, too, when she was carrying over the Holy Stairs?

"Is that really the face of Christ on Veronica's veil? Do many churches have inside a piece of the real cross, as they claim? Did my friend King Louis of France really have the authentic crown of thorns? Is the Church of the Nativity in Bethlehem really the true site of Jesus' birth? Is that really Jesus' footprint inside the Domine Quo Vadis church near Rome? Jesus' *footprint?* Come on! How can any of this be true? How do we know for sure? These are the things I doubt. And then I worry that my doubts and questions make me a man of weak faith. Taking it one step further, I worry then about being judged as unworthy for the kingdom of heaven. But I cannot help it; I legitimately question these things. I just don't buy some of the things in my faith."

Paddy was silent for a few moments.

"Do you want me to leave now?" I joked.

He sipped his coffee before responding.

"You are being a bit too hard on yourself, Bob."

That caught me by surprise. "That's the *last* thing I expected you to say," I said with a sense of relief. "But I don't understand. I thought my admission of having doubts and asking questions would be close to committing a mortal sin."

"One's faith life is not dependent on any of those things you mentioned. One does not have to believe in relics or even apparitions to believe in God and to live according to His will.

"You said so yourself when you recalled the term 'worthy of belief' when speaking of the apparition site in Wisconsin: the church's exhaustive investigation found that the story of the miracle of Mary appearing to the young Sister Adele is 'worthy of belief.' That does not mean that one *must* believe! That does not indicate that one is somehow of little or no faith if one chooses not to believe. Again, that has little or nothing to do with one's belief in God.

"You have promised to be candid with me, Bob, so I make the same promise to you; and honestly the whole idea of relics was big business in the middle ages. The more spectacular the relic then the more people who came to visit your shrine or your church and your city.

"That's not to say that some of these relics aren't authentic. Some may well be! As you said, who can be sure? It's been over two thousand years so facts and stories change. But what does it matter even if some of these sites or relics are not authentic? The Italians have a saying I like: 'If it isn't true, it should be.'"

"Meaning what?" I asked.

"It means that these relics and holy sites, real or not, at the very least get all of us to think about the real thing. And if we spend time thinking about the real cross and how the man on that cross gave salvation to the rest of us, is that not a good thing? If while visiting Bethlehem we spend time thinking about the one true site of the birth of Jesus and how that birth changed all of human history, is that not a good thing?  If we visit Lourdes and it reminds us that Mary takes our prayers to her Son, is that not a good thing?

"Make no mistake, Bob; I choose to believe in many of these things!  However, the fact that you question or doubt some of them does not mean that you are doomed.  Frankly, in most cases, asking questions about one's faith can be viewed as a good thing.  It means you are seeking to understand the truth.  It means you care about the truth.  And as you get older, your faith will become more of an adult faith, one that you can wrap your arms around."

"Well, Paddy, I feel as if I got off fairly easy on that one," I admitted.  "I hope you feel the same way after my next confession; perhaps then you will better comprehend why I often feel unworthy of God's love and forgiveness, why I sometimes feel like a failure in faith."

He sat up straight on his stool.  He had no clue where this next phase was heading.

"Here goes.  I went to an empty church recently on purpose.  I looked around in silence.  I was testing myself.  I wanted to see how much I knew about all the things I saw in that church.  I looked at Jesus on the cross.  I looked at all the statues and paintings and stained-glass windows of Mary and Joseph and the apostles; at least I *think* they were apostles. I looked at the angels and the halos and the doves and the saints and the sheep and the lambs.  And it hit me how little I know about the facts of my faith.  I was humiliated by my ignorance.

"With the possible exception of perhaps three people, I couldn't tell you the life story of any saints.  I can't grasp the concept of grace; is it like good things from God raining down upon us?  Is there really a purgatory; and if there is then what exactly do we do there to make up for all of our sins?  What's an angel and what's an archangel?  How did they become an angel and why do they always seem to play a harp?  What are a seraphim and cherubim?  Are they like a heavenly version of a Simon and Garfunkel?  Who or what is the Holy Spirit?  What is my soul? *Where* is my soul?  Is there a hell?  If I was ever to take a test on the facts of my faith, I'd fail. I know next-to-nothing about all of these things that since birth I've been told to believe.

"All of that forced me to ask myself what it is that I do believe; what is it that I do know. And that was frightening, too. The list is a short one. I believe in God. I believe that God's Son is Jesus and he walked the earth as a human being. I believe Jesus was crucified and that he rose from the dead three days later. I believe that Mary was chosen by God to be Jesus' mother on earth. I believe that God offers to all us the opportunity to spend eternity with Him in heaven.

"*And that's it!* There may be a few other things but most of them would be considered trivial or insignificant. How bad is that? How bad am I? And why would a man like this be worthy of eternal life?

"And here's where it gets really bad, Paddy. Are you ready? Not often, mind you, but more than once I have asked myself if all of it is the largest shell game in the history of mankind. I've wondered if all of it is real. *All of it*, Patrick; do you understand what I am saying? Is any of it really true?

"I know a man who read the Bible every day. He attended Mass several times a week. He prayed the rosary regularly. And near the end of his life he asked me, 'Do you think that all of this was real?' I was stunned. Here was a man who was faithful and religious for his entire life and now as he reached the end he was wondering if he had been taken in by a fairy tale. He asked if his life really made a difference; he asked if anything he did ever mattered; he asked if there was another life waiting for him after death. Is it real or is it all just a story to help us make it through a difficult life? What if, at the moment of death, you hear one voice and it screams at you, 'You fool! It was all a fraud!' Is life really nothing more than you are born, you go to school, you find a career, you get married, you have children, you take vacations, you work, you get old, you get sick, you die: what if that's really all it is?

"Pat, these things are known to only two people: me and now you. I have never told anyone. I've always been afraid to share these things because I'd face certain scorn and ridicule. People would look at me differently. How can a man who really does believe in God and Jesus ever think some of these things, even if just in passing? Why do these thoughts even enter my mind? Other than the belief in God and Jesus, why would one have questions about most things religious or sacred? What if all of it or most of it is a huge hoax? What does that say about such a person? It can't be a good thing. So I ask again: why would a man like this be worthy of eternal life?

"I've tried to live a good life. I try to be a good person. Too often, I fail, but I do try. I do have standards. But I don't do these things only because I'm Catholic; I try to do good because I believe that's just the right way to live."

I lowered my head and stared at the front of the bar. I couldn't bear to look my friend in the eye. I was humiliated. What must he think of me?

Paddy must have sensed my embarrassment for the first thing he whispered was: "Bob, it's OK." Then he waited a few more seconds before adding: "Look at me. I can help."

He adjusted his tweed cap and re-filled his coffee cup. Then, like a good parent would do to a child, he put his left hand on my shoulder and repeated, "It's OK."

I still felt bad, however. I always have. I shouldn't have all these questions but I can't help it.

"You have presented to me a most interesting situation," he began. "On the one hand we have a man who unashamedly admits he believes in God and Jesus and that he loves them. We have a man who believes in everlasting life. On the other hand, we also have a man who admits he knows so very little about the facts and history and tradition of his faith. And, far more seriously, we have a man who acknowledges that every now and then he wonders if any of it is real and true. He then asks the logical question: 'Why would such a man be worthy of God's love? Why would he be granted heaven on judgment day?'

"So, just where do we begin?"

I jumped in as Paddy paused to gather his thoughts.

"Let me add one more thing. Maybe this will help. I've given this some thought. Maybe one reason I have such serious questions and doubts is because I simply can't figure it out; my very limited human brain cannot fully understand the concept of God. *I believe in God but I just don't get Him!* I can't comprehend His power. I can't comprehend all that He has done and all that He is capable of doing. How did He create *everything*? How did Jesus rise from the dead? How is it that God always was and always will be; that concept literally makes my head hurt if I think about it. Are not these things impossible? So, perhaps I doubt it because I don't understand it. Does that make sense?"

Paddy raised his coffee cup in my direction as if in a toast. "Now we're getting somewhere! Yes, that little piece of information helps a great deal," he said.

"Allow me to begin at the most basic level," he went on. "At the very least, Bob, it is apparent that you have accepted Pascal's Wager. Am I right?"

I looked at him as if he was speaking Latin. I had no idea what he just said.

"Who is Pascal? And what is his wager?" I asked.

He chuckled. "I'm sorry. That's my mistake. Pascal was a French philosopher. Blaise Pascal was his full name. His wager, or some people call it Pascal's Gambit, says that there is more to be gained from wagering on the existence of God than from atheism; and that a rational person should live as though God exists. Thus, when you just told me that you try to be a good person and you try to live a good life just because you believe that's the proper way to live, I assumed you had accepted Pascal's Wager. *Why not* live a good life? *Why not* strive to be a good person? What do you have to lose?

"One of two things, Pascal argued, will happen when you die. One: If there is no God then at least you still lived a good life and you left the world a better place. What harm is there in that? Or two: When you die you will learn that God does exist and by having lived a good life you will be justly rewarded."

He leaned in a bit and whispered, "By the way, Bob, just between you and me, I can personally vouch for that second option."

"I am quite sure that you do," I smiled.

"Next, let us move on to the fact that you know so little about your faith. It bothers you that you are ignorant about our traditions and about what we do and why we do them and about the lives of our saints and so many other things; correct?"

"It bothers me very much," I said. "It's as if I missed all those days of catechism. I've lived my life as a practicing Catholic and for the most part I don't even know what I am practicing! I go to Mass, I say a few prayers, I receive Holy Communion, I was confirmed, I go to confession; but if you ask me what it all means I don't know how I'd respond! It's like my faith life has always been on auto-pilot. There's no depth there because I know so little about all of it."

"First, Bob, be assured that living a life of sanctity and goodness is not based on knowledge," Paddy replied. "Some of our saints were illiterate; they didn't know much at all about the specific teachings and traditions of the church. If you love God and you follow Jesus, you most certainly are capable of living a good life and even a holy life. You don't have to pass a Faith-I.Q. test to enter the kingdom of heaven. Knowledge has little to do with salvation.

"That being said, however, if you really love someone then it stands to reason that you then want to learn more about that person. The more you know, the more you love. If you really love God and Jesus then learn more about them! It's as simple as that."

He stopped long enough to stand up from the bar stool.

"Finally, and I think most importantly, let me address your doubts and questions about God Himself."

Suddenly I was second-guessing my decision to tell him those things. What was coming next? Was Paddy going to discipline me? Was he going to tell me that there was no hope for a man such as me? Whatever the punishment, I deserved it. How can one ever question anything about God?

"You tell me, Bob, that you can't comprehend how God created everything; is that right?"

"Yes."

"And you tell me that you don't understand how God didn't

have a beginning and He doesn't have an end; correct?"

"Yes."

"Then you say you don't know how a man, Jesus, could rise from the dead."

"Correct."

"And all of it seems impossible to you."

"Yes. It is impossible. I don't get it. I can't grasp it."

Pat raised his voice for what came next. "Well, join the crowd!"

I was taken back. "Excuse me?" I asked.

*Who does* understand it?" he responded with his voice still at a high level. "To paraphrase what your friend Karol told you earlier, 'God is God and you are you.' It is impossible for us to comprehend what God can do. It is so far above the level of human comprehension.

*"If you understand, then it is not God!"* He lowered his voice now. He sounded scholarly and compassionate. "If with our limited knowledge we think our definition or concept of God adequately explains Him then we have instead an idol of our own making. We can never totally grasp neither the immensity of God nor the inscrutability of His actions. *We will never figure out God!*

"That in itself runs counter to our human nature. We want to solve problems. We want clarification. We want a clear picture. We want to understand. And that's where our doubts come in. That's why we ask questions. God is far beyond our intellect.

"My pal Saint Augustine once said: 'If the thing believed is incredible then it is also incredible that the incredible should have been so believed.'"

"What on earth does *that* mean?" I asked. "Was he drinking at the time he said that? Was he working on no sleep? You saints talk way over our heads sometimes."

"It's not that complicated, Bob. It fits perfectly with our discussion. It is a tribute to God that so many of us believe in these things that are seemingly impossible. We believe because we know with God all things are possible. If one believes in God then even the incredible can be believed with no explanation necessary.

"Here is another example. Have you ever seen the poster

which shows the ocean and a small rowboat?"

"I have," I answered. "I see it frequently in religious book stores or cathedral gift shops."

"Do you recall the caption? It reads, 'Lord, the sea is so vast and my boat is so small.'"

"And how does that fit in here?" I wondered.

"The mystery of life and the mystery of God are so huge that it exceeds our ability to understand. It quite simply cannot be done. I will repeat what I said moments ago: 'If you believe that you understand God, then it is not God that you understand!'

"I have a theory on those who have chosen not to believe in God. I think that many of them at first did believe. Later, like most of us, they tried to explain and comprehend God. They could not. None of us can. But while most of us continue to believe anyway and accept the fact that we will never completely comprehend Him, a few others determine that if they cannot understand something or someone then it cannot be so; in other words, they say, 'If I cannot grasp God, then God must not exist.' They fail to see that it is perfectly human and normal to not comprehend God."

"Let's see if I am hearing you correctly," I said. "I just presented to you a very painful confession. I told you that sometimes I don't get God. I can't get my arms around all of the things He has done. It literally seems impossible to me. All the while, I am thinking that this makes me a very weak man. It means I am a man unworthy of God's love and mercy. But to hear *you* talk, Pat, it sounds like my doubts are completely natural. It even sounds like we all ask these questions; even you!"

"Well, the difference may be, Bob, that you've allowed the doubts to consume you. This situation clearly weighs very heavily on you. Most believers, me included, very soon realize that the effort to fully comprehend God and all of His mysteries is a complete waste of time. We cannot do it. You, however, seem to have a hard time letting go. Accept it. Embrace it. Let God consume you instead.

"Remember this, too. Faith always seeks a deeper understanding. It's a journey. Thus, faith has a traveling companion: doubt! Yes! The one thing you struggle with is in reality part of the deal for if one has faith one also at times feels doubt. This is not a discouraging handicap or a sinful flaw. Rather, it is a reminder that we are incomplete and unsatisfied. When we allow ourselves to entertain honest doubt it encourages us to better seek the truth. It means we are not comfortable with the answers so far. That leads us to a more precise understanding, allowing our journey to continue and to mature. Doubt guards us against stagnation.

"You see doubt as a weakness, Bob. Look at it this way: Welcome it, walk with it, and see it as a challenging friend trying to make you better, trying to make you more whole, and bringing you closer to the truth."

❖❖❖❖❖❖❖

"Bob, I'd like you to meet a friend of mine."

Paddy and I had wrapped up our discussion about my questions and doubts a few moments ago. Our talk had helped me, yes, but I still couldn't shake the feeling that there was something wrong with me; that I still asked too many questions and had too many doubts about God and faith. He told me that my inability to grasp and understand God was in reality an encouraging search for the truth. He said that it didn't mean I doubted the existence of God at all. In fact, he said it meant quite the opposite; that I knew without a shadow of a doubt (there's that word again) there was an all-everything God and I so badly wanted to better understand Him.

Whatever you say, Paddy.

Since then, I had finished my second Coke while thinking to myself all of the points and counter-points made during our long talk. And he had gone about his business as my temporary bartender; cleaning a few glasses, changing the music on the sound system and putting on a pot of Irish vegetable and leek soup.

"What do you mean; you'd like me to meet a friend of yours?" I responded. "I thought you worked solo."

"Well, every now and then I call in the reinforcements. It depends on the subject matter. And what we are about to talk about requires the presence of a special individual; an expert on this next subject, if you will."

Paddy motioned with his right hand to the bar stool to my left.

"Bob, say hello to my friend Vince."

I did a quick spin on my stool and, sure enough, there sat a man! He wasn't there just seconds ago. People sure come and go quietly around here, I thought.

Vince was dark-skinned with a round face and a pug nose. He was a bit overweight and even though he was presently sitting I could tell that he was on the short side. I had no idea about his identity. He did not look familiar.

"Hello, Vince. My name is Bob. It's good to meet you."

He extended his chubby hand and we exchanged a handshake. His grip was firm. He also gave me a polite smile. My first impression was that Vince was a friendly guy, probably humble and down-to-earth. I liked him.

"Vince, would you like to tell me your full name right away so I know who I am dealing with? Or shall we make small talk for awhile and see if I can guess your identity? We can make it like the game Twenty Questions."

He spoke his first words. "Let's make small talk. Isn't that what guys do while sitting next to each other on bar stools?"

"We do indeed," I responded. "It usually starts with a mild argument over which guy is going to buy the first round."

"There is no argument needed, my friend. I will get this first round. Besides, I know our bartender Patrick quite well; he won't take my money anyway. What will you have?"

I looked at all the bottles lined-up on the shelf behind Paddy. One caught my attention immediately.

"Pat, I'll have a Baileys Irish Cream on the rocks. Just a little something to sip on sounds very good."

"And I will have, please, a glass of Chartreuse," requested Vince.

Paddy turned to fill our glasses. There was an uncomfortable silence between Vince and me as sometimes happens when two people have just met for the first time. I couldn't ask him, 'So, what do you do for a living?' because I had already guessed that, like my other friends tonight, he wasn't *among* the living. What's a good conversation starter when you are with a ghost? I was still searching for something to say when Vince broke the ice.

"What is this game you mentioned? I believe you called it Twenty Questions."

"Do you feel like playing? Good! I love games. In Twenty Questions, one person has a secret and the others get to ask up to twenty questions before attempting to guess the secret. The only allowed answers are 'yes' or 'no'.

"In our case, I will ask the questions because you are the one with the secret."

"And what would that be?" Vince wondered.

"The secret is your real name. Who you are," I told him. "Are you ready?"

"Yes. And that was your first question. You have nineteen remaining."

This guy sure takes his games seriously, I thought.

"Is your first name really Vince?"

"Yes."

"I hear an accent in your voice. Are you from France?"

"Yes."

"I thought so! You sound a little bit like a friend I met earlier tonight, King Louis IX. Do you know him?"

"Yes. You have sixteen questions remaining."

"Wait a second, Vince! I was just making conversation with you. I wasn't really asking you an official question in our game. Do you understand?"

"Yes. And now you have fifteen questions left."

Leave it to me to get an ultra-competitive saint. I had to concentrate.

"Did you know Louis when he was alive?"

"No. He died about three hundred years before I was born but I sure read many things about him when I was in school. He was one of my heroes. You can imagine how thrilling it was then centuries later when I met him at an all-saints luncheon in heaven. I even asked him for his autograph."

"Vince, you don't have to give me any additional information in this game. You are required to only answer truthfully with a 'yes' or a 'no'. Are you clear on that?"

"Yes. And that was another question. You are down to thirteen."

I stared at him. I made a mental note to myself to never to play another game with this guy.

I resumed my interrogation. "Were you once a priest?"

"Yes."

"Have I heard of you?"

He took a sip from his drink before he replied. "Yes."

I paused to gather the facts. This was a man named Vince who was once a priest in France. He was born long after Louis had died so I guessed his time on earth to be sometime in the 1600's. And I had heard of him. These facts I knew.

I put my detective skills to work. First, I assumed that this man was either already a saint or he was being considered for sainthood because everyone I'd met previously tonight were one or the other. Everyone but Agca, but he doesn't count. Next, I figured that his formal first name was Vincent. That left me with Saint Vincent Somebody. I had an idea!

I looked at him closely and then asked another question.

"Do you have a window in this cathedral?"

He smiled. "Yes."

I knew it! I recalled briefly looking at his window during my initial self-guided tour. I still had ten questions left so I decided to string it out and make him sweat a little bit.

"Were you also a philanthropist?"

"Yes."

As I had earlier told Patrick, I knew very little about the lives of most of our saints but this guy was a rare exception. I was sure I had him now.

"At one point, did you live a very comfortable life?"

"Yes."

"And later did you purposely lead a life of sacrifice?"

"Yes."

"Did you live a life of charity?"

"Yes.  And by the way, you are running out of questions."

I grabbed my glass of Baileys and lifted it in his direction.

"I don't need any more questions, Vince.  I think I just won the game. My final question is: 'Are you Saint Vincent de Paul?'"

"He is indeed," shouted Paddy from the far corner of the bar. "That is very good, Bob.  You played the game well!"

❖❖❖❖❖❖❖

Paddy walked close to Vince and me and placed in front of us two bowls of soup.  "That was easier than I thought it would be, Bob," he said.  "My money was on Vince.  I didn't think you'd guess his identity."

"It hit me when he told me I had heard of him.  Frankly, he is the only Saint Vincent that I know.  I see his name all the time on all of those clothes collection boxes located in grocery store parking lots.  I used to go with my dad all the time to drop-off our old clothes.  He'd always say, 'Come with me, son.  We need to bring some clothes to Vincent de Paul.'  He never used the title of 'Saint'; it was simply 'Vincent de Paul' like you were just a normal guy standing on the corner waiting for people to drive by with boxes.  When I was a kid I always wondered why you couldn't get your own clothes.  I thought I was going to see a naked man named Vince on that corner. Decades later, my wife and I did the very same thing with our kids.  We always donated our old clothes in your name."

"That's very kind of you," Vince said.

"Do you mind explaining to me just how you became famous for your acts of charity?" I asked. "I know just a little bit about you but not much.  What happened?"

Vince glanced at Paddy.  "Did he not know much about you, either?" he asked.

"All he knew about were snakes and green beer," answered Paddy and both men let go with a hearty laugh.

This was a first; being ridiculed by two saints at the same time.

Vince turned his attention back to me.

"You were correct as we played our game that my early years in the priesthood were quite comfortable. I served as a tutor to a count's family. I did not want for much and we had an active social life.

"However, I was later captured by Turkish pirates and was enslaved for two years in Tunisia. The living conditions were horrific. I was living with convicts and galley slaves and street urchins. This experience opened my eyes to conditions that I never knew existed.

"When I escaped I dedicated my life to relieving the suffering of mankind. I preached to the clergy about the poor and the needy. I set up the Sisters of Charity with the help of a wonderfully compassionate woman named Louise de Marillac. These nuns were the first ever not confined to an enclosure. We went out to the towns and cities to personally care for the poor and the sick. I am just as proud of that work as I am of my work for charitable causes. My highest ambition was to plant the Gospel spirit of charity, humility, meekness and simplicity into the hearts of Christians. Just think, if universal charity prevailed, earth would be a heaven and hell would be a fable.

"Upon my death in 1660, I was remembered as a man with a 'selfless devotion to all.' I cried when I heard that. That was the ultimate compliment.

"And now, here I am in Saint Patrick's Cathedral in New York City visiting with my great friend Pat and my new friend Bob. Who would have ever guessed such a thing?"

My thoughts exactly, I concurred.

"I'm curious as to your drink selection," I said to him as I pointed at his Chartreuse.

"And why would that surprise you? It is an excellent liqueur made by monks in the Chartreuse Mountains in southeastern France. It is said it provides a long life to those who drink it."

"And is that true?" I asked.

"Well, I lived to be nearly eighty years old so it sure worked for me," he laughed.

Again, there was another moment of uncomfortable silence.

Vince tasted his soup and Paddy dropped a couple of napkins in front of us.

Vince seemed like a good guy and I certainly respected the way he lived his life but I had absolutely no idea why he had been sent to be my friend.

"So…" I started.

It was Paddy who replied. "So… what?"

"So, what is Vince doing here?"

Once again it was Paddy who answered. "This time it is a little different, Bob. With your previous friends tonight it was you who had a problem or a question to present. However, Vince is here to present a question to you."

❖❖❖❖❖❖❖

Immediately, I had a bad feeling about this. I was already uncomfortable. Why did Vince want to talk to me? I wished I could jump off my bar stool and sneak away into the night. Do you mean to tell me that he was sent from up above just to talk to *me*? I had that horrible feeling in the pit of my stomach; the one you get when you know you are in trouble but you don't know exactly why.

I decided to confront him. Let's get on with it. I turned away from Paddy and looked straight at Vince.

"Do you not approve of my level of charity?"

He met my stare.

"Why would you think *that*?"

"Duh, let me see; the man most famous for his charitable acts comes to me four hundred years after his death and he wants to talk about *something*. So, I'm just guessing here but maybe that *something* is his area of expertise, charity; and secondly, again just guessing, I hardly think you'd make such a long journey to tell me 'Well done and keep up the good work!' Thus, I ask again: 'Do you not approve of my level of charity?'"

"You seem to be on the defensive," he responded calmly. "It seems like I've touched a nerve and I haven't even said anything yet."

"I think you're right; you *have* touched a nerve. Here's why: I think, all things considered, my charitable actions are certainly above average and probably closer to very good. I think you wouldn't have a hard time at all, Mr. de Paul, to locate family members and friends who would tell you that they consider me to be a charitable man."

"Good for you. I guess I'll leave now."

He got up from his bar stool. Then, two seconds later he sat back down and said with a smile, "Well, maybe not just yet."

First this guy touches a nerve and then he pulls my leg. So far, Vince is a hard guy to figure.

"Tell me about it," he went on.

"Tell you about what?" I asked.

"You just told me that you consider yourself to be a charitable person. And you have friends and family members who would tell me the same thing. So, tell me about it. What do you do?"

"Are you asking me to *brag* about my charity? That seems to defeat the purpose. I'm not comfortable doing that. After all, Vince, you just told me that one of your ambitions in life was to teach meekness and humility. Bragging is neither humble nor meek."

"You are absolutely correct. However, for you, at this time and in this place, I will allow an exception."

I had the feeling that my friend was setting a trap. However, I had no choice but to carry on.

"OK, but I'm not going to give you dollar figures. I'm not going to tell you how much we give and I'm not going to tell you to whom we give. Let me just give you the big picture.

"I think I'm a charitable guy because often I will pick up the dinner tab for friends at a restaurant. Or I'll buy baseball tickets for the extended family. Or I'll treat some in-laws to a weekend at a lake cabin. Or I'll buy the beer after a round of golf. I think I do these things quite often. Is that not generous? We all know people who never pick up a tab or those who will look at a check from the waitress and then add-up and pay for only exactly what they ate and drank. I don't want to be like that! Perhaps I over-compensate with my behavior but I want people to believe that I am generous."

Vince stopped me.

"That's all very good, Bob, but don't confuse generosity with being charitable.  It is 'generous' when you assist someone who really doesn't need the assistance.  For example, I assume these people for whom you buy dinner can afford to pay for their own meal if you'd allow it."

I nodded my head to agree.

"Again, that's very kind of you.  Generosity is a fine trait.  However, it is *charitable* when you assist those who desperately do need the help, those who would literally go without if you didn't assist.  Try this more often: instead of picking up the tab at the restaurant for a group of friends who can easily afford to buy their own, use that same money and buy a few meals for the people at the homeless shelter."

These saints are sure hard to please, I thought to myself.  This guy is actually finding fault in for whom I buy dinner.  I can't win with these guys!  However, as I thought about it, he did have a good point.  His request was a reasonable one.

I thought it best to throw another example at him.  "OK then, Vince, let's see if you can nit-pick *this* one," I said.  "Another reason that I believe I am a charitable man is that I usually worry that I have not given *enough*."

That perplexed him.  "I don't understand.  You are charitable because of what you *don't* give?  Then don't give anything and you'll think of yourself as the most charitable man in history."

I hesitated.  "Well, I suppose that came out wrong.  Let me explain."

"Please do."

"I worry that I don't give enough.  For instance, let's say I am shopping at the mall during Christmas season and I come across a volunteer ringing the bell for the Salvation Army kettle.  I stop and put in a five-dollar bill.  Later, when I leave the mall I see another volunteer with a kettle so I put in a one-dollar bill because I've already given; right?  My next stop is the grocery store where I see yet another kettle.  And when I walk past that volunteer I feel like saying, 'Sorry, I already gave twice at the mall.'  I feel bad

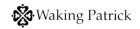

that I cannot give to every bell ringer I see. I wish I could.

"Then there is this: I'm at a fundraiser dinner for a charity event. They have a silent auction. I pick out a few items that I'd like to acquire so I place my bids. Usually, I am out-bid so then I walk away thinking, 'Well, I tried!' But I know full well that I could have beaten the other bids if I would have tried harder. The opposite is true, too: let's say I bid $300 for one-night condominium stay at a local lake and at the end of the night I win that item; believe it or not in this case I'm still not happy because I think I should have bid even more. Or we pledge $1500 to our local seminary but I think to myself that we really could pledge even more. Or we give $500 to the local Heart Association but I think to myself that I should have made it an even thousand. Or I buy ten boxes of cookies from the neighborhood Girl Scout and as soon as she leaves the door I wonder if I should have bought twenty boxes. Do you get what I'm saying, Vince? I never feel like I am *doing enough* even though I usually do *something*, which is far more than most people do. I feel good when I give but at the same time I feel bad because I think I should give more. I write the check and think to myself, 'This is going to help the cause and I am a nice guy to do it.' And then seconds later I think, 'You could have done even more, you cheapskate.' How weird is that?"

Vince leaned in and said, "It's pretty weird." And then he looked at Paddy and once again they had a good laugh at my expense.

Vince continued. "This is going to surprise you, Bob, but I did not come here tonight to condemn or judge your level of charity."

"You didn't?"

"No. As you just told me, you do more than most. And you do it with far fewer resources, too. I am with you tonight to ask you why you think you never give enough. That's a puzzle. Most people who give think they are giving too much; you believe you are giving too little. It's very interesting to me."

"*Why* do I feel that way? Is that what you want to know? Is that why you are here tonight? Well, you're asking the wrong guy, Vince, because I have no idea. I can't figure it out. I can't figure *me* out. If I am a 'puzzle' to you then rest assured I am also a 'puzzle' to me."

"I think I can help. I think I can get to the bottom of it."

"If that's true then you are not only a saint but you are also a magician," I said lightly.

He grabbed his spoon and finished what was left from his bowl of leek soup. "My compliments to the chef," he said, looking at Pat.

Then he turned back to me with a sincere look on his face. "I have two questions," he explained. "We will take them one at a time. One: What *bothers* you about giving? Two: What *scares* you about giving?"

I thought about it and shrugged my shoulders. "I don't know," I replied. "How do you know that I'm bothered and scared?"

"I know it because that's what I was sent here to ask. I understand that these are two unusual questions so take your time and reflect upon them. Let's begin with the first: What bothers you about giving?"

I took his advice; I took my time. I grabbed the small black straw and slowly stirred the ice cubes around the inside of my glass of Baileys. I looked at Pat for some guidance or a suggestion but all he did was lean in on his elbows and wait for my reply. I was on my own.

I repeated the question out loud. "What bothers me about giving?"

I wasn't really sure what Vince was looking for.

"Can you give me a hint? I'm lost."

"I think you know the answer, Bob. You are probably reluctant to admit it in our presence because you know how self-serving it will sound. You've already admitted other things tonight which are far more troubling. Just come out with it and tell us: what bothers you about charity?"

"Well, now that you put it that way…"

"Yes?"

"I suppose I get frustrated, or in your word 'bothered', by the *reaction* to my giving."

"Meaning what?"

"That too often there is *no* reaction! Or there is very little reaction! Or at least there is not the reaction I expect or the reaction I feel I deserve."

"Go on."

"I just want to feel appreciated. Don't we all? I want to know that the receiving party is grateful. I mean, I don't have to give them anything. I could choose simply to ignore them. Instead, I choose to give. But sometimes they act like it's no big deal. Or that it is expected of me to give. Far too often, I don't get what I feel is a genuine and sincere and heartfelt 'Thank you!' Sometimes I get a form letter in the mail thanking me for my gift. A form letter? Are you kidding me? In my mind, it is a big deal to donate to a charity. It is a sacrifice. There are many other things I could do with that money. And all I ask in return is for my gesture to be received with gratitude. Is that asking too much?"

Vince exchanged a quick glance with Paddy before responding.

"That's not asking too much at all, Bob. Of course we all want to feel appreciated."

"There's a 'but' coming here, isn't there?" I asked.

"Yes," he smiled. "As I was saying, it is perfectly natural to desire gratitude and appreciation *but* you seem to have misjudged the spirit of charity."

It's time for the lecture, I thought.

He resumed. "True charity is the desire to be useful and generous and giving and kind to others without ever once considering recompense. It should never be, 'Here is what I am giving you and here is what I need in return.'

"Charity is never lost. It may be met with ingratitude or even in some rare cases be of no service to the recipient but charity always performs a work of beauty and grace upon the heart of the giver.

"You must ask yourself, Bob, if you are giving because you want to be recognized and thought of as a charitable person or are you giving because it is from your heart? Do you give only in order for *you* to feel good about it or perhaps to assuage guilt or do you give because you love God and you love others as you love yourself?

"If you are charitable for the right reasons, Bob, a proper expression of gratitude will be the last thing on your mind and the last thing you will need."

He stopped for a few seconds to let it all sink in.

"Are you clear on all of that, Bob?"

I was still a bit cloudy on some of that but I wasn't about to admit it so I nodded my head and replied, "I understand." But I knew deep down that this was going to be a tough one for me. I like being thanked. I like feeling appreciated. I *don't* like being taken for granted. But I'll work on it. If that's what my buddy Vince wants, that's what I'll do.

"Very good!" he said. "You did well on our first question so now let's move on to our next one: What scares you about charity?"

"You sure don't waste any time, do you Vince? There's not a lot of chit-chat with you, is there? Do you have a taxi waiting for you outside? Are you late for a hot date?"

Vince looked at Paddy. He seemed to not understand my comments.

"I think he is joking with you, Vince," explained Pat.

"Oh. I was confused. I haven't had a hot date in, well, never."

"Paddy was right," I told him. "I was kidding. Sorry. Now, what was that final question again?" Truthfully, I knew full well the subject of the question but I was just trying to buy a little more time. These self-exams were getting tiresome.

Vince obliged. "What is it that scares you about charity?"

I knew where he was going. In fact, I knew back when he asked me that question the first time. I had to give him credit for being perspective and observant for this particular dilemma had troubled me for a long time.

"I am ready for you on this one," I quickly replied. "What scares me is the Gospel passage that I've heard over and over again for most of my life. I think it's from Matthew. I believe the quote is: 'It is easier to put a camel through the eye of a needle than it is for a rich man to get to heaven.'

"By the way, just for your information, I think Matthew is by far the most impressive of the four writers of the Gospel," I added.

Vincent immediately perked up.

"Is that so? That's very good, Bob; obviously you've done some research on this! And why is Matthew the most impressive? Do you feel he is more analytical than Mark, Luke and John? Or more intellectual? Does he add more perspective than the others? This is a fascinating observation. Tell me, why is Matthew your favorite?"

"Because Matthew is my middle name."

Vince said absolutely nothing. I must have really impressed him to leave him speechless.

Vince recovered in a few seconds. "Let us pick up where we left off, shall we? I am familiar with that Gospel about the rich man and heaven and the eye of the needle and the camel. What is your problem with it?"

"What's my problem?" I exclaimed. "Try this: I guess I'm not going to heaven then!"

"Are you rich?" he asked.

"My goodness, we are far from rich. We never have been and we never will be. For the record, that is more than fine by me. I've seen what too much money can do to families. Their priorities are often way out of whack. Their children often are spoiled. So, no, we are not rich. We are, however, comfortable. And when I hear over and over again that it is easier for a camel to walk through the eye of a needle than for a rich man to enter the kingdom of heaven, it sounds to me that many people I know are already doomed. It sounds like I'm being asked to give away in charity most everything we have. And I certainly have never done that. I told you before that I always worry that I don't give enough; then every time I hear that passage I think that I, too, don't stand a chance at heaven. That's what scares me. Can I not have a comfortable life and still stand a chance at heaven?

"I know many people, Vince, who are considered to be rich. And a lot of them are good people! They appear to be generous and charitable. They seem to be men and women of faith. But to hear Matthew tell it, they're not going to heaven! What's up with that?

"Are they really supposed to give up everything? Who does

that?"

Paddy and Vince exchanged glances. "We did," they said in unison.

"Come on guys, you know what I mean! Give me some hope here. Do we really have to be like the two of you to get to heaven? Do we really have to give everything to charity? Cannot we have a good life on earth and still earn an eternal life in heaven?

"So, to get back to your question: that's what scares me about charity. It seems no matter how much I give it won't be enough."

Vince replied with a condescending tone of voice. "My friend, I'm afraid you have taken that passage far too literally. A camel quite obviously cannot walk through the eye of a needle. The Lord did not intend for us to take it that way."

I did not appreciate his tone and his attitude so I fired back with a trace of anger. "Hey, Vince, I may not be the brightest guy in the world but I'm also not a complete idiot. I never have taken literally that passage. Did you think I've been looking for a magic camel for the last thirty years? Give me a little credit, will you?"

I lowered my voice and spoke more calmly. "However, I still grasp the meaning of it. We are being told that a rich man faces a mighty challenge in entering heaven. If one doesn't give away nearly everything in charity or generosity then heaven is unlikely. Is that it? If true, that scares me."

"The passage, Bob, is nothing more than a warning to all of us with any amount of possessions or wealth. We are being told to ask ourselves if we are putting anything in our lives before God. Do we believe anything we possess is more important than God?

"Who or what in our lives prevents us from growing closer to God? And whatever it is, we must surrender. We must re-prioritize. It may well be the acquisition of wealth. It may also be material possessions. It could be a relationship. It could be pride or an addiction or selfishness. When we continue to place God below other things on the totem pole is when we risk our life in His kingdom. That's where the proverbial camel comes into play: when a rich man or any man deems a possession or popularity or power or prestige to be of more value and importance than God is when it becomes impossible to walk that camel through the eye

of a needle."

After so many years, I finally got it. "That's it?" I asked. "There's nothing more to it than that?"

"It all comes down to what is in your heart, Bob. When it comes to charity, don't ask what you *have* to do but ask what you *can* do. God won't look at your financial statements and charitable deductions but he will look at the charity in your heart. Did you love? Did you give? And did you give out of love? The widow with next-to-nothing who gives one dollar out of the goodness of her heart is more charitable than the man who gives one million dollars because he wants the attention and accolades.

"Give with love from your heart and that camel and the needle will be the last thing you'll have to worry about."

❖❖❖❖❖❖❖

That made sense. I turned away from Vince for a few moments to reflect on what he had just said. It was reasonable but it wasn't very comforting because I realized right there that there have been times in my life where God was not my top priority, at least not on a daily basis. He is always up there at #1 in the big picture, I suppose, but if I look at my life in phases then there were certainly times when career and family were all-consuming. At least Vince was able to convince me that I still had a chance; at least I knew the path I must travel from this day forward.

I turned to face him once again to offer my thanks.

And he was gone.

I looked at my bartender friend. "Where did he go?"

"He had other appointments," replied Paddy. "And he had to drop-off some old clothes to one of his collection boxes. That guy is always working. Never takes a day just to himself. Nice guy, though."

Paddy removed my empty glass and placed it in the sink behind the bar. "Can I get you anything else to drink or eat?"

"Is it closing time?" I asked.

"Almost."

"Really?" I said excitedly. Did this mean I was close to being finished in here?

"Almost," he repeated. "There are just a few items of business for us to discuss and then you will be on your way." He motioned to the large silver coffee pot at the far end of the bar. "Would you like a cup of hot coffee for our final few minutes? I proudly serve Starbucks."

I laughed. "You and about nine million other places! That sounds good, Pat. I take cream with mine. Or skim milk. You don't happen to have anything for dessert, do you?"

"Such as…"

"Cheesecake, perhaps?"

With that, he reached into a glass mini-refrigerator that I hadn't noticed before and removed a large piece of cheesecake with a graham cracker crust and covered with cherries. He set the plate in front of me and walked away to pour my coffee.

Best service I've ever had in a pub in my life, I thought to myself. And I bet I don't even have to leave a tip.

As Pat returned with my steaming Starbucks, he got down to business.

"Bob, you've had a remarkable night."

"You can sure say that again."

"As you wish. Bob, you've had a remarkable night."

I grinned. "Pat, I didn't mean for you to literally say it again. It's just an expression one sometimes uses these days. It's a way of confirming that what you just said was very true; perhaps even a huge understatement. In other words, 'Yes! I have had a remarkable night. I whole-heartedly agree with you!'"

"Oh. I learn the most interesting things from you, Bob."

"And vice-versa, Pat. Now, you were saying?"

"Did you find your first new friend Louis to be helpful?" Paddy asked.

"I did."

"Was your second new friend P.J. able to help you with prayer?"

"Yes. He helped me very much."

"And what about your third new friend? Did Karol help you with forgiveness and judgment day?"

"Yes. Karol was a huge help."

"And did your most recent new friend Vince help you with your outlook on charity?"

"Yes. Vince was very sensible. I understood his explanations."

"And if I may be so bold to ask; have I been of assistance to you?"

"You've been great, Paddy. I appreciate everything you've done."

"I am glad to hear it. I am proud that all of us, in our own way, have been of great help to you. The subjects that were discussed with you so far tonight were very lofty and worthwhile. They help to form the foundation of a man. Now, if I may, we move on to our final subject."

'Where is this going?' I wondered silently. I was almost afraid to find out.

"And that final subject would be what?" I inquired.

Paddy leaned in closer and whispered. "You."

That caught me off guard. "Me?" I paused briefly and added: "That's my least favorite subject."

Pat pounded a fist against the top of the bar. "And I find it very appropriate that you should respond with such a statement! It provides to me the perfect opening."

I poured the skim milk in my coffee. "Go ahead then."

"Earlier tonight you told Fulton Sheen the following: 'There is nothing that sets a common man apart.' At that time, Sheen promised to you that your comment would be addressed later.

"Also with Sheen you said, 'I know all about common. I am as common and normal as you get.'

"Also earlier tonight you told Karol that you felt undeserving to meet him when he was alive and you gave that honor to your wife. Later you also told him: 'I am a very common man; what can I possibly do to change the world?'

"While sitting on the bench in Central Park today you said to yourself: 'I love my wife and kids and for some reason they love me.' The key phrase there is 'for some reason.'"

I interrupted him for a moment. "How do you know what I was thinking while in the park?"

"Shouldn't you be beyond that by now, Bob?"

He had me there.

Pat got right back on topic. "And just now you said: 'Me? That's my least favorite subject.'"

"What's your point, Pat?" I wondered.

"It's very simple. You believe you are a common man. You believe there is nothing you can do to change the world. That makes you sad. You feel helpless. In fact, Sheen's opinion was: 'You've given up.'

"You also told Sheen: 'I measure success by the ratio between what a man is and what he is capable of being. My ratio is far too high. I think I am capable of so much more. I haven't delivered.' There it is again! I hear from you that same theme over and over again; you feel 'undeserving', people love you 'for some reason', you are 'capable' of better things, and you know all about 'common'. You clearly feel disappointed that you are just a common man. You may even feel that there is something wrong with that.

"I think it goes even deeper. I think the fact that you feel 'common' also makes you feel alone. It's as if one feeds off the other."

"That may be a bit of a stretch, Pat. Common? Perhaps. But alone or lonely? I don't think so. I have a great family and some fine friends."

Paddy turned away and walked back to the sound system. He grabbed a compact disc from the pile and placed it in the machine. He turned up the volume.

I recognized the song after the first few notes. "Hey! I know that song! It's called *Same Oul' Town*. It's by *The Saw Doctors*. They're my favorite group. They're from Ireland. Do you like them, too?"

"Yes, I do," he responded.

"I love music, Pat. Often my idea of a perfect afternoon is relaxing on my deck or in my home and cranking my Bose to a high volume and listening to Sinatra or Crosby or a Big Band. It helps me think. It relaxes me. I enjoy it. Often I sing along.

"The same is true at a Sunday Mass," I continued. "I think good music makes a mass more meaningful. It helps me get something out of that mass. That being said, the opposite is also true; bad music can totally ruin a mass. I can't wait to leave. Do they have to sing so many verses? Do they have to sing everything? Am I at a mass or a concert? And why did they select the person with the worst voice to be the lead? Sometimes I think the choir believes that it's all about them and not about the mass itself. It drives me nuts."

Paddy had no comment.

"And with that, I will leave my soapbox," I added with a laugh.

We both stopped to listen to the song still playing in the background. I quietly sang along to the chorus.

> *Oh I go out for a walk*
> *To see if there's news*
> *The rain on the path*
> *leaking into my shoes.*
> *And I do talk to myself*
> *'cause I'm my only best friend*
> *It's Sunday night, nearly Monday morning again.*

"That's a great song," I stated. "For some reason it speaks to me."

Paddy walked back from the stereo to stand in front of me. "I find it interesting that a song that 'speaks to you' includes the phrase: 'And I do talk to myself because I'm my only best friend.'"

I threw out my arms in protest.

"Pat, it's a song, it's not my mantra! What's with you? Are you still on that 'Bob is alone' kick? I am no more alone or lonely than most any other middle-aged man or woman. Besides, aren't you the one who just moments ago defined it as a problem that I consider myself 'common'? Wouldn't it be 'common' for people my age to sometimes feel alone or lost?" Most of us feel alone at times."

"Talk to me about that," he urged.

"I am very content, Paddy. I have many reasons to be happy.

I am very lucky. Let's imagine that somehow you gathered every middle aged man in the world and you rated them by their wife, kids, career, status, health and family. Now you arrange them in a line-up with 'happy and blessed' starting on the left and 'unhappy and unfortunate' ending on the right; I'd be placed way over near the start of the line on the left. I know that! I have every reason to feel good about my life.

"These are good days. We are empty-nesters. We have more leisure time. We finally have disposable income. There is less stress. We have terrific relationships with our daughters and those closest to us. These are happy times. This is what we worked for during the last thirty years. I am happier than most people. I am luckier than most people."

Paddy didn't seem convinced. "And yet…?" he asked.

"And yet, who is joyful all the time? I'm not. I feel restless. I get discouraged. As good as I have it I sometimes feel a void or emptiness deep inside. What is it? Why can't I shake it? One can be surrounded by hundreds of people and still feel very much alone. To paraphrase Neil Diamond, 'Feeling lonely makes you wonder why.'

"Who is he?"

"Never mind. In addition, the older I get the more often I feel that so many things I do seem useless or senseless. Too many things seems to be a waste-of-time. I find myself more and more bored or unfulfilled with activities and people. I don't like feeling that way. I'm not proud of that. It's a character flaw. I just feel *lost* sometimes."

"I hear and see this all the time, Bob. There is only one way for you to fill that void," Pat said.

"Let me see if I can guess where this is going," I said sarcastically. "Here's where *God* comes in, right Pat? Only *God* can fill that void, is that it? So now is the time when you are going to say something like, 'You are never alone with God.' Is that it? Is that the best you've got?"

Then, inexplicably, I got a little angry. "Well, where is He then? I'm right here but where is He? Like the great church song says, 'Here I Am, Lord'. And to that I would add, 'But where are

You?'

"Why would God even *know* about me? Why would God even *care* about me? Why would He *love* me? Why would He not forget about me? I wouldn't blame Him at all. There are seven billion people in the world so I think God is going to be just fine with or without me. I'm quite sure that He can carry on without regular-guy Bob here; in fact, maybe He already has."

"Why would you expect God to do all of the work?" asked Paddy. "If at this stage of your life you feel that there is greater distance between God and you, ask yourself, 'Which one of us moved?' God is right where He has always been. He doesn't force His way in, He asks. And He only stays with our permission.

"You ask how it is possible to feel alone sometimes even when your life is full of people who love and support you. You say you sometimes feel restless. You may not want to hear this but we are restless until we rest in Him. It's as if God put inside our hearts a homing device so we realize that no matter how good our lives may be and how successful we may be that there is still something that says, 'This isn't enough!' That restless feeling or that feeling of emptiness may be God tugging at you to remind you that your permanent home is not here on earth but it is with Him in heaven.

"There is something radically solitary about the human condition. You cannot be anyone else. Likewise, no one else can be you. It is in those moments of emptiness that one can realize that God can satisfy our heart unlike any human being.

"From where I stand, it sounds likes you have everything you need to be happy. You have a great family and friends. You have all the resources required to enjoy life. But deep down inside you realize that you don't have a relationship with the best friend of all. You've ignored Him for too long. It is never too late with Him. Work on this friendship. Develop this friendship. And you will fill that void and emptiness with a contentment and joy you never knew was available.

"The world is wonderful. It sets before us countless treasures. It enchants us. It attracts both our reason and our will but in the end it cannot satisfy our spirit. Man eventually realizes that this world, with all its many riches, remains superficial and precarious.  As we get older, as we enter our final years, man finally determines that only one thing, or one Person, can make him whole.  In too many cases it is regrettable that it takes so long to realize this.  Perhaps, Bob, that's where you are in your life at this moment."

These guys make it all sound so simple, I thought to myself. Maybe it's me and all the people just like me who make it so hard.

Paddy returned to the sound system and turned off the music. The cathedral was now eerily quiet.  I only heard the soft sounds of his footsteps as he walked back in front of me.

"And now, let's tackle your one remaining problem," he said. "And for this one I am going to call in one final friend."

❖❖❖❖❖❖

I heard a commotion behind me.  I spun around on my stool and saw a man standing in the open space behind the back pews. I didn't know who or what I expected to see when Paddy told me of 'one final friend' but I certainly didn't plan on this.

There, at the back of Saint Patrick's Cathedral, was a makeshift barber's shop.

A male barber wearing a navy blue barber's jacket was standing behind a leather barber's chair.  He was at work using scissors to cut the hair of a man wearing a white cape to protect his clothing.  Nearby there stood the traditional barber's pole with its revolving red, white and blue colors.  The barber and his customer were engaged in quiet small talk.

What in the world was *this* all about?

Slowly, I turned back to Paddy.  "Would you care to explain?" I pleaded.

"It will become quite clear soon enough," he replied.  "For now, it allows me to bring closure to this last item on my pad of paper."

He grabbed the yellow pad and read from it.  "We are all connected to each other," he recited.  "Do you remember, Bob when you first said that to me?"

"I do not. Remind me."

"It's when we first met. You were explaining to me your visits with Louis and Sheen and John Paul II. You told me of their relevance in your life. You pointed out their place of honor in this cathedral. You said you understood why they had visited you. 'We are all connected to each other,' is how you put it. Soon, you were also able to find the connection between the two of us."

"Sure, I remember now. I don't get the point, however."

He nearly shouted. "Here's the point. We are *all* connected! Don't you see? We are all brothers and sisters in Christ. God is the King of all men and women, not some. Jesus died for all of our sins, not some. We all want the same things out of life: a happy and healthy family and a kind, compassionate and charitable society. These things don't matter in the least: nationality, skin color, material wealth, level of education, success in business, power and prestige. We are all the same. We are all God's children. And as soon as you realize that, Bob, you won't feel so alone in the world. You won't feel so lost. You'll better understand your fellow man. You may even like them. You may even care about them much more than you do now. I appeal to you that wherever you are and whatever you are doing to see the face of a brother or sister in every human being. Our common humanity unites us and it is far more powerful than the things that may divide us."

Again, I heard noise behind me. I turned to see the barber and his customer shaking hands and saying goodbye to each other. The haircut was finished.

The barber returned to his place behind the chair. I suppose he was waiting for his next client. I could use a little trim before I go home, I thought to myself. I wonder what he charges.

To my surprise, the customer began walking over in my direction. And it was at this time that I noticed his clothing.

He wore a heavy insulated jacket. It was open, revealing a white cotton T-shirt and suspenders connected to his very large and baggy pants. He had a small radio, large gloves and a flashlight hanging from his waistband. He wore black rubber boots. In one hand he carried an ax. And in his other hand he carried a helmet.

As he got closer, I could see the letters on that helmet. NYFD. This man was a fireman for the New York Fire Department. And he was coming to talk to me.

❖❖❖❖❖❖

I stood up from my bar stool. He confidently walked right to me and extended his right hand. "Bob, it is nice to meet you," he said.

He was a powerful man. He nearly crushed my hand during our ensuing handshake. He stood much taller than me; I guessed his height to be at least 6′3″. Even with his large clothes I could tell he was solid muscle. He had a square jaw. His hair was jet black. He looked like a model. Sometime in his life he had probably posed in a fireman's calendar for charity.

"And you can call me 'Chief'," he added.

Then he looked at Paddy. "How are you doing, Pat? It's good to see you again!"

"It's always my pleasure, Chief," returned Paddy.

I still hadn't said a word. I was dumbfounded. Why would I be visited by a fireman?

"Would you like something, Chief?" asked Paddy.

"Do you still make that wonderful Reuben sandwich? And a tall glass of milk?"

Pat immediately produced the food and drink for his friend the fireman. Chief grabbed the sandwich with his massive hands and took a huge bite. "It's just as good as always," he said after a few seconds. "Thank you!"

"You two get to know each other," said Paddy. "I'm going to walk over and get a haircut."

Finally I spoke. "Are you leaving?" For some reason I was reluctant to be left alone with the fireman.

"I'll just be across the way there," Paddy explained. "I need a haircut. About once every month our friend Pierre offers a free trim and shave."

"Who is Pierre?" I interjected.

"That's the barber. Chief can fill you in. I want to get over to him before one of the apostles show up. I once had to wait for at least an hour for Paul to get his haircut and his beard trimmed. Those apostles are really picky. They talk a lot, too. They always talk about 'the good old days'. They always brag about being at The Last Supper. It drives Pierre nuts. Anyway, if you two need anything just grab for it from behind the bar. If you want me, just shout."

Pat walked out from behind the bar and started over to see Pierre. After just three steps he stopped and came back to me. He placed his hands on my shoulders. "God bless you, Bob. I am glad we *connected*."

I stared at him as he walked away. I am so sure I've been talking to Saint Patrick, I thought to myself. Did tonight really happen? Was any of this real?

I turned my attention back to the fireman who was just taking his final bite from the Reuben. He wiped his mouth with a cloth napkin and looked me in the eye.

"Well, Bob, you are probably wondering about why I am your new friend and why I am here in this cathedral."

"I thought you were here for a haircut," I replied.

"Ha! That's very funny," he laughed. "I came to see you but I decided to come early because I knew Pierre would be here, too. As they say, I thought I'd kill two birds with one stone."

"Who is Pierre?" I asked, glancing across the floor to briefly look at the man behind the barber's chair.

"That's Pierre Toussaint," he replied.

"You have got to me kidding me," I exclaimed.

"He's the one and only. I assume you know his story? He was born a slave in Haiti. His master emigrated to New York and he had Pierre come with him. Pierre was a very intelligent young man. After he was freed from slavery he became a counselor to the rich but most of what he earned he gave away. He was widely known for his kindness and charity. His wife and he took in black orphans. They cared for the sick.

"When Pierre died in 1853 the church was packed with both rich and poor. Everybody liked and respected him. His eulogist said, 'I have known Christians who were not gentlemen and gentlemen who were not Christians but one man I know was both.'

"Pierre is buried here in this cathedral and he is now on the track to sainthood," concluded the fireman.

"He's buried *here*?" I asked. "That at least explains his presence tonight in my company. But what's with the barber act? Why is he giving haircuts?"

"That was his profession when he first moved to New York. He needed work. He became a hairdresser to women and a barber to men. And he made himself in to one of the most successful and sought-after hairdressers in the city. That's how he met so many rich people. Then later they used him as a counselor because of his intellect and wisdom; and he used them to help the poor and needy."

Chief stopped to make sure I was giving him my full attention.

"Do you hear what I'm saying, Bob? That man accomplished so much in his life. He explained that he overcame all adversity simply by embracing Christ's call to 'love one another.' He was a slave. He was a barber. In other words, he was a *common man*."

As he said those final two words I felt as if I had been punched in the stomach.

"Now I get it," I told him. "Now you are going to give me the speech, right?"

"What speech?"

"You know. The one which goes something like this: 'Louis told you tonight that every saint was first a sinner. He also told you that we are all capable of being a saint. Then Sheen told you that even saints weren't perfect. And Pierre Toussaint, once a very common man, is *going to be* a saint.' That's where this is going, isn't it? And then your little speech will conclude with this: 'Bob, you can be a saint, too.'"

I continued before Chief could jump in.

"I am getting tired of being told,' Be a saint.' Or, 'Look to the saints for your inspiration and your example.' Is that all you people talk about? I've got news for you: it is too late for me to be a saint. I'm a lost cause. If others are trying to live a saintly life then God bless them! I give them credit. But you're talking to the wrong guy. I've made too many mistakes to ever be a saint. If only saints get to heaven then I give up. I just want to be a better person. That's my goal. I have a better chance of becoming the first man on Mars than I do being a saint."

I stopped to take a breath and that's when the fireman responded.

"Bob?"

"Yes?"

"I am sorry to tell you this but that's not where I was going at all. Why would I? I'm not a saint, either. However, you certainly did make some interesting points. Don't immediately dismiss what the others have told you."

"I'm confused," I stated. "Why are you here then? What is your connection to this cathedral? What is your connection with *me*?"

"I'll begin with that first part," he replied as he placed his NYFD helmet on top of the bar. "Engine Company 54 and Ladder Company 4 are both located nearby. Their firemen routinely inspect the ceiling space of the cathedral. From where we are on the floor the ceiling appears to be a work of Gothic masonry but in reality it is an artifice of plastic and lumber. And in the massive attic space between the ceiling vaults and the peaked roof is a collection of wooden trusses and beams. Some of them are over one hundred years old. We call it the Lumberyard.

"During inspection, some firemen will write their name in a dusty window. Others may carve their name in a beam. The names include Paul Gill, Michael Brennan, Michael Lynch and Leonard 'Rags' Ragaglia."

I shrugged my shoulders. "Who are they?"

I noticed a tear in his eye as he replied. "They were killed on 9-11."

I could think of nothing to say. It took Chief a few seconds before resuming.

"The NYFD lost 343 members on that one day. On the tenth anniversary of the attacks, we were remembered in a special prayer service here in this cathedral. The Cardinal of New York said: 'In this, God's house, all are welcome. In this house which belongs to the Lord who wants to save and protect and welcome His people, those who do the same – our firefighters – are also at home. Amid the violence and horror on 9-11 were moments of extreme loyalty, kindness, courage and selflessness.' He called all firefighters 'Hall of Famers' because we 'go against whatever degrades human life.'

"Since 9-11, the cathedral's Building Managers have been instructed to never clear away those names on the beams or in the windows. Their names will remain here forever.

"And that's the reason, Bob, for my presence in this cathedral."

"Chief, I am very sorry," I mumbled. It was the only thing that came to mind. I'm sure it wasn't enough. What would be?

"And now let's turn to the second part of your question: 'What is my connection to *you*'?"

I still had no idea. And after that heart-wrenching first part of his story I wasn't about to guess.

He spoke these next words very deliberately in order to have the greatest impact. "What is so bad about being *common*?"

"What do you mean?" I retorted.

"Please, Bob, do not play poker with me. I call your bluff. You know exactly what I mean. You constantly refer to yourself as a 'common man'. And it hardly sounds like a compliment when you say it or think it. So again I ask: 'What's so bad about it?'"

He paused and pointed at Pierre. "After all, *he* was a common man."

Then he placed his right hand over his heart. "And I was, too," he said. "Do you not think, Bob, that I was proud of what I did in my life as a common man or, like you, do you think I was disappointed with it? Do you not think I was admired and respected at the end of my very common life?"

"You saved lives in your life, Chief," I argued. "And Pierre over there *changed* lives. I consider that to be uncommon."

"We did what we were asked to do. We did what we were expected to do. I think there is something heroic in leading a virtuous and selfless life without expecting or demanding accolades and attention in return."

He continued. "Let me ask you this: 'Do you think I made the

world a better place?'"

"I am quite sure that you did."

"And did Pierre make the world a better place?"

"He certainly did."

"Now honestly ask yourself if you did, too. In some small way, is the world a better place because of your life? Are the people you've touched somehow better or richer because of you? If the answer is yes then I will ask you for a third time: 'What is so bad about being common?'"

I ignored him. I wasn't about to let on that he had a point.

"It goes a little deeper than that for me, Chief," I told him. "I have a hang-up with being 'common' because I equate it with being unable to make a difference. Only uncommon men and women really change the world. But what can I do?"

"Go on," he encouraged.

"There are many things wrong in the world and I feel helpless to change them. There is so much evil in the world; wars and weapons of mass destruction and terrorism and governments slaughtering their own people. And there is nothing I can do about it. I hate that.

"I worry about the direction of our country and I am powerless to change it. I love our country but it is a mess. Everybody says so. There's corruption and conceit. For decades, politicians have spent us into a black hole. They spend our money and then tax us more to pay for it. We throw them out of office only to see the next group do the same thing. Government has taken over our lives by constantly creating new rules and regulations. Lobbyists and special interests have much more influence than do the rest of us. Our education system has suffered. We abort babies and call it a choice. We have too many one-parent families. We have too many two-parent families with parents who don't care or try. Our political campaigns are nasty and embarrassing, full of one lie and smear after another. We find excuses for most forms of bad behavior. We've taken religion and faith out of the public arena; we even have to call the Christmas tree at City Hall a 'Holiday' tree. How far have we fallen?

"We are all so frustrated and discouraged. We're becoming

more isolated. We're more unfriendly and disrespectful than ever before. We are more selfish. We wave to our neighbors while we walk to the mailbox but we really don't want to know our neighbors. We're more rude and impolite. Many of us are angry. What has happened to us? It never used to be this way. It's not *supposed* to be this way!

"There are so many good and decent and kind-hearted and caring and compassionate people in this country but we seem to have been swallowed up. Or maybe we've *given* up.

"And that's what's so hard. I feel so inconsequential. I feel so *normal*."

I stopped momentarily to gather my thoughts. I was surprising myself. Where were these emotions coming from? Was I really this discouraged? Was I really so (here comes that word again) disappointed?

"I walked around New York earlier today. I stood on one street corner and saw thousands of people. It made me feel so irrelevant. Everywhere I looked I saw another person I will never know. And they will never know me. It made me think of my role in the world. Other than perhaps two hundred people, who will even know when I am no longer alive? And of those two hundred, how many will really care?

"And then I go even further and ask, 'Why would *God* even care?' There are seven billion people in the world. I think of all the billions who came before me. I think of all the billions who will come after me. Why would God care about *just me*?

"And maybe that's one reason I am a sinner. I excuse my sin by saying: "I am just one sinner in the gigantic history of mankind. And this is just one sin. So what? What difference does this make? It's one grain of sand in a desert."

I took a sip from my drink.

"And so am I, Chief; so am I. I am just a grain of sand in the desert."

My friend has such a sad look on his face. I had probably given him far more than he expected. He was probably wishing he was fighting a fire right now instead of visiting with me.

"Bob, remember that what I am about to say is coming from

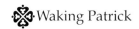 

*me,*" he started. "It's not coming from a saint. It's not coming from someone so holy. It's not coming from someone who has been dead for hundreds of years. I was alive when you were alive. This is coming from a contemporary. This is coming from someone who can relate. This is coming from a common man. OK?"

"OK."

"*I know how you feel!* I had many of the same frustrations. Our lives are very similar. You and I are like so many hundreds of thousands of other people. We try to do the right thing. We take our faith seriously. We love God and we fear Him. We try to be a good spouse. We try to be a good parent. We try to be a good friend. We work hard. We try to teach our kids about compassion and charity and sacrifice. We play by the rules. And we do all of these things for no other reason other than we believe it is the right way to live.

"We also make mistakes. We fall down. We sin. But we get back up and keep trying because the true Christian is not necessarily the one who goes all the way with Christ since birth or childhood; I mean, how many men and women have ever done that? We are all sinners. Rather, the true Christian may be the one who somewhere in life locates the right road and then from that point forward tries their very best to remain on that road; and when they fail they get back on it immediately.

"We get discouraged when we see the world and our country in such a troubling condition.

"Where I am now, Bob, I see things. I hear things. I've learned things. Do you understand? So hear me now, one friend to another, one common man to another.

"It is the common man who holds in their hands the ability to change the world. But we can only do that if we care enough to keep trying. You sound like a man who is ready to give up. Don't leave it to others to be the ones to care. Earlier you mentioned the evil in the world: well, evil has greater impact when good people stop caring.

"You said you feel like a grain of sand. Guess what? *You are!* Is that not what you wanted to hear? Sorry. You are a grain of sand. And so was I. And when you consider the enormity of history, so were your friends Louis and Sheen and Karol and Patrick. Do you not believe that they, too, felt inconsequential and powerless and unimportant? But because they always had love in their hearts, they made a difference. You can, too. Your effort is just as worthy as the efforts as everyone you met here tonight. Realize that any difference made for the good, large or small, is what we are called by God to do.

"I know what you mean when you question the absolute insignificance of your role in God's incomprehensible plan. I felt that way, also. For example, at this precise moment as you and I are talking in this cathedral, someone out there is dying; someone is being born; someone is sick; someone is hungry; someone is homeless; someone is helping; someone is praying; someone is getting married; someone just made a medical discovery; someone is making a difference. It's been like that for every second of every hour of every day of every year of every century in history. God sees all of it. And we must believe that He loves each of us. We must believe that He is guiding this crazy mass of humanity toward some meaningful conclusion that we cannot understand or comprehend.

"To ask, 'What have I really done?' and 'What difference can I really make?' is a healthy awareness that although we are quite normal and common we are also important. We realize that God has networked the human family so each of us has a role to play.

"You probably don't want to hear this, either, but I'm not here to hold your hand: *Accept your smallness*! Make peace with it. Embrace it just like countless others have before you. It is only when one accepts their role in the world that one can change it. And then see what a real difference you will make.

"Pack as much love into your daily life as you possibly can. And by that I mean both the big gestures and the small ones: volunteer, donate to charity, visit the sick, reach out to the lonely, assist the elderly, tutor a child, lead a prayer group, serve food to the homeless and hungry, the list of opportunities is endless. Take care of your corner of the world. Make better your community and watch the ripple in the water become a wave.

"That's when you change the world. That's when you make a difference. That's when you stop being unimportant and inconsequential. That's when you stop feeling powerless and helpless. That's when you are more like Christ. That's when you love one another.

"That's not bad for a grain of salt. That's not bad for a common man. That's when you can approach judgment day with hope that you will hear the words: 'Well done, thy good and faithful servant!'"

*Going Home*

I woke up in my hotel room thanks to my beeping alarm clock on my cell phone. I was going home today.

I lay in bed for a few minutes because I didn't sleep very well. Maybe it was all the noise from the busy streets of New York City. Or maybe it was that weird dream I had.

I took a shower and then turned on the television to watch the morning news as I got dressed. The cute anchorwoman gave me the usual headlines about protests and shootings and unrest in the Middle East and a political war-of-words in the United States.

Same old stuff.

I sat at a table in the hotel's complimentary breakfast room and looked at the sports page from the *USA Today* while eating an English muffin and a bowl of Frosted Flakes.

The food in these places is never very good but I always eat it anyway. After all, I paid for it.

I had some time to kill before going to the airport so I decided to attend the morning mass at St. Pat's. I enjoy weekday morning mass. They go so fast. There are no bells and whistles or singing or homilies; it's just the scripture readings and a few prayers and the Body of Christ and have a good day. I like that.

After mass I took a quick walk around the inside of the cathedral just like I did last night before I went back to my hotel. For some reason I linger at a few places more than others, including the Saint Louis side altar, the bust of Pope John Paul II and the statue of Saint Patrick himself.

As I near the exit of the cathedral I look to my left and see the cathedral's small gift shop. It's kind of odd but it reminds me of

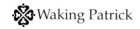

an Irish pub I once enjoyed.  Why would that be?

Once outside I immediately hailed a taxi cab.  They are everywhere in this city. "LaGuardia, please," I instruct the cabbie.

Traffic is heavy.  We crawl from one stop light to the next.  I look up at the Empire State Building as we drove by and I tell myself once again that there is no way I will ever go up to the observation deck.

The taxi arrives at the airport.  My driver nearly ran over two people with suitcases crossing in front of him.  I paid with a credit card in the small machine attached to the back of the front seat. I like that new payment procedure because you no longer have that uncomfortable moment waiting for the driver to give back your change because he is hoping you will tell him to keep it.

I printed my boarding pass at the hotel so I proceed directly to security.  I can't even see the end of the line!  It wraps around a corner and down a second hallway.  There are only two employees manning the security booth.  'I will never make it in time,' I think to myself.  I always think that.  And I always make it.

A woman in front of me is complaining to nobody in particular about the TSA pat-down up ahead and having to remove her jacket and shoes and jewelry.  I look at her and think about asking if she'd prefer instead to be blown out of the sky by a bomb.  I look at her a second time and think she'll probably *enjoy* the pat-down.

I stop at the Dunkin' Donuts counter on my way to the gate and order a cup of coffee and two blueberry donuts.  And I grumble when the woman at the cash register tells me that I owe six dollars.

I grab a copy of *The New York Post* and read it while waiting for my plane to board.  One headline screams, 'Cuomo Says No-No to Soho.'  Where do they find these headline writers?

I board my plane and locate my aisle seat.  I like the aisle seat more than the window seat because I don't have to crawl over anyone when I have to get up and use the restroom.  Plus, I don't like to look out the window because I'm afraid of heights.  I usually look the other way.

I see a woman approaching from up ahead and she is holding

a crying baby. Please, God, don't let her sit next to me. I hold my breath and she approaches my row. She walks right by me and goes to the back. Thank God! There is only one thing worse than sitting next to a screaming baby on an airplane and that is sitting next to an overly-large passenger who literally spills over my arm rest and I have to spend the entire flight trying not to touch that person.

We take off. While everyone else is looking out a window I am looking at my feet. Or I try to look calm and nonchalant as I page through that silly Sky Mall magazine.

My first ever trip to New York City has ended. I am finally on my way home. It's been a good trip. My work was successful and I saw some of the city's landmarks. The people were kind. It's odd but I feel like I even found a few new friends.

I rest my head on the back of my seat and close my eyes. I am relaxed. I am comfortable. For some strange reason I feel good. I feel happy and serene. I feel at peace. I feel like I have a plan. I feel like I have a purpose. Where did *that* come from?

I'm very lucky. I have a great life.

And I can't wait to get home.